小学生最想读的课外读物

101 个美丽故事

变成星星的七兄弟

[韩]铅笔头 编著　[韩]车保兰 插图　金钟 译

花山文艺出版社

图书在版编目(CIP)数据

变成星星的七兄弟：小学生最想读的101个美丽故事 /
[韩]铅笔头著；金钟译. —石家庄：花山文艺出版社，2005
(小学生最想读的101个故事系列)
ISBN 7-80673-699-9

Ⅰ.变... Ⅱ.①铅... ②金... Ⅲ.儿童文学—故事—作
品集—韩国—现代 Ⅳ.I312.685

中国版本图书馆CIP数据核字(2005)第073116号

冀图登字：03-2005-021号

丛 书 名：小学生最想读的101个故事系列
书　　名：变成星星的七兄弟——101个美丽故事
编 著 者：[韩]铅笔头
插　　图：[韩]车保兰
译　　者：金　钟

策　　划：张采鑫
责任编辑：于怀新
特约编辑：高长梅
美术编辑：齐　慧
装帧设计：红十月工作室
责任校对：童　舟
出版发行：花山文艺出版社(邮政编码:050061)
　　　　　(河北省石家庄市友谊北大街330号)
网　　址：http://www.hspul.com
销售热线：0311-88643226 / 7 / 8 / 9
邮购热线：0311-88643235
传　　真：0311-88643225
印　　刷：北京国彩印刷有限公司
经　　销：新华书店
开　　本：860×1290　1/24
字　　数：60千字
印　　张：8.75
版　　次：2005年9月第1版　2005年9月第1次印刷
书　　号：ISBN 7-80673-699-9 / I·325
定　　价：19.60元

目 录

●序言(1)

1.捡玻璃瓶碎片的老人(2)

2.意外的处方(4)

3.看台上的父亲(6)

4.等待了几十年的爱情(8)

5.洗手水(10)

6.面包里的金块(12)

7.老头子做的事肯定是对的(14)

8.把幸福藏在哪里(16)

9.约定(18)

10.影子(20)

11.乞丐西莱蒙(22)

12.被油漆工拯救的生命(24)

13.战胜小儿麻痹症获得金牌(26)

14.不说谎(28)15.兄弟情深(30)

16.为了真正的和平(32)

17.懒儿子挣钱(34)

18.不死的蜥蜴(36)

19.强生号船长(38)

20.沾上土的豆腐(40)

21.送给奶奶的阳光(42)

22.印地安的灰姑娘(44)

23.报恩的喜鹊(46)

24.与狮子在一起(48)

25.杰杰的爱(50)

26.兄妹塔(52)

27.变成星星的七兄弟(54)

28.遗产(56)

29.一对穷夫妻和五个孩子(58)

30.门(60)

31.用苹果树做成的船(62)

32.养花人(64)

33.旧蚊帐(66)

34.心中的小提琴(68)

35.心中的晚霞(70)

36.小鸟(72)

37.小王子(74)

38.竹子呀竹子(76)

39.埋在地里的银锅(78)

40.写在手绢上的信(80)

41.八马碑(82)

42.白色的花边(84)

43.这个人也是朝鲜人(86)

44.草坪上的癞蛤蟆(88)

45.马夫的心(90)

46.希波克拉底誓言(92)

47.令人高兴的"水"(94)

48.做你想做的事(96)

49.霍尔莱婆婆(98)

50.管仲和鲍叔牙(100)

51.老马(102)

52.装满稻谷的船(104)

53.司令的怀表(106)

54.砖瓦匠的孩子(108)

55.跨越湖水的爱(110)

56.奈尔的梦想(112)

57.比大人更明智的孩子们(114)

58.小火车头(116)

59.伤疤脸(118)

60.金色盒子(120)

61.林肯和梯子(122)

62.给哥哥的信(124)

63.忠诚的狗(126)

64.别被雷声吓到(128)

65.精灵和鞋匠(130)

66.善良的少年(132)

67.做汤圆的老奶奶(134)

68.热情的力量(136)

69.庄子的故事(138)

70.小偷的儿子(140)

71.鸡毛蒜皮的小事(142)

72.坐马车的弟弟和奔跑的哥哥(144)

73.凡·高写给弟弟的信(146)

74.最后一课(148)

75.剑君的故事(150)

76.兄弟之间的信任(152)

77.孝子和老虎(154)

78.人生的秘密(156)

79.刻在石桥上的名字(158)

80.跟在灵车后面的皇帝(160)

81.奥兹国的魔法师(162)

82.价格昂贵的小猫(164)

83.老鼠新娘(166)

84.世上最容易也是最难回答的问题(168)

85.被响尾蛇咬伤的母亲(170)

86.与大猩猩同行(172)

87.胡楂子树和爱情(174)

88.老奶奶的挑战(176)

89.我请求(178)

90.魔法暴风(180)

91.儿童和儿童节(182)

92.热心是财产(184)

93.亚历山大大帝的遗言(186)

94.青鸟(188)

95.想要一把小提琴(190)

96.跃过小溪(192)

97.汉斯救人(194)

98.守泉人(196)

99.可爱多多龙(198)

100.蓝色阳伞(200)

101.酒友(202)

序言

从美丽故事中寻找自身的幸福

　　小朋友们,你知道要想寻找到自身的幸福首先该做什么吗?我们要做的第一件事就是给自己一个独立思考的时间。你想知道潜藏在自己身上的幸福吗?那么就请你留给自己一点儿时间与这本书交个朋友吧。

　　这本书由101个美丽故事组成,其中包含了美丽的人们所传递出来的爱、笑声和感动。这些短小的故事如同甘霖一样,温暖地滋润着贫瘠干枯的世界。读完这些故事后,你会感到平时蜷缩紧张的心灵一下子得到释放,正是这些如小溪般潺潺流过的感动,会让你在不经意中找寻到埋藏在自己内心深处的幸福。

　　通过这101个美丽故事,希望更多的小朋友能够拥有一个美丽的心灵,寻找到自己的幸福。

铅笔头

捡玻璃瓶碎片的老人

一个衣衫褴褛的老人在公园里踱来踱去,往口袋里不知塞着什么东西。

"有点儿可疑,不知道他刚才在捡什么?"

在公园里巡查的警察决定对这个老人进行监视。

老人仍在不停地捡着东西。他的口袋已经鼓鼓的,看来再也塞不进东西去了。

"不管怎样,应该带回去调查调查。"

警察把这个老人带到了派出所。

"老大爷,你口袋里都藏的是什么呀?赶快把里面的东西一件不落地全部掏出来。"

老人按照警察的吩咐如实照办,但令人惊奇的是,口袋里装的竟然是玻璃瓶碎片、尖锐的钉子和锋利的铁块等物品。

"你想把这些东西用在什么地方?快一五一十地回答我

的问题。"

老人低声地回答：

"噢，我只是担心大人们随意扔掉的东西会伤害到小孩子，小孩子要是光着脚跑来跑去踩到碎玻璃片的话，那可就麻烦大了。要是你们的调查结束了，我可以走了吗？我得赶紧捡完才行呀！"

后来人们才知道，这位老人就是瑞士著名的教育家裴斯泰洛奇。裴斯泰洛奇主张教育要尊重人的天赋、没有强制和压抑使受教育者心情愉悦平和，他一生始终以一颗谦逊的心致力于孤儿和青少年教育工作。

意外的处方

奥立佛·格登·史密斯是一名医生。他为人亲切善良,经常和穷人们在一起聊天。

一天,一名家境贫寒的妇女急匆匆地找上门来,恳求医生去她家上门治疗。

"先生,我的丈夫痛苦得连饭也吃不下了, 整天病恹恹的,求求您一定要救救我的丈夫呀!"

来到这名妇女的家里,格登·史密斯了解到这名妇女的家境不太好,丈夫由于长期失业整天生活在忧郁之中。

"我会给你开一剂处方,今晚请您来我的办公室一趟。"

天色变黑后,妇女来找格登·史密斯。

只见格登·史密斯递给妇女一个沉甸甸的药箱子。

"这里面有药和处方单, 拿回家后请按处方单所写内容服药。"

妇女怀着急迫的心情赶紧跑回家,和丈夫一同打开了箱子。

"亲爱的,快服下这些药吧。你一定要打起精神、振作起来哦。"

"没有用的,医生能知道我为什么而操心吗?"

出人意料,药箱子里装的竟然是满满一箱子钱,最上面放着一个纸条,写着这样一行文字:

必要时请服用。

看台上的父亲

有个少年与父亲生活在一起，两人相依为命。这个非常喜欢美式足球的少年尽管个子矮、身体单薄，但在初中和高中都是美式足球校队的一员。可是他老是打替补，以致于一次都没有上场打过比赛。但是这个少年没有放弃希望，他训练得十分刻苦。

时光流逝，进入到大学的儿子又一次被选进美式足球校队里。虽然体格上不如其他选手，但他凭惊人的斗志得到了教练的高度评价，所以最终才得以入选。

听到这个消息后，父亲怀着喜悦的心情把 4 年期间大学足球比赛的门票全部都买了，尽管儿子在这 4 年里一次也没有上场比赛。

但只要有比赛父亲就会一如既往地守候在看台上。

在毕业前，离最后一场比赛还有一周的时间，父亲突然离开了人世。儿子十分悲伤。

终于到了比赛的那一天，比赛开始后儿子所在的队一直比分落后。

儿子请求教练让自己上场，眼神中流露出坚定的决心，最终教练将他派上场。儿子上场后，场上的形势发生了逆转。他比任何人表现得都更好，球抓得也更牢。

比分终于被扳平了，在比赛还只剩下 1 分钟的时候，儿子得到了制胜的一分，奇迹就这样出现了。

比赛结束后，儿子接受了记者采访，儿子哽咽着说道：

"我的父亲是个面前一片漆黑的盲人，只要我有比赛父亲一定会来看我表现，他却不知道我从来就没有上场过。但是如今父亲去世了，所以我今天在场上的表现父亲一定会在天堂里看得到的。父亲，我爱你！"

等待了几十年的爱情

喜马拉雅山脉连绵不断,积雪常年不化,因此被称为"世界屋脊"。

在常年积雪的喜马拉雅山脉深处的山谷里有一个村庄,一天,村子里来了位陌生的法国少女。从那天起她在村子里住了下来,每天都到村子前面的河畔走一趟。这条河是由山上积雪融化后形成的,少女总是很怅然地望着河面。

人们看见她都会不住地摇头,还有人认为她是一位精神病人。

日升日落,斗转星移,不觉中几十年就这么过去了,少女那美丽的脸上平添了一道道皱纹,黑发也变成了白发,但是少女每天去村子前河畔这件事一天也没有中断。

在一个春暖花开的日子里,已成为老婆婆的她坐在河边,这时河面上有个东西朝她漂了过来,这是一具年轻人的尸体。

老婆婆急忙跳进河水里,把青年的尸体捞了上来,随后紧紧地抱着尸体,泪水顺着脸颊流了下来。

　　"这个人到底是谁,你干吗这么伤心?"

　　人们不禁问道。

　　"他是我年轻时与我结伴攀登喜马拉雅山、后来下落不明的我的未婚夫。由于没有办法将他的尸体从雪堆里找出来,所以我相信总有一天雪会融化,尸体会随着水流漂下来……"

　　在河边等待几十年就是为等到未婚夫的尸体,听完了老婆婆的话,所有人的眼眶都是红红的。

　　已变为老婆婆的她抱着容颜仍似从前的未婚夫,深情地亲吻着他,泪水不断地滴落下来。

洗 手 水

在英国皇室举行的一次豪华晚宴上发生过这样一件事。宴会招待的是一位外国首相,因此,气氛十分和谐融洽。品尝完美味的外国首相忽然觉得有点儿口渴。

"我想喝点儿水……哦,这水看起来能喝。"

对英国饮食习惯不太了解的外国首相端起桌上的水杯,咕咚咚地喝起来。这一举动引得在场的所有人都瞠目结舌,也不乏有人暗自嘲笑外国首相。因为水杯里的水不是饮用水,是用来洗手的。

大家不动声色,全都呆呆地盯着首相喝杯中的水。

此时,看见首相喝水的英国王子也跟着喝起了桌子上的水。

"为了不让外国客人出洋相,我也要跟着一起喝。"

这么一来,餐桌上的人们也纷纷效仿王子,喝起了洗手水。

那天的晚宴虽然抛却了形式上的饮食礼节,却充满了对客人浓浓的关爱之情。

面包里的金块

有个搬运工,每天下班后,总是买些面包,当做他和年幼女儿的晚餐。

这天,和往常一样,他和女儿又用面包代替晚餐。正吃着面包的女儿突然皱起了眉头。

"爸爸,面包里有什么东西。"

"是吗?可能是石头,赶快吐出来。"

但是让人惊奇的是,从面包里取出来的不是石头,而是一个金块。

"如果把这个金块卖了,好几天的伙食就有着落了。"女儿有些欣喜地说道。

但是，搬运工却拿着金块出了门，来到面包店，找到年事已高的面包店老板。

"大叔，我从你这买了面包，发现面包里有个金块，我把它放在这儿了，告辞了。"

面包店老板拦住他，微笑着说道：

"我一直在寻找像你这样正直的人。我没有妻子儿女，所以没人能继承我的财产，因此我最终决定在外卖的每个面包里都放一小块金子，但是直到现在只有你把金块拿了回来，请你一定要接受我的财产，安心在这里工作吧。"

面包店老板紧紧地握住他的手。

老头子做的事肯定是对的

一个老农夫在卖马的途中看见了一头母牛。

"要是有头母牛的话,不就能天天喝到牛奶了吗？喂,我用马换你的母牛,你干不干？"

农夫用马换来了母牛,走着走着,一只身形肥硕、有着浓密卷毛的绵羊映入他的眼帘。

"哦,如果我是那个家伙的话,我就可以不用为毛线不够用而操心了。"

于是,农夫又用母牛换来了羊,接着又用羊换成鹅,用鹅换成鸡,最后用鸡换来了一袋烂苹果。

人们从农夫那里听说了这件事后全都哈哈大笑,嘲笑他回家肯定会被老伴臭骂一顿。

"咳,绝不会发生这种事的。"

有两名非常有钱的英国人听完这句话后,拿出一箱子金币与农夫打赌。

回到家里后,农夫对老伴说:

"最开始我用马换来了母牛。"

"这样我们就能每天喝到牛奶了。"

"但我又用母牛换来了羊。"

"太棒了,这样就可以穿上用羊毛织成的袜子了。"

"但我用羊又换来了鹅。"

"是吗?我们在圣诞节就可以吃鹅肉了。"

"可是我又用鹅换成母鸡。"

"哦,真是太好了,这只鸡既能生鸡蛋又能孵小鸡。"

"这倒是,但我又换成了一袋子烂苹果。"

"天哪!晚饭没有洋葱我就向隔壁邻居借,但那家吝啬鬼妻子跟我说,别说是洋葱就是一个烂苹果也没有。现在我就是借给那个女的 10 个苹果也没问题,太谢谢你了,亲爱的!"

老伴深情地拥抱了老农夫。看到此种情景,两个英国人相互击掌,高高兴兴地拿出了一箱子金币。

把幸福藏在哪里

当这个世界刚被创造出来的时候,人们不知道什么是不幸,因为神把幸福这件贵重的礼物赠送给了人类。

"哼,看看那些人类,瞧瞧他们笑的样子,真是看不下去了!"

"是啊,那些家伙真讨厌,怎么能和我们天使一样呢?"

天使们聚在一起开会讨论,最后他们决定把幸福从人类身上夺走。

但是把夺来的幸福放在哪里成了一个问题。

一个天使说:

"放在遥远的大海深处,让他们找不到。"

"人类的脑袋那么聪明,放在大海里有什么用?他们可能马上就会找到。"

"那放在深山里怎么样?"

"这也不行,你不知道人类有多么强烈的探险精神吗?"

天使们又陷入苦恼中,最后他们达成一个共识,就是无论把幸福藏在哪里人类都会很快找到。

"啊,有个地方他们很难找到!"

天使们的目光全都聚集到说这句话的天使身上,这个天使眼中放着光芒,继续说道:

"藏在他们的心里,无论他们脑袋多么聪明、探险精神多么强烈,都很难找到藏在内心中的幸福。"

"对,就这么干,藏在他们心里!"

就这样幸福被藏进了人们的心里。当你孤单、疲倦、痛苦的时候请静静地倾听一下自己的内心,将藏在里面的幸福小心翼翼地捧出来吧! 所有的事情都将取决于你的内心,不是吗?

约　　定

　　在一个闷热的夏日里,有个企业家吃完午饭后来到公园里散步。公园里有很多人在卖冰激凌,其中有个少年也在卖着冰激凌。

　　由于阳光太晃眼了,企业家低着头走路,一不小心撞在了少年的身上,冰激凌桶被打翻在地,少年一脸哭相。

　　"实在对不起,冰激凌钱我……"

　　企业家把手伸进了口袋,但是口袋里空空如也。他还有个重要的约会,再回公司的话恐怕就不能再出来了。

　　"这样,我今天出来没有带钱,明天上午 10 点钟你能来这个地方么？到时我会把钱给你,可以么？"

　　回到公司的企业家与一个想购买自己公司产品的人见了面。这个人决定购买他们公司的很多产品。

　　"好的,那么我们明天 10 点钟签合同吧,其他时间恐怕我方有些困难。"

企业家犹豫了一会儿。

"是遵守和少年的约定,还是遵守与这个人的约定?"

很快,企业家作出了这样的决定:

"明天上午 10 点钟恐怕不行,我有个约会……"

"还有什么约会比这么大一笔合同更为重要?"

企业家对这个人说出了与那位少年之间的约定。这个人被企业家的话深深感动了。

"原来是这样,那我无论如何也要调整一下签约时间了,因为我相信连小小约定都如此重视的人做出的产品肯定是最棒的产品。"

第二天,企业家遵守了与少年之间的约定,不仅如此,那份对公司发展有很大帮助的大合同也如愿签订了。

影　　子

　　有个人和他的影子之间的关系十分亲密,影子总是默默地追随着他的左右。

　　有一天,嫉妒心很重的风吹了吹他,问道:

　　"你为什么对影子这么好?"

　　他回答道:

　　"因为它总是在我的身旁。"

　　风把旋风刮了起来,激动地说道:

　　"你是不了解情况才会这么说。好好想想吧,当你在漆黑的夜晚行走时,当你在暴风雪中举步维艰时,影子可曾在你的身边?影子只会在阳光明媚的晴朗白天里出现在你的身旁。"

　　这个人听完风的话后,一想确实是这样。

此后他对影子的态度就变得非常冷淡。

"你对我来说没有什么用,赶紧走吧!"

影子听完此话,只好孤零零地将自己的身体隐藏了起来。

之后他就和风玩在了一起,但是他们之间的关系总是显得不那么协调。

风就像一开始来的那样悄悄地溜走了。

最后只剩下他一个人,不甘寂寞的他突然思念起影子来。

"影子呀,我的影子呀,如果你不再讨厌我了,请你回来好不好?"

于是影子露出了白色的身躯低声答道:

"我一直都在你的身旁,只是你在黑暗寒冷的夜晚走路时我离你太近了,你没有察觉到而已。"

后来影子又像平时一样始终守候在他的身旁。

乞丐西莱蒙

盲眼孩子西莱蒙是一个到处流浪要饭的乞丐。

那天，西莱蒙为了讨到晚饭直到太阳落山了才回到海边。

西莱蒙蜷缩在海边岩石下面准备入睡。

"奇怪，今晚灯塔怎么灭了，怎么回事？也没有月光。"

西莱蒙揉了揉自己的双眼，但是仍看不到任何灯光。

"波泰罗爷爷生病了吗？大事不妙，灯塔要是不亮的话船可怎么航行？"

西莱蒙开始有些不安。

当，当，当……

从大海的远方穿来了急迫的钟声。虽然没看见任何物体，但很明显这钟声的含义就是让人赶快把灯塔点亮。

"糟了，一定要把灯给点亮，这可关系到好几百人的生命！"

西莱蒙摸索着爬到了灯塔顶部，灯塔守护人波泰罗爷爷好像不在。

西莱蒙又摸索着掏出了火柴，脱下身上的外套用火柴点燃扔向窗外。西莱蒙很快又将衬衫和裤子脱下，连自己最喜欢的拐杖也扔向了火堆。

海面上的船只看见灯塔上的亮光后都平安靠了岸。

西莱蒙用手背擦了擦满是汗水的额头，露出了纯真的笑容。

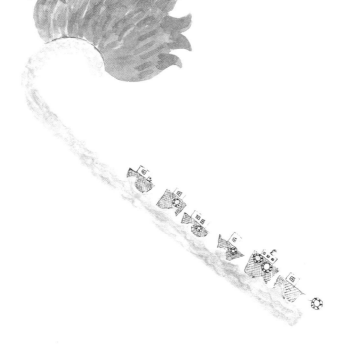

被油漆工拯救的生命

有个人拥有一艘小船,一到夏天他经常会和家人一同划着小船游玩,或在船上钓鱼。

夏天过完后,他把小船拖到陆地上,发现小船底部有一个小洞。

"明年夏天再修理吧。"

他就抱着这个想法准备以后再解决这个问题。

"是不是该给船刷漆了呢?"

他找来了一个油漆工让他给船刷一层漆。

第二年春天,尽管还是春天但天气已经十分炎热。

"爸爸,我想划船,我们可以去湖里划船么?"

父亲完全忘了船底还有漏洞这件事,答应了两个儿子的要求。

大概在船上呆了有两个小时的时间。

"哎呀!船上有个漏洞……糟了!"

他直到这时才想起船上有个洞,他感到眼前一黑,迅速将小船划向岸边。

靠近岸边后,孩子们不再嬉戏了,将船拖到陆地上。

他仔细地将小船检查了一遍,却发现漏洞被堵上了。是

谁把船上的漏洞给堵上的呢?

"难道是那个油漆工?"

他买了礼物找到油漆工。

"我已经收了给你船刷漆的报酬,为什么还送我礼物呢?"

油漆工疑惑地问道。

"是这样,我让你给我的船刷漆,你却连我船上的洞都给堵上了,托你的福我的孩子们都得救了。真是太谢谢你的关心了,我感到非常抱歉,因为我的这份礼物实在无法表达出我此刻的感激之情。"

战胜小儿麻痹症获得金牌

沃尔玛·鲁道夫生于美国田纳西州一个很小的窝棚区里,沃尔玛 4 岁时得了肺炎,伴随严重发烧,最终导致患上小儿麻痹症。医生诊断说沃尔玛决不可能像正常人一样行走。

"上帝啊!请您不要让这个孩子丧失掉自信吧。"

沃尔玛的母亲诚恳地祈祷着。

"沃尔玛,虽然你的腿行动不便,但无论什么你都可以做得到的。"

沃尔玛的母亲总是这样激励着沃尔玛。母亲相信沃尔玛也能和正常人一样行走,为此经常训练她走路。但是沃尔玛没走几步就摔倒在地上。

"妈妈,我走不了,走不了!"

"这是什么话?快起来,再走走看!"

每次的摔倒都会让沃尔玛的脸上和身上多一处淤伤。

"表现非常好,今天走一米,明天走两米,听见了吗?"

几年后,在母亲的努力下沃尔玛走得越来越好,几乎和正常人一样,这是用医学理论完全不能够解释的。

"我要成为世界上最出色的田径选手。"

沃尔玛为了圆自己成为田径选手的梦而努力训练,但是沃尔玛在田径比赛中每次总是最后一名。

"还是放弃田径比赛吧。"

沃尔玛一点儿都没有因周围人的话语而泄气。

进入到田纳西州州立大学学习的沃尔玛遇见了泰姆普教练,埃德·泰姆普教练发现她拥有良好的天赋。经过刻苦的训练,沃尔玛被选拔为奥运会选手,代表国家参加比赛。

她在奥运会中发挥出色,获得了100米和200米赛跑的金牌,还作为400米接力赛的最后一棒赢得冠军。众多的观众都将掌声毫不吝惜地送给了这位战胜小儿麻痹症、在奥林匹克比赛中胸前挂三块金牌的选手——沃尔玛·鲁道夫。

不 说 谎

1963 年,29 岁的乔·克里蒂安当选为下院议员,此后从政 40 余年,对于自己身体上的障碍和由此而引起的苦痛他从不回避。正是由于率直反而让他赢得了更多国民的支持。

加拿大总理乔·克里蒂安出身贫寒,在 19 个兄弟姐妹中排行第十八,他患有先天性脸部肌肉麻痹症,导致一边的耳朵失聪、口部歪斜和说话口吃。

乔·克里蒂安这种身体上的障碍有时会成为政治漫画家的讽刺对象。不仅如此,一些小的事情也会被任意夸大,成为好奇的人们所关注的对象。

这是在他为选举而四处游说时发生的一件事。

"我的确有语言障碍,事实上我所担心的是由于我的语言障碍,我的思想和意志能否全部表达出来。国民们,请耐心地听我说话吧,你们可以不听我那些口吃的发音,但请你们一定要留意倾听包含在里面的我的思想和意志。"

人们对他自信而又率直的演说报以热烈的掌声。

可有个人高声问道：

"但是代表一个国家的总理因语言障碍连话都讲不好，这难道不是最大的毛病吗？"

于是，乔·克里蒂安虽有点儿结巴但非常坚定地回答说：

"你说的对，我的确是话讲得不好，但是我绝对不会说谎。"

话音刚落，人们再一次鼓起了掌，掌声持续了很长时间。

"话说不好但不说谎"的这种率真和诚实，给了乔·克里蒂安以巨大的力量，在有身体障碍的情况下，他于 1993 年当选总理后接着又连任三届。

兄 弟 情 深

在一个村子里住着诚实善良的兄弟俩,兄弟俩望着低垂的金黄色稻穗,感到非常满足。

"我家从今年起也能过上充裕的生活了吧?"

"是啊,要是庄稼长得好,一切都没有问题!"

这天是哥哥家打场的日子,大汗淋漓地忙完后,金黄色的稻谷堆占满了整个院子。

"一堆,两堆,三堆……三十堆。"

数了数收获的稻谷堆正好是三十堆。

"三十堆,和我的一样多。"

几天前打完场的弟弟笑了。

当天晚上,哥哥看了看堆在院子里的稻谷堆,挑起其中的一堆朝弟弟家走去。

"对了,弟弟现在也要开始居家过日子了,好好弄的话应该比我们家过得还好。"

哥哥偷偷地来到弟弟家，把一堆稻谷放在院子里。

当晚，没怎么睡的弟弟也悄悄地把一堆稻谷挑到了哥哥家里。

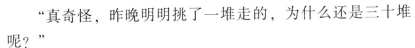

"哥哥家里人要比我家多，三十堆会不够的。"

第二天早上，兄弟俩各自数着稻谷堆，边数边摇头。

"真奇怪，昨晚明明挑了一堆走的，为什么还是三十堆呢？"

兄弟俩等到晚上又各自挑一堆送给对方。

"真是太奇怪了，是鬼神在作怪吗？"

这天晚上，哥哥又挑着稻谷走过田头，准备通过独木桥的时候从远处走过来一个人，这个从对面来的人正是弟弟。

"喔，是哥哥您呀！"

"是呀，现在我才弄明白，原来把稻谷放在我家里的人就是你呀！"

月光下对面而立的兄弟俩紧紧地拥抱在了一起。

为了真正的和平

甘地主张以非暴力抵抗运动来反抗侵略印度的英国，并且极力推动印度团结为一个整体，他被人们尊称为领导人民斗争的圣雄。

他向人们强调反抗决不能使用暴力，应该用爱和解，但是也有一些人对他的观点嗤之以鼻。

"我们的祖国都落到了别人的手中，光谈和平有什么用？难道是要我们乖乖地坐在那儿忍受？"

他们大声地主张以暴制暴，所以追随甘地的群众和反对他的群众之间也经常发生摩擦。

一天，一名反对非暴力抵抗运动的人对甘地犯下了严重的暴力，这名暴徒当场被捉住了。

几天后，甘地要站在法庭证人席上对施暴者提出证词。人们都希望甘地在场——历数这名施暴者犯下的暴行。

身负重伤的甘地好不容易站在了证人席上，他平静地陈述道：

　　"坐在被告席的人看来非常恨我，但是我却不恨他。不管他恨我的理由是什么，不管这个理由是对还是错，只因为他恨我，我也没有必须去恨他的理由。如果我在这里用他对待我的方式来对他，我们之间的纠纷就永远不会消失。只有抛却仇恨，我们之间的铁丝网才会被剪断。法官大人，我请求您能将他释放。"

懒儿子挣钱

很久以前，有个姓宋的老头儿由于非常勤劳而远近闻名，因为他的勤劳也积攒下了一笔不小的家产。

但是，宋老头有个好吃懒做的儿子，这个儿子什么活儿也不愿意干，即使做事也是半途而废。

一天，宋老头把儿子叫过来。

"你要是能靠自己的能力挣出一枚金币的话，我就把财产都传给你，否则你就别想继承我的财产。"

第二天，儿子在房间里踱来踱去，不知道怎样才能挣到钱。这时，宋老头的老伴把儿子叫过来。

"孩子啊，你把这钱拿去交给你老爸，就说这是你挣来的钱。"

母亲给了儿子一枚金币。

儿子按母亲所说把金币交给了宋老头，宋老头一拿到金币就把它扔进了火炉里。

第二天,母亲又给了儿子一枚金币。

"这是我挣来的钱。"

儿子把钱给了宋老头,可老头还是把金币扔进了火里。

母亲后来觉得自己这么做是错误的,就不再给儿子钱了。最后,儿子自己在外面辛苦工作了好几天,终于挣来了一枚金币。

"这钱真是我自己挣来的。"

但宋老头还是把钱扔进了火里。

儿子十分气愤,大声地喊道:

"不要,您知道我为了挣这枚金币吃了多少苦吗?"

儿子从火苗蹿升的火炉里找出了那枚金币,这时宋老头开心地笑了。

"这就对了,这才是你自己挣来的真正有价值的钱啊!"

宋老头紧紧地抱住儿子,拍了拍儿子的后背。

不死的蜥蜴

　　这是发生在日本东京的事。日本为准备东京奥运会决定对主体育场进行扩建,这样周边的几座民宅就需要拆迁。

　　工人们为将房屋拆掉开始卸去房屋的屋顶。

　　突然里面有个东西蠕动了一下。

　　"咦,那是什么东西? 好像有个活的东西!"

　　"是老鼠么?"

　　"不是,要是老鼠的话早就跑了。"

　　好奇的工人们仔细地查看着屋顶,发现一只尾巴被钉子钉住的蜥蜴在不时地蠕动。

　　"哦,天啊! 这只蜥蜴住在这里有多长时间了?停一下,停一下,工程暂停一下!"

　　工人们从屋顶上下来决定问一问这间屋子的主人。

　　"我根本不知道这里住着蜥蜴,但是这么长时间它是怎么活下来的呢? 钉子钉在这里已经有三年的时间了。"

"什么？三年了？这么说，
这只蜥蜴一动不动在这里呆
了三年了！那么它吃什么呢？
要是什么也不吃的话不早就
死了么？"

"我们赶快上屋顶把这只蜥蜴救下
来吧。"

工人们又爬上了屋顶，但是令人惊奇的事情
发生了。另外一只蜥蜴不知什么时候爬上来，正
在对尾巴被钉住的蜥蜴进行喂食。

这只蜥蜴一天要对被钉住的朋友喂食好几次，就这么一
直做了三年。

强生号船长

很久以前发生过这样一件事。

往返于美国和新西兰的强生号遇到了飓风,在海面上漂流着。当时无线电还没有被发明出来,所以没有任何能够对外求助的办法。

"继续在这么浩瀚的大海上漂流的话,最后我们会全部丧命的。"

"粮食还剩多少?我肚子好饿。"

"什么也看不见,还要走多远才能抵达陆地?"

"我们已在大海中迷路了,在海面上不停地打转,现在我们犯下了大错误。"

人们都已显露出疲惫的神色,渐渐放弃了生的希望。

突然,船舱里传来了一阵爽朗的笑声,这是一个搭乘强生号的孩子的笑声,刚出生不到 6 个月。

人们朝这个孩子聚拢过来,孩子则笑吟吟地望着大家。

有人说话了：

"孩子这么可爱地笑着呢，决不能让这个微笑着的幼小生命就这样夭折了，我们必须救他，一定要找到生路回到美国！"

人们凝视着孩子微笑的脸庞又重新一点点燃起了希望，他们每个人在精疲力竭时都会来船舱里看孩子一眼。

就这样过了100天，最后强生号平安无事地抵达了目的地。

船长对强生号上的所有人敞开心扉说道：

"强生号的船长不是我，是这个孩子，因为是这个孩子的笑脸给了我和其他人以巨大的动力，这个孩子救了我们所有人。"

沾上土的豆腐

　　无论刮风还是下雨,总会有一个骑着自行车卖豆腐的老大爷出现在人们的视野内。

　　当嘟嘟,当嘟嘟。

　　老大爷敲打着钟穿梭于胡同之间。

　　"哟,卖豆腐的大爷来了,快给我来一块吧。"

　　大婶们听见老大爷的钟声都出来了。

　　当嘟嘟,当嘟嘟。

　　突然,骑着自行车的老大爷失去了重心,哐地一声摔倒在地上,瞬时间装豆腐的箱子沾满了泥水。

　　"老大爷,有没有事？"

　　一个常买老大爷豆腐的大婶赶紧扶起了老大爷。

　　"啊,我没事,哎呀,豆腐可全完了,看来今天您得去别处买豆腐了。"

　　老爷爷掸掸衣服上的土,站了起来,脸上露出了"今天生意全完了"的失望表情。

老大爷开始把沾上土的豆腐重新放进箱子里。

大婶也帮助老大爷将豆腐放进箱子里，问道：

"老大爷，我要买两块豆腐。"

老大爷一脸懵懂地望着大婶。

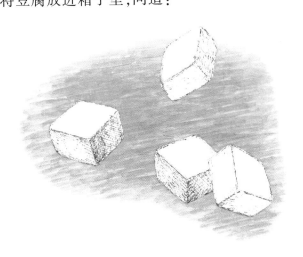

"豆腐都沾上了土呀！"

"我经常买大爷您的豆腐，所以即便您的豆腐沾上了土也没法吃别的豆腐，把沾上土的地方去掉不就能吃了吗？"

"给我也来一块吧。"

"给我来两块。"

看见此种情形的其他大婶们也走过来要买沾上泥土的豆腐。

送给奶奶的阳光

在山坡上有个很大的屋子,里面生活着一位名叫艾儿查的孩子。艾儿查有一位白发苍苍、满脸皱纹的奶奶。浑身无力的奶奶整天在屋子里一动不动地躺着。尽管每天早上太阳都会升起,但由于奶奶的房间是朝北方向的,没有一丝阳光能照射到那里。

"爸爸,为什么奶奶的房间没有阳光照进来?"

艾儿查的父亲这样回答:

"阳光不会从北面的窗户照进来的。"

"那么我们把房屋的方向转一下吧,爸爸。"

"哈哈,但是我们的屋子太大了。"

"那么奶奶的房间就永远也进不来阳光了吗?"

"如果你办不到这件事,那就不要再提了。"

艾儿查为了找到能让奶奶的房间照射到阳光的办法而冥思苦想。

　　"奶奶看到明媚温暖的阳光,一定会很高兴的……"

　　一天,艾儿查感觉到阳光照射在自己的金发上,他低下头发现膝盖上也有阳光。

　　"我要把阳光装起来送给奶奶。"

　　艾儿查用裙子装满了阳光走进奶奶的屋里,把裙子一下子摊开,但是阳光却消失得无影无踪。

　　"我想给奶奶带来些阳光,可是……"

　　艾儿查哭丧着脸,奶奶笑着说:

　　"艾儿查呀,阳光就在你的眼睛和你的金发上,只要你在这里,对我来说没有阳光也无所谓。"

　　艾儿查虽然不能理解为什么阳光在自己的眼中,但是他看见奶奶幸福的表情感到十分高兴。

印地安的灰姑娘

印地安战士风被各部落尊为英雄。很多姑娘都想和力大无比、动作敏捷的风结为夫妻，但是除了风的姐姐以外，风不会让任何人看到自己的样子。

风回到家后，他的姐姐问这些姑娘：

"你们看见我弟弟了吗？"

姑娘们异口同声地回答说看见了，但风是不可能和不诚实的女人结婚的。

在另一个部落的村子里，酋长有三个女儿。两个姐姐十分讨厌她们的妹妹，她们把她的长发剪掉了，只让她穿又脏又难看的衣服。

这两个姐姐也非常想和风结婚，一天她俩也去见风。

天黑后，风牵着雪橇回到家里。

"看见风了吗？"

"是的。"

对风的姐姐的提问撒了谎的两个姐姐同样只能回家了，这时样子难看的妹妹找到了风的家里。

"你看见他了吗？"

"没有。"

风的姐姐对这个说实话的妹妹感到奇怪，又问了一遍。

"现在看见了吗？"

"是的。"

"看见什么了？"

"我看见他用彩虹牵着雪橇，怀抱着用银河做成的弓弦。"

"你的确是看见他了。"

由于妹妹诚实的回答，风露出了自己的模样。就这样她和风结了婚，从此过上了幸福的生活。

报恩的喜鹊

有个射箭技术娴熟的书生去参加科举考试,走在山路上的书生听见了喜鹊凄惨的鸣叫声,于是顺着声音传来的方向找去。原来是一条大蟒蛇吐着蛇信子正爬向喜鹊巢。

"不好,那条大蟒蛇……"

书生觉得鸟巢里的小喜鹊很可怜,迅速拔出箭射死了蟒蛇。小喜鹊的父母在书生的头上不停地盘旋以表示感谢。

由于是在深山里,天色很快就黑了下来。书生看见远处传来微弱的灯光,走近了发现原来是座小寺庙,这时一个身穿白色衣服的女子打开门走了出来。

书生在女子的指引下来到屋子里,放下行李躺在床上。由于走了太长的路的缘故,刚躺下去就进入了梦乡。

没过多久,书生感到胸口堵得慌,几乎喘不上气来,于是睁开了眼睛,原来一条大蟒蛇把自己的身体层层缠住了。

这条大蟒蛇就是书生白天所杀死的蟒蛇的妻子。

"看来你也不喜欢就这样不明不白地死掉，所以我给你一个机会，这个寺庙的后院有一口年代久远的钟，只要你能在子时来临之前把那口钟敲三下我就放过你，哈哈哈！"

于是，大蟒蛇消失了。书生来到寺庙后院一看，那口钟高高地悬挂着，根本不可能敲响。

离子时越来越近了，大蟒蛇又现身了，将书生紧紧缠住准备吃掉他。

"当……当……当……"

就在此时，钟声响了三遍，大蟒蛇立即消失了。好不容易获救的书生来到了钟的下面，发现地上有两只头部全是鲜血的喜鹊。

原来，为了报答白天救自己孩子性命之恩，喜鹊夫妇用尽全身的力量撞向了钟，最后用自己的生命敲响了钟。

书生选择了一个向阳的地方悉心地埋葬了这对喜鹊夫妇。

与狮子在一起

1956 年在非洲的肯尼亚,有一对英国夫妇保护着人们和农作物不受野生动物的侵犯。

一天,他们射杀了一头袭击人类的狮子,发现有三头刚出生不久的小狮子正蜷缩在货车的后面。

"天哪,看来我们杀死了这些孩子的母亲。"

他俩把这些幼小的狮子抱在怀里,用装满牛奶的奶瓶喂养这些小狮子。尽管狮子每天都将家里搞

得乱七八糟,不时还闯一些祸,但是夫妇俩与狮子之间渐渐有了深厚的感情。然而终究不可能将具有野性的狮子一直养在家里面,丈夫向妻子建议把狮子放归自然,但是妻子不同意,最后决定只留下最小的艾尔兹。

就这样,小艾尔兹和夫妇俩住在了一起,艾尔兹把乔伊夫人当成了自己的妈妈。乔伊夫人散步时一定要跟着去,一块儿玩水,连躺在床上也要四脚朝天耍耍小淘气。两年过去了,艾尔兹长成硕大的母狮子,村里的人开始感到不安了。

"把艾尔兹送进动物园吧,人们都在对我们怒目而视。"

"不行,我们不可以把它关起来,还不如把它放回到丛林里。"

从那天开始,乔伊训练艾尔兹成为一个强者,让它和其他野生狮子共处,自己去寻找猎物。但是艾尔兹丧失了野性,经常被其他狮子咬伤,最后跑回夫妇家里。

乔伊开始冷淡地对待艾尔兹,为了能让它自己找食而不给它吃的。几个月后,乔伊带着瘦得不成样子的艾尔兹来到了丛林深处。

最后艾尔兹抓住了一头野猪,它终于成了一头真正的狮子。当乔伊看见艾尔兹走向一头公狮子后,就转身慢慢地离去了。事实上这个故事被拍成了一部名为《野性的艾尔兹》的电影,全世界的人都知道这个讲述狮子和人类之间互爱的故事。

杰 杰 的 爱

6 岁的杰杰虽然还不太懂事，却是个让人恨不起来的捣蛋鬼。这个孩子竟然能和树聊天，拥有令人称奇的感受能力。

杰杰有一个失业的爸爸、在工厂上班的妈妈、两个姐姐和一个哥哥，家里条件十分困难。由于家境贫寒，杰杰有时候还得饿肚子，所以个子长得很矮。

圣诞节来临了，但是杰杰没有收到一份圣诞礼物。

"看来耶稣只是为了富人家的孩子而降临到这个世界上的。"

杰杰望着天空喃喃自语道。

几天后，杰杰回到了学校，但是杰杰却没有钱买午饭，看着杰杰楚楚可怜的样子，班主任有时会塞给杰杰一些硬币。

"拿去买个面包吃吧。"

可杰杰不想要老师给的钱，急忙躲开，当老师想叫住他时，他已跑得无影无踪了。

但是有一天,杰杰没有再拒绝老师给的钱,一言不发地接受了。老师感到有些奇怪,后来才知道其中的原因。

杰杰的班里有一个比杰杰还要穷的孩子,这是个比杰杰个子还小、还要穷、谁也不和他玩的黑人孩子。杰杰把老师每次给的钱买来面包和这个小孩一起分着吃。

从把面包分给比自己还困难的孩子并和他一起玩的杰杰身上,班主任老师领悟到了很多东西。

"是啊,不是只在富裕的时候才去帮助别人啊!"

兄 妹 塔

鸡龙山下面有个小寺庙,百济灭亡后,一个皇族就在这里出家当了和尚。

一天,这个和尚在梦中被奇怪的声音所惊醒,于是他打开房门。门外有一只斑斓猛虎,和尚不禁汗毛倒竖起来。

老虎张开大口,一副奄奄一息的样子。

"怎么了?"

和尚问道,但是老虎只是张大嘴巴,不住地流着眼泪。

和尚看了看老

虎的嘴巴,原来老虎的嘴里面插着一支簪子。

"看来,大概是吃了人才会弄成这样,但不管怎样你也是条生命……"

和尚将老虎口中的簪子拔了出来。

"今后不准害人,知不知道?"

和尚训斥完老虎后,老虎点了点头,转身离开了。

几天后,和尚听见"咚咚"的声音,就打开了房门,老虎背着一个女子放在了他的房门前。

这个女子看见老虎后当场昏过去了,什么也记不起来。和尚每天喂女子进食,悉心照料着她。

一段时间后,和尚把这个女子送回到故乡,但是女子的父母认为,既然和尚救了自己女儿一命,和尚就应把她带走。就这样,这个女子决定出家当尼姑。

之后,和尚和这个女人结为兄妹,毕生都伺奉着佛祖。后世的人们为了赞颂这两人的情意和修行成果,分别修建了7层石塔和5层石塔,这就是"兄妹塔",也被叫做"男妹塔"。

变成星星的七兄弟

　　从前,有个村庄里住着一位寡妇,这个寡妇有七个儿子,七个儿子都非常孝顺,为了母亲什么事情都可以做。

　　一到冬天,儿子们担心母亲冻着,就把房间里的火炕烧得旺旺的。

　　"哎哟,真冷呀!"

　　但是母亲好像把抱怨冷的话语当成了口头禅。

　　"应该把火再生大一点儿。"

　　儿子们又往火炕里添进了很多木头,火炕烧得嗞嗞直响。

　　一天晚上,大儿子起夜,却发现母亲不见了。清晨时分,大儿子发现母亲偷偷地跑回来躺下。

　　第二天晚上,大儿子佯装熟睡,看见母亲出门后就悄悄地跟在后面,母亲正在过着一条没有桥的小河。

　　"哎哟,真冷! 哎哟,真冷!"

母亲脱下鞋子，趟过冰凉的河水，之后不住地咳嗽。

母亲来到对面村子一个卖鞋的光棍老汉家里，两个人一直聊到天亮。

大儿子无法理解母亲的想法，赶紧跑到家里把这件事告诉了弟弟们。

"应该为母亲在河上放上垫脚石。"

于是，七个儿子连夜拿着大石头在河上安放好垫脚石。

第二天清晨，往家赶的母亲看见了垫脚石。亏得这些垫脚石母亲没有脱鞋就安全渡过了河。

"老天爷呀，把石头放在这里的人肯定是心肠十分善良的人，请让他们死后变成星星吧。"

母亲向上天祈求道，上天答应了她的要求，七兄弟死后变成了北斗七星。

遗　产

有个富翁有 10 个儿女。

"我死后会给你们每人 100 个金币。"

富翁经常对儿女这么说，但是在富翁快要死去的时候，他发现要想维持和儿女之间的约定，钱有些不够。

富翁把儿女们叫到面前，按照次序先给了大儿子 100 枚金币。

临到最小的儿子了，富翁让其他儿女都出去一下。

"孩子呀，我给

了你哥哥和姐姐每人 100 枚金币,现在只剩下了 10 枚金币。"

"但是不可能每个人都拿到一样多呀……"

小儿子很难过地回答说。

"最好尽量去遵守与更多人之间的约定,所以我这么做了。至于你,我把我最亲密的 10 个朋友介绍给你,我和他们之间的友情比金币还要珍贵,请你一定要好好珍惜。"

说完此话富翁就咽气了。

置办完丧礼后,拿到 100 枚金币的 9 个儿女们开始四处游玩,整日忙于购买房屋和物品。

小儿子用不多的金币招待了参加父亲葬礼与父亲关系很好的朋友们。

"能想起我们的人就只有你了。"

父亲的朋友们都称赞着小儿子。每个人都送给小儿子一两头家畜,还忠告他要把钱存起来花。

没过多久,在这些兄弟姐妹中小儿子生活得最好。

"比金币更重要的东西是友情。"

小儿子经常会对自己的子女这么说道。

一对穷夫妻和五个孩子

有一对穷夫妻生了五个孩子,但是对面村子里有一对富夫妻却一个孩子也没有。

一天,富夫妻来找穷夫妻。

"大家都知道我们没有孩子,你们可不可以把你们五个孩子中的一个给我们做养子?我们会让他丰衣足食,吃穿不愁的。"

"只要你们能像亲生子女一样对待他,反倒是我该感谢你们了。"

孩子们都入睡后,穷爸爸开始和妈妈商量把哪一个孩子送走,爸爸说:

"还是把最小的老五送走吧。"

但是,妈妈摆了摆手说:

"这个孩子还在吃奶,不行,不能把他送走。"

"那么送二儿子?"

"那个孩子生病了浑身难受着呢，我们应该把他一直照料到病好为止。"

"送大儿子？"

"不行,他是我们家的顶梁柱。"

"四儿子怎么样？整天就知道哭。"

"不行,那个整天哭不懂事的孩子怎么能送给别人呢？"

"那么三儿子可以,他是个就知道捣蛋的淘气包。"

"那更不行了,他更需要我们的爱。"

直到凌晨,穷夫妻俩也没有拿定主意。第二天早上,穷爸爸来到富夫妻家里,这样说道：

"请你们把昨天的事当做没有发生过，无论生活多么艰苦,我们也要用自己的手把子女抚养长大。"

门

深夜,雨淅淅沥沥地下着,街道一片漆黑。

一个女子拖着疲惫的身躯回到故里,因为从小就在这里长大,所以无论再黑找到回家的路总不是什么困难的事。正当她准备敲门时,手却停在了半空中。

"妈妈会欢迎我吗?离开家已经有 10 年了……这么长的时间都没和家里联络,只是自顾自地生活着。"

看见从家里透出来一丝微弱的灯光,女子鼓足了勇气敲了敲门。

意外得很，门就这样被打开了。

"妈妈！"

女子细声地抽泣着，跪倒在母亲的面前。

母亲拍了拍女儿，热情地接待了她。

两个人畅谈了很长时间，最后女儿问：

"以前天黑后，你担心有人进来把门锁得紧紧的，为什么现在你开着门睡觉？要是小偷进来可怎么办？"

女儿说完，母亲用自己粗糙的双手握着女儿的手说道：

"过去10年我一天也没有把门锁上，我是担心，你哪一天回来了，看见门锁了，转身又会走掉……我一直在等着你回来呀。"

用苹果树做成的船

一艘船失事了，船上一个小孩被海浪冲到一个孤岛上，独自活了下来。岛上只有一棵苹果树迎接这个孩子。

"孩子，阳光是不是太晒了？快躲到我的树阴下吧。"

"谢谢！"

孩子坐在阴凉的苹果树下，突然觉得肚子很饿。

"孩子，快摘我的果实吃吧。"

小孩摘下苹果，吃了个痛快。但是还感到肚子有些空荡荡的。

"这样，你掰断我的一支胳膊，用来捉鱼吧。"

小孩用树枝做了一个钓鱼竿，来到海边钓鱼。

但是小孩一想起远方的家人泪水就不住地流下来。

"原来你想妈妈了，可是有你在身旁，我不觉得孤单呀……孩子，不要悲伤了，快用我的身体做艘船吧。"

在一个电闪雷鸣的日子里，喀嚓一声苹果树折断了。

小孩用树做了一艘船，平安地回到了家里。

小孩长大后成为一艘大船的船长，他又找到了小时候曾经停留过的那个孤岛。

"找到了，找到了，就是那个岛！"

船长在船上装着一些苹果树树苗，终于在出发两个星期之后找到了那个岛。岛上的老苹果树只剩下折断的枝干。

"我回来了，从今以后我再不会让你感到孤单了。"

船长精心地在老苹果树的周围种下了几十株苹果树树苗。

养 花 人

　　有个花园里种植了很多鲜花,好像风景画一样美。有个养花人每天照料着这些鲜花,给花浇水拔草,为这些花倾注了全部精力。

　　无论是谁来到这个花园前都会停下脚步。芬芳的花香和美丽的花朵吸引了行人,让人在花园里驻足,流连忘返。

　　但令人无法理解的是,养花人根本看不见这些花。

　　一天,经过花园的人询问道:

　　"听说你是个盲人,那你是怎么照料这些花朵的呢?"

　　养花人回答说:

　　"第一个理由,在我因事故失明前我就喜欢养花了,即使失明后我也没有放弃对养花的喜爱。眼睛虽然看不见,但是我可以触摸花瓣,抚摸叶子,闻到花香。另外一个理由就是因为有着像你这样的人。"

　　"什么? 为了我? 这怎么解释? "

　　"因为你们看见鲜花会感到心情愉悦, 对我来说给别人带来快乐就是我最大的快乐。"

旧 蚊 帐

在日本,有个名叫岩崎的人,他是创建三菱公司的大企业家。

他花了很多钱买了一座豪宅,并将家里装修得富丽堂皇,过着令人羡慕的生活。

一个阳光刺眼的夏日。

已经 80 岁高龄的母亲把一个包袱递到了岩崎的面前。

"孩子呀,这是我们家的宝物,希望你能好好地保管。"

母亲拿出了一个破旧的蚊帐。

"这不是我小时候睡觉时用的蚊帐么?母亲,你为什么没扔掉一直保留到现在?"

"还记着闷热的夏夜里我和你在月光下挂着蚊帐,听着虫叫声进入梦乡吗?我想让你不要忘记过去虽然艰苦但十分珍贵的日子。"

岩崎想起了童年时与母亲相依为命的艰苦岁月,于是把

旧蚊帐紧紧地抱在胸前。

　　"今后我一定不会忘记母亲的话。"

　　岩崎的眼中泛着泪光，旧蚊帐所蕴含的意义已深深地印在了他的心中。

　　岩崎对自己过去豪华奢侈的生活重新做了一番审视。

心中的小提琴

"我长大后要成为一个出色的人，要为人们带来美的享受。"

怀有这种想法的安东尼奥·斯特拉迪巴利乌斯既学习演奏小提琴又埋头苦练歌唱技巧。

但是要想成为音乐家决不是一件简单的事情。

"我既没有萨尔瓦多那样的嗓音，也没有朱利奥那样超凡的小提琴演奏技巧，看来我肯定成不了一个优秀的音乐家了，但是……"

安东尼奥没有继续迷惘下去，他拿着用爷爷传下的雕刻刀做成的作品，找到了一位叫阿玛提的老人，老人是意大利最有名的小提琴制作工匠。

"老爷爷，我也可以制作小提琴么？"

"为什么你会这么想？"

"我的嗓音条件不好，也不太会演奏乐器，但是为了音乐我愿意做任何事。"

"是吗？搞音乐有很多种方式,但不管哪一种方式最重要的是内心,在做每一把小提琴时你要把自己的心全部倾注在里面,这样才能诞生出优秀的乐器。"

在阿玛提老人的激励下,安东尼奥开始学做小提琴,直到40岁他的名字才被人们所熟知,他一生共制作了1116把小提琴。

在他逝世260年后的今天,斯特拉迪巴利乌斯制作的小提琴那神秘而又美丽的音色仍在打动着人们的心弦,大概是由于小提琴不仅凝结着他的手艺,也蕴藏了他内心的歌唱。

心中的晚霞

英国年轻的画家特纳正在画一幅名为《晚霞》的画。

一天，一个天文学家找到特纳，天文学家仔细地欣赏着正在创作中的画，显示出极大的兴趣。

当特纳终于完成这幅画的时候，天文学家这样说道：

"真是太美的晚霞了，美得令人窒息，从来没见过有这么美的晚霞，嗯……以我天文学家的眼光来看，这个世界上不可能有这样的晚霞，那你是看什么画出来

的呢？"

特纳平静地回答说：

"博士您的话很对，这样的晚霞连我自己到现在也没有看过，所以我要把它画出来，博士，您也希望看到这样的晚霞吧。"

听到这里，天文学家不禁脸红了。

"年轻的画家，我似乎暂时模糊了学术和艺术之间的差别了。我忘记了把实际中不存在、只存在人们梦中的美丽世界表现出来这才是艺术家要做的工作呀。"

感动天文学家的特纳，凭借着对阳光的绚丽呈现而获得了极高的评价，这对后来的印象派画家产生了深远的影响。

小　鸟

有个因犯下杀人罪被关在看守所的犯人，他的名字叫罗伯特·斯特拉伍德，因为脾气火爆，和所有人的关系都十分紧张。

一天，狱警编造了各种借口把来探视他的母亲打发走了。生气的斯特拉伍德追问这个狱警为什么这么做，最后两人发生了激烈的冲突，狱警在冲突中死亡。

为了救儿子母亲四处奔走，最后在母亲的帮助下罗伯特·斯特拉伍德被轻判为无期徒刑。

他被关在单独牢房里，过着沉闷而毫无意义的日子。

有一天，他在散步途中看见一只快要死去的麻雀。

"你的处境和我没什么两样啊。"

他想让这只麻雀获得自由，在他的精心护理下，这只麻雀又飞上了天空。

麻雀飞走后，感到空虚的他又买了一对金丝雀喂养起来。

在单独牢房里养金丝雀不是一件简单的事。为了把鸟养好,他开始去图书馆找书看,还拜托母亲找一些有关鸟的书籍和药品,独自开始研究起来。

最后,他为喜爱鸟的人在一份学术杂志上,发表了一篇有关鸟的疾病和治疗方法的文章。

他的研究结果震惊了全世界,他用自己小学都没毕业的学历在单独牢房里攻克了鸟类学家都难以解决的难题。一个女子在看完了报纸有关他的报道后深受感动,便时不时和他见面。两人在一起讨论有关鸟的话题,这个女子渐渐地感到其实他是个热心肠人,最后两个人结为夫妻。

小 王 子

"星星真的很美丽呀，它美丽是因为上面有很多看不见的花儿……"

"那当然。"我答道。尔后，我便默默地望着月光下的沙丘。

"沙漠也很美……"

小王子又说道。的确是这样，我一直很喜欢沙漠。我们坐在沙丘上，什么也看不见，什么也听不见。但是在这一片寂静之中，有个东西在闪光。

"使沙漠变美丽的，是不知在什么地方藏着一口井。"

小王子说道。听到此话，我突然理解了沙漠的神秘。

小时候，传说我住的那栋房子下埋着宝贝。当然了，没有人能发现它，也许根本就没人想去找它。但是就因为这一点，那栋房子才令人神往，其中深藏着这个秘密。

"是啊，不论是房子、星星或是沙漠，这些美丽的东西都是因为有着肉眼看不见的东西。"

　　"我很高兴叔叔和我的狐狸有着相同的看法。"
小王子说。

　　这时,小王子睡着了,我把他抱在怀里重新上路了。

竹子呀竹子

在古代中国的吴国,有个叫孟宗的人。孟宗的母亲生了病躺在床上,孟宗悉心照料着母亲,可母亲的病却一天比一天厉害。

"孩子呀,我很想吃一种东西。"

"母亲,您就说吧,我一定会为您找到的。"

"我想吃竹笋,吃了竹笋后我就会感到有力气了。"

"母亲,您先等一下,我这就去给您找。"

为找到竹笋,孟宗来到竹林里,开始四处寻找。

但是在地面被冻得硬邦邦的严冬季节是不可能有竹笋的。

孟宗一屁股坐在地上哭了起来。

"竹子呀竹子,你快帮帮我吧,我的母亲很想吃竹笋呀。"

孟宗伤心地哭了好一阵子,孟宗流下的眼泪温暖了已上冻的地面,这时两棵竹笋冒了出来。孟宗用衣袖擦了擦眼泪,对着竹子行了一个大礼。

　　"竹子呀竹子,太谢谢你了,我要赶紧回去为母亲煮汤。"

　　孟宗摘下竹笋回到家中,为母亲煮了一锅热腾腾的汤。久病不起的母亲喝完汤后,很快就精神抖擞地坐起来了。

　　"连老天爷也被孟宗的一片孝心所打动了。"

　　村里的人都十分高兴,称赞着孟宗。

埋在地里的银锅

这是发生在朝鲜时代的事。有个很早失去丈夫、靠做针线活来抚养两个儿子的母亲。

一个下雨天，从屋檐落下的雨水滴答滴答地落在地面上，地面被敲出了一个个水坑，突然有个水坑里露出了一个银制锅盖的一角。

"天哪，这里怎么会有一口锅呢？"

母亲赶紧打开锅盖，锅里装的全是闪闪发光的银子。

"哇，不管是谁放在这里的，从今往后再也不用过苦日子了。"

母亲长舒了口气，决定把锅取出来，突然，她又改变了想法。

"不行，不行，飞来的横财可能会带来灾祸的。"

母亲又重新把银锅埋好，卖了房子，搬到别的地方住了。

时光流逝，两个儿子在科举考试中全都金榜题名，在他

们荣归故里的时候,母亲这才把银锅的事情说了出来。

"现在即使我死去和你爸爸相见,也不会感到羞愧了。要是有了那口银锅你们变得懒惰的话,恐怕我也享受不到现在的快乐了。"

母亲望着在贫苦生活中仍保持着正直和善良优秀品格的两个儿子,心里感到十分满足。

写在手绢上的信

夏尼是名被错判入狱的法国男子,监狱里既没有书也没有笔和纸,夏尼在监狱里过着郁闷的日子。

一个温暖的春日,夏尼在院子里散步,忽然,他发现石头缝里冒出了一株浅绿色的嫩芽。

"好险踩上,我要小心照看它。"

夏尼每天守护着嫩芽,为它的生长担心,是不是蔫了,有没有被人踩死。每次在看守清扫院子的时候,他都把心提到了嗓子眼里,生怕扫走了那株嫩芽。

最终夏尼向看守吐露了心声。

"那儿长着一株十分娇小柔弱的花儿,您在打扫时能注意一下吗?"

"哈哈,你认为我会杀死那株花吗?"

幸运的是,看守热情地答应了他。夏尼直向这名看守点头致谢,此后他就更把全部精力倾注在这株花上了,还给它起了个美丽的名字——皮奇奥拉。

皮奇奥拉在爱护下长得越发动人,但有一天它开始凋零了,原来是院子里的石头挤住了皮奇奥拉。

夏尼想让皮奇奥拉活下去。夏尼请求看守帮助他,但是根据监狱里的规定任何人都不能随便移动石头,只有一个人例外,那就是国王。

夏尼掏出一条手绢,用自制的墨水把自己虽然简短但十分诚恳的心声写在了上面。

之后,夏尼请一位少女帮他把这条手绢交给国王,但是写在手绢上的信没交到国王手中,却传到了王后那里。

"喜欢鲜花的人是不可能犯罪的, 把这么善良的人关在监狱里是不对的。"

经过长时间的等待,国王最终下旨了,同意为了花把石头移走,并且释放了夏尼。

八 马 碑

　　崔石是高丽忠烈王朝顺天府的巡抚,他清正廉洁,从不收受贿赂,反而会捐钱给遭遇不幸的人们。

　　"他要是能一直在这里当官就好了……"

　　但情况与村民们的愿望有所不同,崔石得到升迁要去汉城上任。村民们听到这个消息后都很难过。

　　村民们送给即将去汉城上任的崔石八匹骏马,送给离开巡抚职位的官员八匹骏马是当时的风俗。

　　"我不能收下这些马,这么珍贵的礼物我怎么可能收呢?"

　　崔石对村民们说。

　　"不行,您必须带走这些马,这是我们祖上传下来的风俗。"

　　"是的,如果您不拿走的话,我们会受到惩罚的。"

　　既然村民这么说,崔石没有再拒绝下去,带上所有的马

前往汉城。

一天，养马的仆人慌慌张张地跑了进来。

"老爷，有喜事了，刚才马下了一个崽。"

听到仆人的话，崔石也感到非常高兴。

"太好了，等到这匹小马驹有力气了，就把这些马都送回顺天吧。"

"老爷，可是……"

"哎，不用再说了，被人说成关心百姓的我，怎么可以把八匹对百姓十分珍贵的马拿走呢？按我说的去做吧。"

不久，包括小马驹在内的九匹马被送回到顺天，顺天百姓们为了感谢崔石的爱民之心，特意立了一座八马碑。

白色的花边

很久以前,一名像孔雀般优雅的女子和一名像狮子般强壮的男子生活在一起。男的出门打猎,为家里换取食物,女的则在家里纺线,两人过着幸福的生活。

可是有一天,突然爆发的战争打破了村子里的宁静,这个男人和其他男人一同被派往战场。

"你一定要回来呀,要自己保重身体。"

几个月过去了,女子还在漫长的等待中受着煎熬。

最后部落终于赢得了战争的胜利。参与战争的其他男人都回到了家人的怀抱,但这个女人的丈夫却没有回来。

沉浸于悲伤之中的女人不和任何人说话,也不再跳舞了。

有天清晨,女子进入茂密的丛林里。

东方破晓,天空渐渐变红,树叶上凝结着摇摇欲坠的露珠。

"那个花边真美啊，咦？我好像在上面看见了我丈夫的面容。"

女子始终注视着那个花边，最后发现那不是什么花边，而是结在树枝上的蜘蛛网，所谓丈夫的面容是蜘蛛网上悬挂的树叶所形成的影子。

"对，从今天开始我要编织花边，编个和那个蜘蛛网一样洁白美丽的边，万一找到我丈夫的话，我要用编织的花边盖在他的身上。"

此后，女子就拿出针线编起花边，她所编的花边已经超越了一般的花草图案，对丈夫的爱、思念甚至痛苦全都编织在了里面，可以说那是世界上最好看的花边。从那以后，全世界的女人都开始编织像蜘蛛网一样优雅美丽的花边。

这个人也是朝鲜人

　　流亡的金九先生在中国东北掀起朝鲜独立运动时,采用各种方式同日本人进行斗争,被日本人视为眼中钉。

　　日本宪兵队为抓住金九先生绞尽了脑汁,他们在得到金九先生在中国东北活动的消息后,制定了暗杀计划。

　　"总是有很多人保护金九,我们日本人很难接近他,怎么办呢?"

　　"既然日本人不行的话就用朝鲜人……"

　　于是日本宪兵队开始了暗杀金九先生的行动,日本宪兵队买通了一个朝鲜青年,并对他进行训练。不久之后,那个青年人接近了金九先生,但是那个青年可疑的行动引起了其他独立运动家的注意,于是抓住了他。

　　"处死这个败类! 处死他!"

　　独立运动家们高声大喊要处死这个青年。

　　此时,金九先生走到青年的面前,把这个低着头的青年紧紧抱在怀里。

"能在中国东北的土地上遇见我想见却见不到的朝鲜青年真是高兴,放这个青年走吧。"

周围的人面面相觑,感到十分诧异。

"饶了他?也许他会再暗杀先生的,不行。"

"就放过他吧,这个人和我们一样也是朝鲜人啊。"

金九先生微笑地望着青年这样说道。听了金九的话,青年低下头,流下了眼泪。

此后,青年加入了光复军,为了朝鲜的独立一直斗争到底。

草坪上的癞蛤蟆

有个富人拥有一大片草坪。

这个富人把"不劳无获"这句话当做家训,非常讨厌懒惰的人。

富人有一个上小学的女儿,但即使是自己的女儿,只要她不做事也照样不给她零花钱。

"你把草坪好好修剪一下,我给你零花钱。"

父亲让女儿去剪草,女儿毫无怨言,认真地修剪起草坪,最后草坪被修剪得十分整齐。

父亲环视了一下草坪,对女儿的表现十分满意,但是有一处草坪没有被修剪。

"你没剪那里,你必须对自己所做的事负责,因为这次你没做好,所以我要从给你的零花钱中扣除一些。"

"好的,爸爸,听您的。"

见女儿宁愿放弃一部分零花钱也不剪那块草坪,父亲摇了摇脑袋。

"有什么特别的理由吗？"

"这……"

女儿停顿了一下,接着说道:

"请不要剪那块草坪,可以吗？"

女儿的话让父亲更加疑惑。

父亲想搞清楚怎么回事,就来到那块没被剪的草坪前。他仔细看了看草坪,发现那里有好几只癞蛤蟆,很明显是一家子。原来女儿是担心把这些癞蛤蟆赶走才没有剪那里的。

父亲的脸立刻由阴转晴。

"把癞蛤蟆看得比零花钱还重要,我为你感到骄傲。"

父亲抚摩着女儿的头发,给了女儿更多的零花钱。

马 夫 的 心

寒冷的冬日,一辆载着旅客的马车行走在山路上。一个年轻女子抱着吃奶的孩子坐在雪地里,看见马车后,年轻女子挥着手费力地喊道:

"请把我带上马车吧。"

马夫下车看了看,也许再过一会儿这个年轻女子就会被冻死。

马夫不知是出于什么想法,他只把孩子从女子的怀里抢过来交给马车上的人,随后驾起马车就走了。

被突然抢走孩子的女人试图登上马车,但是就在女子要追上马车时,马车又跑开了,总离女子一段距离。

"你这个坏蛋,快把孩子还给我!"

女子大喊着,使劲追赶着马车。

但是马夫在女人快追上时马上会给马一鞭子。就这样,马车像生了气一样总是和女子保持着一段距离。

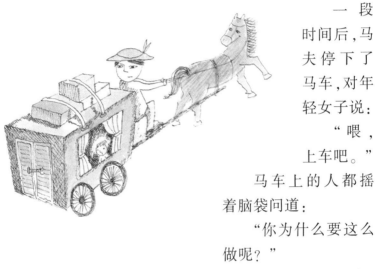

一段时间后,马夫停下了马车,对年轻女子说:

"喂,上车吧。"

马车上的人都摇着脑袋问道:

"你为什么要这么做呢?"

"这是因为,当时就那样让她上车的话,她会马上死去。我想让她身体发热、血液循环起来,所以故意让她在后面追赶。"

年轻女子出了一头汗,脸色也好多了,最后女子向马夫表示了衷心的感谢。

希波克拉底誓言

被称为"医学之父"的希波克拉底是古希腊的医学家,他毕生致力于对疾病症状、致病原因和治疗方法的研究,但更令世人称道的是他首先对医生必须承担的责任和遵守的伦理道德进行了阐述,他的医术很特别,在记录病人病情时表现得很冷静,在治疗时又给病人温馨的感觉。

时至今日,希波克拉底誓言仍是所有从医人员的行医准则,让我们再重温一下这些让人心头一热的文字吧。

我会像对待亲生父母一样去尊敬和爱戴教授我医术的老师。

如果谁需要分享我的财产或需要我的帮助,我会义无反顾。

我会把他的子女当做我的兄弟,在他们需要我的医术时,我会不计代价地传授给他们。

我会按照医疗法规，用训导、讲义以及一切能动员的方法不仅把医术传给我的儿子，还要传给我老师的子女们，或誓约规定的其他人。

我所使用的疗法都是为了患者的利益，决不能对患者有害。

不管什么人来请求，也决不使用毒药，也不再和这人交往。

尤其不能帮助女人堕胎。

不论何时都要克制自己错误和堕落的

行为，尤其在面对男人和女人的诱惑时，也不要去尝试不论是否会造成后患的不端举动。

在照料患者的时候，看到或听到与患者私生活有关的事后一定保持沉默，把它当成一个神圣的秘密。

纯洁和神圣将始终陪伴在我的从医生涯中。

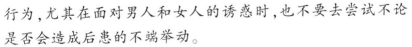

令人高兴的"水"

从小就不能看、不能听、不能说的海伦·凯勒在自传中写道,由于遇见了安·瑟里本先生自己才明白"水"这个单词的含义:

冰凉的水从我一只手上流过,在我另一只手上瑟里本先生写下了"水"这个单词。刚开始很慢,后来逐渐变快了……我一动不动地站在那里,集中全部精力去体会他手指的移动。突然间我感到曾经失去的什么东西一点点地又重新回来了,是语言的那种神秘感向我走来。我认识到"水"这种东西是一种会在我的手上流过、有些冰凉但十分有趣的物体。这个鲜活的单词唤醒了我的灵魂,给我带来光芒和希望,让我获得自由。离开井的时候,我心里充满了对学习的渴望。所有的东西都有自己的名字,这些名字给了我许多新的想法。回到家里,我感到我手触碰到的物体都是有生命的。对事物的神秘感和新鲜感又重新回到我身上,我看见了所有的东西。

进门后我想起了被我打碎的玩偶，我朝壁炉方向摸过去，捡起了玩偶碎片。我想把它们粘在一起，但这只能是徒劳。我的眼睛噙着泪水，我这才明白了我都做过了什么，生平第一次感到悔恨和痛苦。

后来我又学了很多话，虽然不能全都记住，但爸爸、妈妈、弟弟、老师这些词我还能记住。那天晚上我躺在床上想：这个世界上大概没有比我更幸福的孩子了。我很高兴，第一次期待新的一天赶快到来。

做你想做的事

19世纪的女探险家伊达·法伊福是在哥哥和弟弟的陪伴下长大的,因此小时候她从不玩洋娃娃和过家家,喜欢舞刀弄棒。

"孩子呀,你怎么玩得和其他女孩子不一样呢?女孩子家要端庄点儿。"

母亲总是在伊达·法伊福的耳边唠叨,想把她培养成为一个淑女。时光飞逝,伊达·法伊福与母亲安排好的男子结了婚。

但是这种强迫的婚姻生活没过多久就走到了尽头,伊达天天无聊地打发着时光。

一天,伊达去叔父所在的地方旅行,生平

头一次看见了大海。

无边无际的水平线，深绿色的大海，翻滚的波涛，在天空中不时朝前冲刺的海鸥，看到这些伊达暗下决心。

"这世上竟还有这样的地方……是啊，以前我都白活了，今后我不要再做傻瓜了，傻到认为是女人就把自己关起来。"

当时，伊达·法伊福40岁。之后，伊达很轻松地只拎着一箱行李，开始了长达9个月的旅行，她去了耶路撒冷、埃及和意大利。她在旅途中坚持写的日记被出版成书，此后的16年她一直在旅行。伊达·法伊福所走过的路程加起来足足能绕地球8圈。

理所当然，伊达·法伊福成为"柏林地球科学协会"最早的女会员。

霍尔莱婆婆

有个寡妇有一个美丽又勤劳的继女儿和一个丑陋又懒惰的亲女儿。

一天,继女儿来到井边转动辘轳时,辘轳一下子掉进井里了。继女儿想把辘轳捡上来,不料扑通一声掉进了井里。

她醒来后,睁开眼看了看四周,发现自己正躺在明媚阳光下的绿色草地上。继女儿穿过草地,看见烤炉里的面包。

"快把我们拿出来吧!再过一会儿我们就要被烧焦了。"

少女赶紧用长木头勺子把面包取了出来。

又走了好一阵子,少女来到一棵结满累累果实的苹果树前。

"来晃晃我吧,我结的苹果都熟到可以吃的程度了。"

心地善良的少女摇了摇苹果树,少女将如雨般落下的苹果仔细地堆好后,又上路了。

这回出现了一个小草屋,牙齿有一扇门那么大的一个老婆婆正看着窗外。

"孩子呀,不要害怕,我叫霍尔莱婆婆,你和我住在一起,帮我好好抖一抖我的被子,好么?如果你那么做的话全世界会下一场大雪的。"

少女留下来真心帮助霍尔莱婆婆。几天后,少女开始想家了,猜到少女心思的婆婆说道:

"你真是个诚实勤快的孩子,我要送给你一件礼物。"

霍尔莱婆婆打开房门,金子哗地倾泻在地上,少女的身体也被金子所覆盖。

知道了这件事的继母出于对黄金的贪婪,也让她丑陋懒惰的女儿跳进井里。但是懒女儿怕手弄脏没有去救炉子里的面包,担心打到自己头上也没有晃苹果树,来到霍尔莱婆婆家也整天什么活也不干,最后霍尔莱婆婆把金子换成了漆黑的油,就这样懒女儿淋了一身回到家里。

管仲和鲍叔牙

生活于春秋时代的管仲和鲍叔牙从小就是非常要好的朋友,但是由于皇帝被侄儿所杀,王位被夺后,鲍叔牙就跟随太子、管仲跟随太子弟各自流亡到别国。

后来太子登上王位,跟随太子弟的管仲要被处死。这时鲍叔牙恳求大王放过他的朋友。

免于一死的管仲后来做了大官,受到众人的尊敬。

管仲留给了人们这样的话。

"我之所以能有今天的成就全都与我的朋友鲍叔牙分不开。以前我和鲍叔牙一起做过生意,挣来的钱我会多拿些,但是鲍叔牙知道我是因为家境困难才这样做的,所以没说。我也曾做过本是为了鲍叔牙却反令他很为难的事,这个时候鲍叔牙认为人做的事既有有利的一面,也有不利的一面,所以也没指责我。我升过三次官,也有三次被贬的经历,这个时候鲍叔牙知道是我运气不好,所以也没有说我无能。当我在战

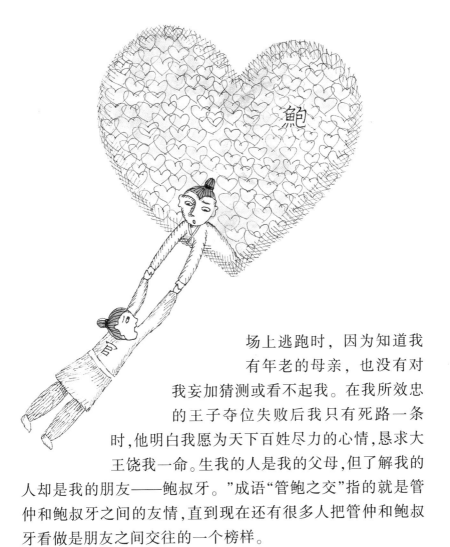

场上逃跑时，因为知道我有年老的母亲，也没有对我妄加猜测或看不起我。在我所效忠的王子夺位失败后我只有死路一条时，他明白我愿为天下百姓尽力的心情，恳求大王饶我一命。生我的人是我的父母，但了解我的人却是我的朋友——鲍叔牙。"成语"管鲍之交"指的就是管仲和鲍叔牙之间的友情，直到现在还有很多人把管仲和鲍叔牙看做是朋友之间交往的一个榜样。

老　　马

我们村子里住着一位名叫皮蒙·奇莫珀的老人，今年90岁。老人驼着背，走路拄着拐杖，满脸的皱纹。

我们家有一匹名叫奥洛劳克的老马。一次，母亲对我们说骑马会使心情变得很舒畅，大哥就骑在马上围着园子转，不时给奥洛劳克一鞭子，它飞快地向前冲去。

二哥和三哥也都骑上马绕着园子跑几圈后，一直跑到山脚下，然后回到马厩里。

奥洛劳克喘着粗气，脖子上都是汗水。

我想在哥哥们面前表现一把我骑马的技术。

"快起来！快跑起来！"

我使出浑身力气鞭打着马，但是奥洛劳克摇摇晃晃的像是要往前走，却直往后退。

"再狠抽一鞭子，使点劲儿。"

这时，佣人拉住我的袖口，阻止了我。

　　"少爷,以后再骑吧。为什么要让马受苦呢?我的马已经 20 岁了,它太累了,连喘气都十分费劲。你看看它有多老了,和皮蒙·奇莫珀爷爷差不多一样老,少爷你不觉得它很可怜么?"

　　我赶紧从马背上下来,马的胸部被汗水浸透了,从鼻孔中呼出的气息也很微弱,不时摇一下已经掉光毛的尾巴。我吻了一下奥洛劳克湿透的脖子,祈求它原谅。

　　如今已是大人的我时常会觉得那匹马真可怜,每当人们给马带来痛苦的时候奥洛劳克和皮蒙·奇莫珀马上会浮现在我的脑海中。

装满稻谷的船

宋朝有个叫范顺仁的人。范顺仁为人善良, 心胸宽广。一天, 父亲让顺仁去运 500 石稻谷。

顺仁运着 500 石稻子往家赶, 走到端阳时遇到了好久没见的朋友, 这个朋友看起来浑身没有力气。

"你怎么一点儿精神都没有? 有什么烦心事吗? "

"我父亲去世了, 但是家里太穷, 连后事都办不了。"

听到此话, 顺仁便把装满稻谷的船整个送给了那个朋友, 随后回到家里向父亲复命。

"终于平安无事地回来了, 累

不累？”

"不累,但是我在回来的路上遇见了一个朋友,他的父亲死了,但让我朋友痛苦的是他竟没钱把父亲安葬。"

"什么？你没把装满稻子的船送给他吧？"

"我是把船给他了。"

范顺仁的父亲非但没有责怪他,反而捋着胡须,非常满意儿子的举动。

"哈哈哈,做得好,这才叫友情呀。"

司令的怀表

在陆军司令的生日宴会上，司令钟爱的怀表不翼而飞。司令和警卫队长顾不上礼节，对每个人搜身，众人心里虽然很不好受，但都强忍着接受了搜身。可怎么搜也找不出那块表。

最后只剩下一个人了，他是司令忠实的部下。警卫队长这样说道：

"十分抱歉，你也得接受搜身。"

"不行，你们不能搜我的身。"

"什么？那我只能怀疑是你干的了！"

"就算你怀疑我也没办法，反正我不会答应你们搜身的。"

此时站在一旁的司令发话了：

"他是我最喜爱的部下，也是我这些部下中最正直的一个。那就别搜他身了。"

警卫队长只好不再要求司令的这个部下接受搜身。

　　当天晚上,回到家里的司令在换衣服时从脱下的衣服里找到了那块怀表。他满脸通红,羞愧难当,立刻想起了拒绝搜身的部下。

　　"为什么他要冒着被误认为是小偷的风险也要拒绝搜身呢?"

　　第二天,司令把这名部下叫过来,问他原因。

　　"司令您也知道,我家里很穷。在昨晚的宴会上我在口袋里装满了剩余的食物,我想带回去给我的孩子和辛苦劳累的妻子。听说要翻口袋我感到非常难为情,所以甘愿接受处罚。"

　　司令拍了拍部下的后背,说道:

　　"你真是一名优秀的军人。"

砖瓦匠的孩子

　　爱德蒙多·戴·阿马奇斯写了一本书叫《爱的学校》,全书讲述了一个名叫爱利克的 4 年级孩子一年里与家人、朋友之间相处的故事以及学校里的生活,书里还包括了其他很多美丽的故事。

　　爱利克的父亲让爱利克在每个星期天把朋友们召集到自己家里玩,这样班里的孩子都成了爱利克的朋友。

　　12 月的一个星期天,一个砖瓦匠的孩子来爱利克的家里玩。砖瓦匠的孩子穿着他爸爸的衣服,衣服已被石灰全部染成了白色,砖瓦匠的孩子把湿漉漉的帽子插在口袋里。

　　爱利克和砖瓦匠的孩子坐在沙发上一边吃着面包和葡萄,一边兴高采烈地玩着积木。

　　但是当砖瓦匠的孩子从沙发上起身时,只见坐的地方覆盖了一层白色的粉尘。

　　正当爱利克想去掸掉粉尘时,父亲没让砖瓦匠的孩子察觉,悄无声地阻止了他。爱利克不明白父亲为什么这么做。

后来父亲这样说:

"孩子呀,你知道我为什么不让你掸沙发吗?要是你掸沙发,你的朋友看到后会自责的,觉得对不起我们。那么做是不对的,因为那个孩子不是故意的,那个孩子的父亲不是在做着肮脏的工作,粉末、石灰、油漆,这些都是我们所必需的东西。劳动是不脏的,看见从工地里回来的劳动者,说他们'脏'是不对的,应该说'衣服上有劳动过的痕迹'。这一点你要牢牢记住。还有,你要好好对待砖瓦匠的孩子,他是你最为重要的朋友,因为他是认真工作的人的儿子。"

跨越湖水的爱

　　新西兰有个名为劳特鲁尔的湖泊,关于这个湖泊流传着一个美丽的传说。

　　从前,在劳特鲁尔湖中的毛拉伊尔岛上生活着阿莱哈部落,在劳特鲁尔湖畔居住着辛斯特部落。

　　阿莱哈部落酋长的女儿希奈莫奈和辛斯特部落的青年杜塔尼卡背着所有人偷偷相爱。

　　杜塔尼卡无时不思念着敌对部落酋长的女儿希奈莫奈,一到晚上就会来到湖边吹起笛子。

　　"杜塔尼卡在呼唤我呢,我马上就来了。"

　　希奈莫奈听见笛声,在月光下划着独木舟渡过湖面。两人总是紧握着对方的手,一直呆到天亮。

　　但是这件事最终还是被希奈莫奈的父亲发现了。

　　"去把我们村子所有的独木舟都烧了,让希奈莫奈再也渡不了湖。"

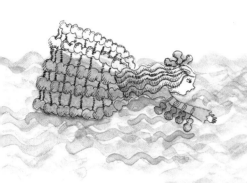

　　希奈莫奈的父亲火冒三丈，不让女儿再划船去那里，但是一无所知的杜塔尼卡那天晚上仍旧吹起了笛子。

　　听见笛声的希奈莫奈无法入睡。

　　"杜塔尼卡，你等着我，无论如何，我都要渡过湖水。"

　　希奈莫奈在身上绑上了几十个水瓢，游过了宽阔的湖面。

　　希奈莫奈的父亲被他们的爱所打动，决心与辛斯特部落和好，就这样两人终于走到了一起。

奈尔的梦想

牛奶配送员奈尔有一个梦想。奈尔最想做的事是用画笔把天空和田野、男人和女人、高兴和喜悦表现出来。奈尔梦想成为鲁本斯那样出色的画家,每当送牛奶和躺在田野里的时候他都会对小狗法特拉谢说出自己的梦想。

"我一定要成为知名的画家,这样我就可以让爷爷穿上毛衣,给他画一幅非常精神的肖像画了。给法特拉谢买一条金项链。然后对着周围邻居们说:'嗨,只有这条狗才是我的朋友。'再盖一栋用白色大理石建造的豪宅,把生活贫穷但喜欢做好事的人们叫来住在一起。就像我对鲁本斯的画产生梦想和希望那样,我也要把我的画拿给他们看,和他们通宵达旦地聊着梦想和希望。"

但是人们不能理解奈尔的梦。女朋友阿尔劳亚的父亲考杰兹看不起奈尔,想拆散他俩。

爷爷对奈尔说:

"奈尔呀,我们是穷人,我们必须欣然地接受贫困这个现实。我们首先要做的事情应当是为了赶走贫困而努力工作。"

　　奈尔听到爷爷的话点了点头,但是仍没有放弃梦想。

　　在圣诞节的晚上,奈尔又冷又饿,在月光下见到了鲁本斯那光芒四射的画作。

　　"法特拉谢,仔细瞧瞧,这就是鲁本斯的画,名叫《世界的宝贝》,我一直梦想着看到这幅画,能和你一起看到这幅画我真是太幸福了。"

比大人更明智的孩子们

早春的一天，马拉夏和阿克流西卡走在路上。突然两个少女发现路边有个水洼儿，于是两人脱下鞋袜，把裙子挽起来，走进水里。

"马拉夏，不要撩水了，小心脚下。"

阿克流西卡的话音刚落，马拉夏就扑通一声大力踩了一下水。阿克流西卡的外套上立刻沾满了泥水，十分生气的阿克流西卡跑过去想揍马拉夏一顿，马拉夏开始往家里逃去，这时阿克流西卡的母亲看见了女儿身上的外套全是泥水。

"这是怎么回事？谁干的？"

"马拉夏干的。"

阿克流西卡的母亲发火了，抓住马拉夏一顿痛打。马拉夏声嘶力竭地哭喊着，马拉夏的母亲听到哭声，跑了过来。

"你凭什么打我的孩子？"

马拉夏的母亲开始理论起来。听见两个母亲在吵架，男

人们出来了。认识马拉夏和阿克流西卡的人聚在一起，邻里之间的吵架越闹越大。结果拳脚横飞，相互推搡着，难听的话脱口而出。

阿克流西卡的奶奶想来劝架，但毫无用处。

在大人们打架的时候，阿克流西卡掸掉了衣服上的泥土，又来到水里准备弄一个过道。看到此种情形，马拉夏坐在旁边，手里拿着木块，帮着阿克流西卡干活。两个人像没打过架一样开心地打闹着。

这时，阿克流西卡的奶奶喊道：

"快看那里，孩子们早已忘掉刚才的事，正在高兴地玩着呢。孩子们比大人要明智得多呀！"

大人们都感到十分羞愧，陆续回到家中。

小 火 车 头

小火车头是一个勇敢诚实的火车头。小火车头用力地拉着客车车厢去往各地。

"喊嚓喊嚓！喊嚓喊嚓！"

终于来到高耸的山坡下。

"喊嚓喊嚓！喊嚓喊嚓！没有我去不了的地方。"

但是他突然有种异样感觉，他的身体根本无法移动。

小火车头赶紧把客车车厢从自己的身体上分开，自己先跑到山坡上，向大火车头请求帮助。

"你帮帮我好么？车厢又长又重，我一个人很难上去。"

"孩子呀，我要马上干完活，现在我正在仔细地擦着身体,好让它露出光泽,所以我帮不了你。"

小火车头喊嚓喊嚓地又跑到另一个很有力气的火车头那里,说出了同样的请求,但同样也遭到了拒绝。

过了一会儿,小火车头遇见了一个和自己体型一样廋小的火车头。

"你能帮帮我吗? 我一个人很难爬上这个山坡。"

"好的,我们一起试试看。"

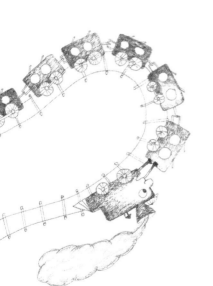

就这样两个小火车头一个在前面拉,一个在后面推,开始艰难地翻越山坡。

喊喊喊! 喊嚓嚓,喊嚓嚓! 嘟嘟嘟! 嘭嘭嘭!

客车车厢缓缓移动了,他们开始慢慢地行驶在山坡上。

"我们成功了! 我们成功了! "

两个小火车头一起朝前移动着,最终翻越了山坡。他们心里都十分满足,又开始喊嚓喊嚓地上路了。

伤 疤 脸

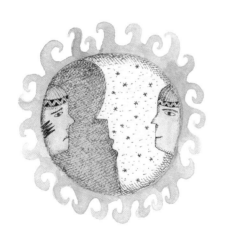

有个被称做"伤疤脸"的印地安青年，由于小时候打猎遇到了灰熊，在与灰熊的搏斗中脸部受伤，留下了很大一块疤痕，因此而得名。伤疤脸深爱着酋长美丽的女儿，他犹豫了好几次，终于鼓足勇气说道：

"我除了弓箭和长矛外一无所有，但是我的内心充满了对你的爱，你愿意和我在这个简陋的草棚下一起生活吗？"

"你的目光流露着真诚，但是我已经对太阳神发过誓，这辈子不会结婚。与太阳神之间的约定即使天塌下来了也要遵守。"

"我要去找太阳神,请求他的同意。"

伤疤脸翻山越岭,想见太阳神一面。

但是他却根本找不到通往太阳神国度的黄金之门。

伤疤脸没有灰心,继续勇敢坚定地朝前走着。

当他到达了湖对面,发现地上放着一只做工精致的弓和一捆箭。伤疤脸对这些东西毫无贪心,那个弓和箭是太阳神的儿子——阿匹西拉兹的。阿匹西拉兹背着太阳神偷偷来到湖边,想除掉居住在湖边的凶狠怪物。一种不祥的预感朝伤疤脸的心头袭来,于是他勇敢地站出来,挽救了阿匹西拉兹的性命。

就这样,太阳神满足了伤疤脸的心愿。

"你去和酋长的女儿结婚吧。我和你约定后,之前我和酋长女儿的约定就不存在了。"

"太好了,我这就去和她结婚,我要亲口告诉她我要娶她为妻。"

太阳神给了伤疤脸很多礼物,连脸上的伤疤也为他去除了。

伤疤脸和酋长女儿结了婚,过着幸福的生活,后来人们把他的名字换成了"温柔脸"。

金色盒子

平安夜里。

3 岁的小女儿正在用价格不菲的金色包装纸包装着纸盒,玩得十分起劲。看到这种情形,父亲发火了。

"家里条件这么不好,你怎么还用这些纸呢?你不知道这些纸很贵么?"

生了气的孩子一句话也没说,把盒子放在圣诞树下,回房去了。

圣诞节早上。

女儿小心翼翼地把金色盒子递给父亲。

"原来你是想把送给我的礼物包装一下呀,昨天真是错怪你了。"

父亲想起昨晚的事,感到十分过意不去。他小心地打开了盒子。

但是盒子里什么也没有。

父亲发怒了，用着比昨天还大的嗓门喊道：

"如果这是个礼物盒，里面就应该装东西。可这算什么？你怎么用这么贵的包装纸来包装一个空盒子……"

女儿抽泣着说道：

"爸爸，那不是空盒子，我对着盒子亲了很多下，那就是我送给爸爸的礼物……"

听到这里，父亲把女儿紧紧抱在怀里，连声说对不起。

从此以后，父亲就把女儿送的金色盒子放在床头。

每当悲伤或疲惫的时候他都会悄悄地打开盒子，这样他就能马上感受到女儿的一片爱心。

林肯和梯子

"你的幸福程度取决于你为此付出了多大的努力。"

留下这句名言的美国著名总统林肯在结束了一天的工作后,会和普通人一样洗手帕和袜子,亲自擦皮鞋。他认为人们所做的事情没有贵贱之分。

林肯小时候住在木头房子里,生活很贫苦。

林肯非常喜欢读书,一次,他从邻居那里借了一本书,他十分喜欢反复看了好几遍。可是由于屋顶漏水,书被淋得透湿。

林肯拿着湿透了的书,找到书的主人如实地说出了事情真相。

"叔叔,您借给我的书被雨水给淋湿了,实在对不起,我愿意为叔叔家干一个星期的活以作补偿,不管什么事您尽管吩咐我做吧。"

对于林肯郑重其事的道歉,叔叔不禁感叹道:

"你有颗正直善良的心,我感到十分高兴,我就把它当做你对我的补偿吧,那本书就送给你了。"

　　林肯即便是在贫苦和艰难的岁月里也总是以微笑面对,他后来成长为一个正直、诚实、谦逊的人。在多次落选之后他终于当选为总统。

　　他去世后,一个漫画家给他画了一幅画。

　　那幅画画了一座山,山下是一个破旧的木屋,木屋上面有一个梯子,梯子的顶端是白宫。这是在称赞林肯并没有因为家境贫寒而陷入绝望中,而是像爬梯子一样,经过不懈的努力终于成为白宫的主人。

给哥哥的信

　　今天是 12 月 22 号,是我们这些死刑犯要被拉到塞米约洛夫斯基广场执行处决的日子。再有一分钟我就要和这个世界告别了,再有一分钟。这一刻我突然想起哥哥和朋友们,等到最后一刻我心里面只剩下了哥哥。我第一次清晰地认识到原来我是这么思念和深爱着我的哥哥。

　　最后的钟声敲响了,可是突然有人朗读起圣上免去我们死罪的赦免状。

　　哥哥,我没有悲观,也没有失望。我周围的很多人遇到不幸时,始终坚持做人的原则,不会堕落也不会被击倒。所谓的人生不就是这样吗?这才是生活的目的。哥哥,我们肯定能再次见面,请你一定要保重身体。未来某个时候我们会互相拥抱在一起,也许会想起我们小时候和遥远的过去、我们的黄金时期、我们的青年时期以及各自的梦想。在今天一个小时还不到的时间内我站在了生与死的岔路口,但现在我还活在世上。如果我给别人留下过不好的记忆，如果我和他们打过架，哥哥您在邂逅他们时，请对他们说把所有的一切当成过往云烟全部忘却吧。现在对我来说已不存有任何的憎恶和愤怒。

　　此时此地我真心地爱着所有认识我的人，想去拥抱他们。这就是生命的喜悦……

　　这是从俄罗斯著名作家陀思妥耶夫斯基（1821~1881）在1849年写给哥哥米哈日的信中节选的一段。由于他是政治犯,这封信没有寄到哥哥的手里,却流传于世。

忠 诚 的 狗

　　从前,有个孤身一人的老爷爷买了一条狗,老爷爷精心地喂养着这条狗,狗也很喜欢和老爷爷在一起。

　　一天,老爷爷收到参加朋友生日聚会的邀请。老爷爷在聚会上遇见好久没见的朋友,大家在一起度过了一段愉快的时光。聚会结束后,喝醉了酒、摇摇晃晃往家走的老爷爷倒在小溪边的草地上睡着了。

　　狗也趴在他的身旁。突然狗闻到了一股异味,抬头一看,原来在不远的地方山火着起来了,浓烟直冲天空。

　　汪! 汪汪!

　　狗大声地叫着,又是推老爷爷,又是咬住衣服来回摇动,但是总也喊不醒醉梦中的老爷爷。

　　火越来越近了,狗跳进小溪里,把全身浸湿后用身体摩擦着老爷爷的脸和身体,可老爷爷就是不醒。

　　狗又跳进小溪, 从水里出来后在老爷爷的周围打滚,把草地弄得湿湿的。这样反复几次后,在草地上滚来滚去的狗逐渐没有了力气。

熊熊燃烧的大火很快就把老爷爷包围了,但值得庆幸的是,因为老爷爷周围湿漉漉的,火靠近不了。

过了好一阵子,老爷爷才醒来,发现黑色的灰烬上躺着已被烧焦的狗。老爷爷明白了一切。

老爷爷哭着将狗埋于向阳之地,还折断了附近的一棵树当做墓碑。

此后,这节树干开始生根,冒出枝叶,长成为一棵大树。人们给这棵树取名为"狗树",后来人们把这条狗住过的村子叫做"狗树村"。

别被雷声吓倒

宋朝有个叫吴二的人,吴二对年老的母亲十分孝顺。

一天晚上,吴二梦见有个神仙对他说:

"明天白天你会被雷劈死。"

"神仙呀！这是怎么一回事呀？"

"没听见么？你明天白天会被雷劈死,这是上天的意思,谁也不能违抗。"

从梦中惊醒的吴二被不祥的预感所笼罩,一想到万一自己死了只剩下母亲就无法入睡。

吴二狠下心来,对母亲这样说道:

"妈妈,我今天要出远门,你要是一个人寂寞的话就暂时到姐姐家住吧。"

"不去,我就和你一起住,我在这里等你,你快去快回。"

于是吴二上路了。突然间乌云密布,天空逐渐昏暗下来,一场倾盆大雨就要到来。

"看来马上就要打雷了,别让雷声吓倒了妈妈!"

吴二担心母亲被吓倒,又跑回家里赶紧把门关上。之后他再次来到外面等着雷电的到来。

但是奇怪的事情发生了,乌云渐渐散去,天空又放晴了,好像什么事没有发生一样。

回到家里的吴二一边给母亲揉揉肩,一边百思不得其解。

那天晚上神仙又出现在吴二的梦中,这样说道:

"你的孝心感动了上天,你不会被带走了,好好地照顾你母亲吧!"

精灵和鞋匠

从前,有个鞋匠,和妻子过着相依为命的生活,鞋匠整天坐在椅子上捶捶打打,裁剪着皮革,一双双皮鞋就这样被做出来。

一天,鞋匠生了病,无法再工作。钱也都花光了,只剩下能做一双皮鞋的皮革了。

鞋匠带着疼痛早早入睡了。

第二天早上,发生了一件让鞋匠感到惊讶的事情。在工作台上放着一双做工细致、样子十分可爱的皮鞋。

"亲爱的,这是你做的吗?"

"不是,我不会做鞋呀。"

路过的一个绅士看见鞋子后,想把它送给自己女儿,就花很多钱买下了。鞋匠用得来的钱买来了可做两双皮鞋的皮革。

那天,他又带着疲惫的身体早早进入了梦乡。

到了第二天早上,令人吃惊的是,工作台上又放着两双做工出色的皮鞋。

"看来是有人在帮助我们,我们今晚可要盯紧了,看看是谁干的。"

当天晚上,夫妇俩躲在床单里,偷偷地注视着外面。时钟响了 12 下后,出现了一群不知来自何处的精灵。精灵们有的在做着针线活,有

的在捶捶打打,兴致勃勃地做着皮鞋。

看着在寒冬里光着身子干活的精灵们,鞋匠和妻子决定送给他们一点儿小礼物。他们为精灵们做了衣服、帽子、袜子和鞋子。

平安夜到了,看见工作台上放着衣服和鞋子,精灵们争先恐后地穿上。他们又唱又跳,最后消失不见了。此后精灵们再也没有出现。

"我们要去帮助那些把帮助别人视为应做之事的人们。现在我感觉身体好多了,我们又能和从前一样生活了。"

善良的少年

在皮雷切有个名叫朱里奥的 12 岁少年，少年的父亲在铁路部门工作，由于家里人口较多，工资又不高，日子总是过得紧紧巴巴的。

父亲每天晚上回到家里后还要做事。最近做的事是将报纸和杂志的定期购买者的姓名和住址抄写在小纸条上。

朱里奥想帮助父亲，但是父亲叫他好好学习，没有同意。

深夜里，朱里奥等父亲入睡后，悄悄地来到书房里，开始模仿父亲的笔迹写起来。

"朱里奥呀，昨天晚上我工作了两个小时，竟然比平时多干了三倍的活儿。真是太神奇了。"

此后，为了让父亲高兴，朱里奥每晚都会代替父亲做事。可是他的学习成绩却一塌糊涂。

一个月过去了，父亲赚到的钱比上个月多出很多，在家人面前露出了满意的表情。但是父亲却骂了朱里奥一顿。

"朱里奥,我为了这个家累得快不行了,你不是都看到了吗?但是你真的太让我失望了。"

朱里奥心里十分痛苦,但之后的几个月,每天晚上还是帮着抄写地址。

但是有一天,父亲终于发现了这一切。

"现在我全明白了,我要请求你的原谅,我善良的儿子呀!你现在快去睡觉吧。"

几个月来朱里奥终于睡了一个安稳觉。当他睁开眼睛醒来时,发现父亲趴在床边,花白的头发贴在自己的胸前。

做汤圆的老奶奶

从前,有一个总是笑容可掬喜欢做汤圆的老奶奶。一天,老奶奶做好了当做晚饭的汤圆,其中一个汤圆却掉进了厨房地板下的洞里。

老奶奶把手伸进洞里,哪知道整个人掉了下去。过了好一阵子,老奶奶发现自己站在阳光灿烂的道路中央。老奶奶问站在路边的石像。

"你看见我的汤圆了吗?"

"是的,看见了,快藏在我后面,无常鬼来了。"

老奶奶笑了,赶紧藏在石像后面。但是无常鬼闻到了老奶奶身上的气味,把老奶奶带到在江对岸自己的家里。

"我不会吃你的,但你要为我们无常鬼做饭。这样,你在那口锅里放一粒米,用这个木头铲子好好搅拌搅拌,之后米会越来越多的。"

老奶奶按无常鬼所说的照做了。果然,米由一粒变为两粒,两粒变为四粒、八粒、十六粒,很快锅里盛满了米。

老奶奶为无常鬼们做了很多天的饭,但是她想回家做汤圆。于是,她只拿了一个木头铲子,乘船过了江。无常鬼们追到江边,把江水一饮而尽。

"哈哈哈!无常鬼们,再见了,木头铲子我拿走了!"

无常鬼们觉得老奶奶的笑容很滑稽,把喝进去的江水又吐了出来。

平安回到家里的老奶奶生活得非常幸福,因为她可以随时做自己喜欢的汤圆了。

热情的力量

1945 年被丢下原子弹的日本可以说是一片废墟。在废墟中日本积攒着重新站起来的力量。

这个时候，有个叫市村的人为了让首都东京繁荣起来，到处寻觅着好的地段。市村对新宿 4 号街很感兴趣，这个地方的主人是一个头发花白的老太太。但是无论市村怎么劝说，老太太十分固执，表示决不会卖掉这片土地的。老太太这样表达了自己的决心：

"不管你说什么就是不行，你来找我，我跟你说不卖，这就板上钉钉了，不会改变的！"

一个大雪纷飞的寒冷冬日里，老太太不顾严寒来到市村的办公室。

办公室里的女职员抖落掉老太太外套上的雪，说道：

"这么冷的天您受累了吧？请换上暖和一点儿的拖鞋吧。"

女职员并不知道老太太是谁,细致热情地招待着对方。老太太被女职员的热情打动了。

"是啊,职员待人接物都这样热情,那么社长肯定是个更不错的人了。"

老太太改变了主意,决定无条件地卖出那块地。

在日本东京新宿有一条叫"高岛屋"的街道,是日本最繁华的地段,这个地方的主人就是"上河会社"的市村社长。

庄子的故事

请听一个关于战国时代思想家庄子的故事。

首先讲一下庄子的"蝴蝶梦"。庄子有天梦见自己变成蝴蝶，扑闪着翅膀在花丛中飞来飞去。梦醒后庄子陷入沉思中。

"刚才变成蝴蝶的时候，我也许是庄子，现在从梦中醒来，我就是庄子，那么现在的我是真正的庄子吗？还是蝴蝶在梦中变成庄子呢？现在的我是真正的我吗？还是蝴蝶变成我了呢？"

庄子常常是一身破旧衣衫，穿着一双破草鞋，整个人

沉浸在对人生的喜悦以及对道与自然的探索中。一次,大王看见了庄子这个样子,不禁皱起了眉头,庄子却说:

"一个人即便有道德,但不去实践它,这才叫丑陋。我贫穷因为我处的时代是个不幸的时代,而且我又没遇到贤明的君主。"

他就这样过着悠闲自得的生活。在他死之前他交代弟子们把他的尸体扔到荒野里,弟子们对庄子的嘱托不能理解。庄子说:"我以天地为棺,日月为双璧,星辰为珠玉,还有比这个更为隆重的葬礼吗?"弟子们担心那样尸体会被乌鸦啄食,他又说道:"我要是被埋进土里,还不是被地鳖虫和蚂蚁啃咬吗?你们为什么要站在地鳖虫和蚂蚁那一边,而冷落乌鸦呢?"说完他露出了轻松的笑容。

最后让我们来读一篇庄子留下的文章。

有一个只有一只脚的动物,它十分羡慕有很多脚的百足虫。

百足虫羡慕没有脚也能爬得很快的蛇,蛇羡慕没有形体却骤来骤去的风,风羡慕只呆在一个地方就能从很远处看见的雪。

雪羡慕虽然看不见却能很自然地明白一切的心。

小偷的儿子

很久以前,在一个国家里,偷别人东西的人要被施以剁手的残酷刑法。

塔克生活在这个国家里,他的爸爸因生活所迫偷了别人的东西。

他的爸爸被拉到皇上面前,准备接受处罚。

"你知罪吗?"

"是的,请马上治我罪吧!"

此时,年幼的塔克跪倒在地,给皇上连连磕头,恳求皇上开恩。

"皇上,救救我的父亲吧,父亲要是没有了手我们一家人可怎么活呀?我们家共有 10 口人,我们 10 口人的性命都系在父亲的这双手上,请您就放过他这一次吧!"

"不行!任何人都必须遵守国家的法律。"

"那么请允许我代替我父亲接受处罚,请砍断我的手吧,求求您了。"

泪水从塔克的眼睛中流了出来。

"好吧,就砍断你的手!但是有一条,这里的几十名士兵要是全部都拒绝的话,我就放了你们俩。"

塔克伸出两只胳膊,慢慢地闭上了眼睛。

"一,二,三!"

刀子落下了,但是刀子没有落在塔克的手腕上,而是砍在了地上。

"你真是一个孝子,而且很坚强!你

的孝心救了你的父亲,也救了你自己。"

塔克的行为深深触动了皇上,此后皇上废除了剁手的刑法,并竖立了一块小石碑来表彰塔克的孝心。

鸡毛蒜皮的小事

从前，有个孝子和他年老的母亲住在一起，年老力衰的母亲几乎每天都呆在昏暗的屋子里。

孝顺的儿子从外面回来后一定会先来到母亲的房里，呆一段时间后才出去。每当儿子进屋的时候，母亲都显得很开心。

邻居们都很好奇，想知道这个孝顺儿子到底在做些什么，于是趴在窗外偷听他俩的对话。

"母亲,我刚从市场上回来。最近一坨猪肉二两钱,五个苹果一两钱,一匹土布五两钱。"

"噢,噢。"

听着儿子的话,母亲边点头边回应。

"母亲,回来的路上我还看了看庄稼地,现在稻子和大豆都熟透了,我想给母亲熬粥,就带回来一个老南瓜。"

"年纪也不小的人了,怎么和母亲说这些鸡毛蒜皮的小事?"

"就是呀,和听都听不清楚的老人家说这些有什么用呢?让母亲穿好看的衣服,吃可口的饭菜,这才算尽孝道啊。"

村里有一个小伙子回到家里学孝子那样做。

"父亲,我今天去看树了。在山上看见一只很大的獐子,我本想抓住它,可是……"

"哈哈哈!"

听了小伙子的话后,父亲很高兴,笑个不停。

这件事很快传遍了整个村子,不知不觉中这个村子里像孝子那样给自己父母亲讲述外面世界故事的人越来越多了。

最后这个村子里的人都成了孝子,这个被称为"孝子村"的故事一代又一代地流传下去。

坐马车的弟弟和奔跑的哥哥

去往法国巴黎的马车就要出发了,这时,突然走过来两个人,哥哥大约 15 岁,弟弟 12 岁左右。

哥哥递给马车夫车费,弟弟上了马车,一脸担心地望着哥哥。

"哥哥……"

"没事的,不用担心!"

哥哥笑着挥挥手,马车开始启动了。

登上马车的弟弟老是透过后门望着哥哥,哥哥跟在马车后面奔跑着。马车里的人都以为哥哥是舍不得与弟弟分别才会追在后面跑。

但是过了好一阵子,哥哥仍然跟在后面,渐渐地离马车越来越远了,泪水从弟弟的眼中流了出来。

"怎么一回事?哥哥为什么还跟在后面?"

乘客们问弟弟。

"我们要一起去巴黎。"

"那两人一起坐马车去不就行了么？"

"因为钱只够付一个人的车费，所以哥哥在后面跑。"

弟弟说到这里，号啕大哭起来。乘客们让马车停下，为兄弟俩凑齐了车费。

听到乘客们的叙述后，马车夫没收钱就让哥哥上了马车。

"真是不错的孩子，拿着我们凑来的钱去巴黎花吧。"

乘客们都称赞着兄弟俩，此时哥哥和弟弟的脸上都绽放出灿烂的笑容。

凡·高写给弟弟的信

　　今天早晨我一早起来给你写了这封信，之后我来到外面，描绘着太阳照射下的院子，我把画拿到屋里，又带着一张空画布来到室外，完成了另一幅画。

　　我之所以又给你写信，是因为我从没有见过这么美轮美奂的自然美景。天空湛蓝，太阳放射出金色的光芒。蓝色和黄色的搭配如同范·戴尔米的作品，既温柔又充满了诱惑。我虽然无法按原貌表现出这种美景，但是我要用我自己的方式来予以再现。

　　抱着这种想法，我又以我寄宿房子对面的院子为对象画了三幅画，之后又画了两幅咖啡馆的画，我还给伯克画了一幅肖像画，给自己画了一幅自画像。此外，我还描绘了从工厂上方升起的红日、搬运沙子的人们和年代久远的风车。

　　我觉得我现在画的画要比最近我寄给你的画更好一些，因为通过这些画我的收获要高于我的付出，我的画能不能全

部卖光，这是我现在最关心的事。

　　我在这里因我的工作而感到十分幸福，我想让你和我一起来分享这种幸福……

　　为后世留下《向日葵》的画家凡·高(1853~1890)其画风强烈，生前他的才华没能得到世人认可，终生穷困潦倒。是弟弟泰奥一直在支持着他的绘画创作。哥哥凡·高和弟弟泰奥两人一生都在相互通信，共同分享着浓浓的兄弟情谊。

最 后 一 课

　　和平时一样,少年眼看又要上学迟到了,于是赶紧穿过原野,跑向学校。

　　平日里吵吵闹闹的教室此刻却十分安静。

　　"快点儿坐好。"

　　老师轻声地对少年说。老师今天穿的是正装,小镇里的人安静地坐在教室后面。

　　"各位同学,今天是我给大家上的最后一堂课。"

　　老师用缓慢的语速说道。

　　"从明天开始学校要教德语,因此我……"

　　少年这才明白老师身着正装、镇上的人坐在教室里的原因。

　　少年在上课时受到老师的提问,但却没答上来。可老师没有像平时那样训斥他。

　　"一直以来,你是不是被我骂了很多次?把今天的学习任

务推到明天是最
坏的习惯。"

老师的话深
深地铭刻在少年
的心中。

"法语是世界
上最美丽的语言，
你们决不能忘记
这个事实。即使我
国人民成了别国
的奴隶，只要还保
留着我们的语言，
就等于是攥着打
开摆脱奴隶身份
的钥匙了。"

这堂课就快
要结束了，老师的脸开始变得苍白。

"同学们，同学们，我……，我……"

老师虽然已经不能说出一句完整的话了，但他来到黑板
前工工整整地写下几个大字——

法兰西万岁！

剑君的故事

新罗真平王八年,天降大霜,到了第二年春天,庄稼歉收,百姓们整日饥肠辘辘。

此时,一位出身于花郎道名叫剑君的青年负责看管宫里的粮仓。一天,朋友们找到剑君。

"现在天下是怎么一种情况你也很清楚,没有放着眼前的粮食却让家人饿死的道理,你就偷偷地拿些粮食分给我们吧。"

朋友们让剑君从宫里偷一些粮食出来。

"不可以,即使饿死了,作为保管员的我也绝不会蒙骗国家的。"

剑君拒绝了朋友们的劝说。然后他来找平时和他关系最好的朋友——勤郎。

"如果你看不到我了,请不要找我。"

勤郎对剑君的话感到很疑惑,就追问其原因。剑君这才把和其他朋友之间发生的事情吐露出来。

"他们也许不会就这样放过我的。"

"那么你先告发他们不就行了么？"

"他们也是我的朋友，尽管现在为生计所迫和我的想法不同，但他们心眼其实并不坏。再说在这么艰苦的时候谁都可能产生那种想法。"

剑君与勤郎分手后就往家里走。但是在剑君的家门口，白天来找过他的朋友们正等着他。

"刚才我们的想法太幼稚了，和我们出去喝一杯吧。"

剑君猜出了他们心里打的算盘，但是剑君没有拒绝他们递来的毒酒，一饮而尽。

朋友们后来才知道剑君竟然还曾为他们着想，最后朋友们也都喝下毒酒，结束了他们的生命。

兄弟之间的信任

法德战争爆发后,法国的一对亲兄弟自愿入伍,来到战场上。兄弟俩被分在同一个部队里,两人并肩作战。

不久,和德军的战斗打响了,子弹如雨点般倾泻过来。

"啊!"

哥哥被德军的子弹击中倒下了。弟弟在远处看见了这一切,但是没有人去救哥哥。

"上士,请允许我把哥哥带回来。"

"你的心情我能理解,但是你哥哥一定死了,你没有必要把自己的性命也白白搭上。"

"请您就让我去吧!"

弟弟再三向上士请求,上士终于点了点头。

弟弟穿越枪林弹雨,来到哥哥的身旁。弟弟把哥哥背了回来,但是哥哥已经死了。

"这样可不行,搞不好连你也丢了性命,今后不要冒着生命危险去做没有意义的事情。”

弟弟把哥哥的尸体放下,说道:

“不是,这绝不是没有意义的事情。”

弟弟流下了眼泪。

“我来到哥哥身边,把哥哥抱在怀里的时候哥哥还活着,哥哥还对我说'就知道你会来的,好像也只有你会来'。说完后他笑着闭上了眼睛。”

上士听完弟弟的话,什么话也没说,只是为弟弟抹去脸上的泪水。

孝子和老虎

朴延是朝鲜时代最有名的音乐家,他早年丧母,小小年纪就在父母的墓地旁盖了窝棚,在那里开始了长达 3 年的守墓生活。

一天晚上,一只老虎出现在朴延的窝棚旁。朴延吓了一大跳,可是老虎来到朴延母亲的墓前悠闲地坐在那里,似乎没有害人的意思。

天亮了,老虎悄悄地走了。从此以后,只要天黑后,老虎都会出现,守护着墓地。

有一天很晚了,老虎还没来。朴延担心老虎出事,一晚上没睡,直到凌晨才勉强合上眼。就像一直在等着朴延一样,老虎出现在梦中。

"请您一定要救救我呀,我现在掉进安在村口的陷阱里,救救我吧!"

老虎凄楚哀切地喊着。

朴延一下子从梦中惊醒,可刚才那个梦仍很鲜活地留在脑海里,老虎悲伤的眼睛里闪烁着泪光。

　　朴延上气不接下气地跑到村口,村民们已把掉进陷阱里的老虎扛出来了,大家团团把它围住。没错,这就是守护着母亲墓地的那只老虎,可惜老虎已经断气了。

　　"我来晚了一步,要是再来早一点儿的话我还能把你救下……"

　　朴延抱着老虎伤心地哭了,对围成一圈的村民讲起了这只老虎的故事。朴延把死去的老虎埋在了母亲墓地的旁边,每年都会为老虎祭祀上坟。

人生的秘密

　　一个小孩走到坐在愿望泉前的老人面前,问道:

　　"老爷爷,您是非常有智慧的人吗?您能不能告诉我人生的秘密?"

　　老人慈祥地望着孩子,这样回答道:

　　"孩子呀,我也带着问题活到现在。那么我就说说我所得到的结论:人生共有四个秘密,第一个秘密是思想,思考一下你是以什么价值观来面对生活的;第二个是信心,要完成定下的目标,首先应该相信自己;第三个是梦想,在以价值观和信任作后盾的情况下,去构筑你最大的梦想吧;第四个是勇气,用你的价值观和信任去实现你的梦想还需要勇气。"

　　这个老人就是卡通电影的先行者——沃尔特·迪斯尼。

　　从小沃尔特·迪斯尼就非常喜欢画画,但在他最初当设计师的时候,却被告知没有才华而丢了饭碗,辛辛苦苦制作的卡通电影也因为发行商的破产而被搁置,但即使事业陷入

最低谷的时候,他也没有放弃希望。

　　最终的结果是,他以他在贫困中惟一的朋友——老鼠为原型,创造了小巧可爱的"米老鼠",从而走上了成功之路。

　　"思想,信心,梦想,还有勇气!"

　　这四样东西就是沃尔特·迪斯尼所说的人生秘密。

刻在石桥上的名字

故事发生在 100 年前的英国乡村里。父母双亡、住在叔父家里的戴比德·罗德·乔治经常会遭到小伙伴们的讥笑。

"喂！乔治！小鞋匠的孩子怎么这么大声说话？再有一次我们绝对不放过你。"

"没有父母的野孩子。"

乔治感到很委屈，伤心地哭了。

"呜，呜！"

"哈哈，修鞋匠变成了小哭孩。"

在当时等级制度森严的英国，鞋匠的儿子就一定是鞋匠，面包师的儿子就一定是做面包的，子承父业是很普遍的事情。

乔治在朋友们都走后，独自一人坐在石桥上哭泣，望着流动着的河水，他突然抬起头，仰望着蓝天暗下决心。

"好，从现在起我要奋斗，长大后我一定不做鞋匠，要干一番大事情。"

　　乔治为了坚定自己的决心,从口袋里掏出小刀在石桥上一笔一划地刻上自己的名字。

　　几年后,乔治白天工作,晚上学习,为实现自己伟大的梦

想而努力着。每当遇到困难时,他都会去石桥看一下自己刻下的名字。

　　这个少年就是后来的英国首相罗德·乔治。他成为许多出身低下遭遇挫折的人实现自己理想的一个榜样。直到现在,在英国乡村的那个石桥上还隐约能看见 D.L.G 的字样。

跟在灵车后面的皇帝

100 年前的奥地利首都维也纳被瘟疫所笼罩，瘟疫以可怕的速度蔓延着，染上瘟疫后无人能继续存活下去。

每个医院里都塞满了病人，甚至连床都放不下了。但即便是来到医院里，病情也不见得就能转好。

弗兰茨皇帝双手抱着头，表情十分痛苦。

"快增加医疗设备，另外对每个街道进行彻底消毒。"

随着时间的推移，不断增长的患者数量得到了遏止。

一位大臣对皇帝说：

"现在您可以放心了，街道逐渐恢复到以前的模样了，人们也开始精神饱满地投入到自己的工作中了。这所有的一切都与殿下的关心和操劳分不开。"

"我要亲自去街道看一下，给我准备马车！"

首都维也纳果真如那位大臣所说，情况好多了。皇帝准备去穷人聚集的偏远地区看一看，但是大臣们立刻劝阻了皇帝。

"那边……，那边瘟疫还在盛行，殿下您别去那里了，小心染上瘟疫啊！"

"这叫什么话吗？我出来一趟，就是想知道患者都在哪些地方，总共有多少，以及都是怎么治疗的，你们却叫我不要去有患者的地方，这像话吗？"

此时，一辆灵车从皇帝的马车旁经过，但奇怪的是，看不见一个人跟在灵车的后面。皇帝就疑惑地问周围的人。

"此人一家子全染上瘟疫了，所以没有人跟在后面。"

"那么我就跟在后面吧，好让他最后一程路不至于太凄凉。"

皇帝跟着灵车来到墓地，直到尸体被掩埋、灵车走后为止，一举一动已完全把这个人当成自己家人一样。皇帝这样说道：

"如果我今天不参加这个葬礼，死的这个人会很凄凉，但我的心将会更加的凄凉。"

奥兹国的魔法师

100 年前作家弗朗克·鲍姆写了一篇童话,名为《伟大的魔法师奥兹》,讲述了多萝茜和朋友们所经历的神秘有趣又充满幻想的故事。

被龙卷风吹到奥兹王国的多萝茜在那里遇见了稻草人、铁皮樵夫和胆小鬼狮子。为了回家,她和这些人找到掌管爱迈拉尔德市的奥兹国王,请他帮助自己实现愿望。

和多萝茜想回家一样,她的朋友们也都有着各自的愿望,稻草人希望得到智慧,樵夫想得到爱心,狮子则希望获取勇气。

于是奥兹国王决定按次序把

他们一个个叫来,聆听他们的愿望。

首先是希望得到智慧的稻草人,奥兹国王把掺杂着钉子和针的粗糠注进了尽是稻草屑的脑袋里。

对于想得到爱心的铁皮樵夫,他打开了铁皮胸腔,把里面装满锯末、外面是绸缎的心形口袋塞了进去。他又把装在绿色四方瓶里的不明液体倒在金盘子里,让狮子喝下。

从奥兹国王的房里出来,稻草人、铁皮樵夫和狮子都高兴地说道:

"我脑袋好像变聪明了。"

"我好像有了一颗能爱的心了。"

"我觉得自己已经变得勇敢了。"

奥兹国王真的给他们都施了魔法吗?还是有其他的原因呢?小朋友们,请你们好好想一想。

价格昂贵的小猫

在英国的一个乡村里住着名叫迪克·惠丁顿的少年，他每天靠着邻居们分给他的土豆和面包渣度日。有一天，他揣着梦想来到了大城市伦敦。

但是在伦敦，等待迪克的是难以忍受的饥饿和痛苦。他想找一份工作，但是人们不会轻易雇用乞丐打扮的孤儿的。

在街头游荡了好几天的迪克最终倒在了一位名叫皮茨威来的商人家门前。

"喂，年轻人，为什么躺在这里？应该干活去呀。"

"我也想干活，但是没有人雇我。"

皮茨威来觉得迪克很可怜，就让他帮厨师干一些杂活。但厨师是个脾气古怪的人，经常用扫帚和汤勺打迪克。幸运的是，皮茨威来的女儿爱莉斯觉得迪克可怜，对他很亲切。

但是问题又来了，迪克住的阁楼里有很多老鼠，让迪克每晚都不能入睡。跑到外面的迪克用给别人擦皮鞋挣来的钱买了一只猫。

一天,皮茨威来对佣人们说:

"我快要出海了,如果你们有想卖掉的东西,就不要错过这次机会了。"

佣人们把自己的东西拿出来,可迪克只有一只猫,迪克只好将猫送到船上。

皮茨威来的船抵达了非洲的巴巴里海岸,正赶上当地的老鼠已经成患,国王和王后受尽了老鼠的折磨。

巴巴里国王对船长说要用很多价格昂贵的珍宝来换那只猫。正直的船长把情况告诉了皮茨威来,待人亲切随和的皮茨威来让迪克·惠丁顿成为一个幸运儿。

之后,迪克与皮茨威来的女儿爱莉斯结了婚,做了一段行政管理工作后,最后成为伦敦市长。

老 鼠 新 娘

一天,农夫把三个儿子叫来,让他们各砍三棵树,每人再根据树倒的方向去寻找自己未来的新娘。大儿子和二儿子去往北方和南方,各自都遇见了平常的农家女子。

小儿子贝克沿着森林里的道路来到一个草屋前,屋子里一个人也没有,贝克叹了口气。

"你怎么了?"

这么温柔的嗓音发自于一个老鼠的口中。

"我在找结婚对象,这件事你可帮不了。"

"你看我怎么样?我将会用真心去爱你。"

老鼠看起来十分可爱和优雅,炯炯有神的双眼传递着秋波,贝克渐渐地喜欢上了这只老鼠。

几天后,父亲对儿子们说,他想尝尝他们的未婚妻烘烤的面包。

听贝克说了这件事后,老鼠用精细的小麦粉烘制成又香又松软的白色面包,比哥哥拿出的黑麦面包和大麦面包更出色。父亲这样说道：

"赶快去准备婚事吧，我很想见见这个儿媳妇。"

老鼠乘上黑色鼹鼠拉的花生壳马车，与贝克一同上路了。贝克并没有因为新娘是老鼠感到难为情，而是非常关心呵护着她。然而，有个路过的男子一脚把老鼠乘坐的花生壳马车踢到了水里。

"可怜的老鼠！亲爱的，你就这么离去了吗，呜呜……"

伤心哭泣着的贝克面前出现了一位有着白雪一样肌肤、垂着金色长发、带点儿淡淡腮红的年轻女子，她正坐在一辆黄金马车上。

"贝克，是我呀，在我是老鼠的时候你没有嫌弃我，现在我变回公主了，你该不会离开我吧？是你解开了我身上的魔法。"

于是，贝克和公主在得到父亲的祝福后，两人回到公主的王国里，过着相亲相爱的幸福生活。

世上最容易也是最难回答的问题

邻国国王向被当做俘虏抓获的年轻的亚瑟王提出一个问题：

"女人最想要的是什么？如果你能在一年内寻找到这个问题的答案，我就放了你，否则就会把你处死。"

亚瑟王为了找到这个问题的答案，接触了非常多的人，不论对方身份高低贵贱，没有一个人能给他答案。他的一个手下说：

"在北方住着一个又老又凶的魔女，或许她知道答案。"

亚瑟王找到了魔女，但是魔女提出，作为告诉他正确答案的条件，必须同意自己与他率领的勇敢骑士——格威因结婚，格威因为了拯救亚瑟王的生命，毫不犹豫地答应了这门婚事。

于是，魔女说出了这个问题的答案。

"女人们最想要的是自己能够掌控自己的生活，自己的事情自己能做决定。"

　　亚瑟王把这个答案告诉了邻国国王，邻国国王对这个回答很满意，就饶了亚瑟王一命。但是对亚瑟王来说，还有一件让他担心的事，那就是对为了自己而与凶恶的魔女结婚的格威因放不下心。

　　但是格威因却对年老的魔女十分体贴。

　　结婚仪式结束后，到了晚上，走进房里的格威因吓了一大跳，凶恶的魔女变成了异常美丽的女子坐在那里。那个女子这样说道：

　　"你不顾我是个丑陋的魔女与我结婚，作为报答，从现在起我生活的一半时间是丑陋的魔女，另一半时间将会是美丽的女子。好了，做出选择吧，是白天变为魔女好呢？还是晚上变成魔女好呢？"

　　格威因平静地回答：

　　"还是由你自己来选择吧。"

　　"你果然是懂得尊重我生活的好男人，那么从现在起无论白天还是黑夜我都会是美丽的女人，做你的好妻子。"

被响尾蛇咬伤的母亲

一天,父亲要出门去集市里卖柴火。

"过一个星期后我才能回来,你不要担心我,好好照看孩子吧。"

母亲和孩子们并排站着,目送着父亲踏上征程,直至父亲的背影消失在视线之外。

一条响尾蛇慢慢地靠向母亲,但是母亲仍和平时一样劈着柴,浑然不觉。

"啊,好疼!"

劈着柴的母亲被蛇咬伤了,毒液很快就遍布全身,母亲的眼前一片漆黑。

"难道就这么死了吗?那么谁来照顾我的孩子呀?丈夫还要一个星期才能回来……"

母亲用尽全身力气继续劈着剩下的柴火,然后她来到厨房,为孩子们准备了一个星期的食物,母亲的额头上渗出了

一粒粒汗珠。

母亲平静地把大儿子叫过来，低声说道：

"孩子呀，妈妈现在很困，想睡觉，无论妈妈睡得多么熟，你们也不要叫醒我。你们每天要按时吃三顿饭，你还要记着喂弟弟吃饭。天气冷了的话，就把柴火点燃……"

母亲躺在房里等待着死亡的到来。大概三四个小时过去了，大儿子晃醒了母亲。

"妈妈，妈妈，弟弟哭了。"

母亲听见孩子的哭声后竟奇迹般地从床上站起来，原来母亲干活时出了很多汗，被蛇咬伤后留下的毒液通过汗水排除到了体外。

与大猩猩同行

　　达伊安·波西最早对大猩猩产生兴趣是在 1963 年，那时，他为了看野生动物而来到非洲。

　　几年后，35 岁的达伊安遇见了动物学家路易斯·里奇，于是她请求里奇能让自己成为他的助手。

　　"我想下半辈子都为大猩猩而活着，请让我做你的助手吧，我想大猩猩们的头领也会喜欢我的。"

　　就这样达伊安在山岭间展开了追踪大猩猩的探险生活。

　　"大猩猩，我是你们的朋友，不要害怕。"

　　整整 3 年过去了，达伊安终于赢得了大猩猩们的认可。达伊安独自在森林深处建造了草屋，和大猩猩生活在一起，研究它们的生活状态。

　　她甚至曾单身一人对抗过想置大猩猩于死地的几百名猎獗盗猎者，对达伊安·波西来说，大猩猩已成为她的家人。

　　"那么多的盗猎者，你一个人怎么可能对付得了？倒不如教育这个国家的孩子们,从小培养他们对动物的爱心,这样反而收效会更快些。"

当人们这样劝阻时,达伊安斩钉截铁地说道:

"这么做太迟了,在孩子们成为大人前大猩猩恐怕早已经全部消失了。"

1977年,达伊安·波西喜欢的大猩猩被盗猎者杀害后,她感到非常愤慨,开始在全世界范围内募集大猩猩保护基金,最终使国立公园的巡警队比以前有了很大的改观。

在非洲的六个火山热带森林里曾经生活着600多只大猩猩,现在已减少到400多只,但据动物学家说,如果没有达伊安·波西的辛勤工作,大猩猩已经全部消失了。

故事 87

胡楂子树和爱情

从前,有个美丽的姑娘叫罗斯佩泰。她十分倾慕王子,但是却无法向意中人吐露心声。

"王子啊,什么时候我能把这个手镯送给你呢?"

罗斯佩泰把想送给王子的金手镯埋在了半山腰的胡楂子树下。

由于与邻国发生战争,王子来到了战场上。但是王子被深受信任的将军所出卖,好不容易才活着从战场上逃出来。

罗斯佩泰在王子走后每天都来到埋有金镯子的胡楂子树下,虔诚地向神灵祈祷,求神保佑王子能平安地回来。

一天,一个衣服被撕碎的青年躺在胡楂子树下。

"喂!快醒醒。"

罗斯佩泰用葡萄酒润了润青年的嗓子,给他吃面包。后来她一看,这个人并不陌生,他的手上戴着刻有花纹的宝石戒指,这是王子的标志。

"啊,王子,原来你就是王子!"

罗斯佩泰虽然认识他,但表面上仍装作不知道。她把王子撕破的衣服缝好后,想从胡楂子树下挖出藏在里面的金镯子。可是金镯子已经溶化消失了,胡楂子树也因此而染上了金黄色。

罗斯佩泰折断一节树枝递给王子,说道:

"这就是指挥棒,快站起来投入战斗吧。"

很快她又给王子准备了一匹马,王子从她那里获得勇气,重新回到战场上,最终取得胜利。罗斯佩泰与王子结了婚,过着幸福无比的生活。

直到现在胡楂子树里面仍是金黄色的,这是因为当年胡楂子树把罗斯佩泰埋下的黄金当成养分的缘故。

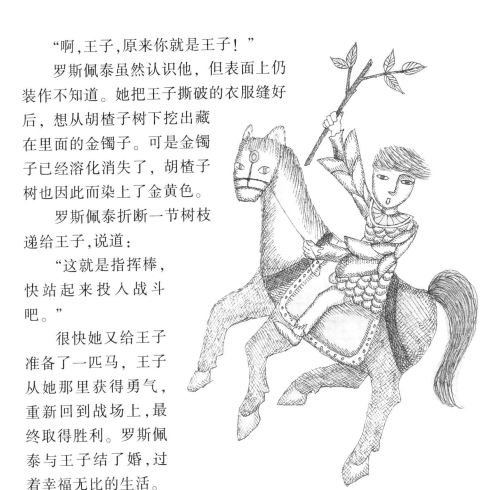

老奶奶的挑战

美国的胡尔达·克鲁斯老奶奶不是总安静地呆在家里，因为她曾用矮小的身躯、花白的头发征服了海拔3000米的日本富士山。富士山终年积雪不化，由不易断裂的花岗石所构成，要登上这座山不是一件简单的事。据说老奶奶为了登上富士山，在高层建筑里上上下下，进行腿部力量锻炼。

老奶奶还参加80岁以上的老人马拉松大赛，创造了8项世界纪录，曾22次攀上美国最高峰——惠特尼峰。

"你为什么喜欢挑战难度这么大的事呢？你年纪也不小了。"

对于记者们的提问，老奶奶这样答道：

"如果因为自己老了就什么也不想做的人才是真正的老人，一个人不管多么年轻如果非常懒惰，那么这个人也是个老人。年龄妨碍不了我做想做的事情。在不知不觉中，我被岁月推上了挑战的舞台，我想让老人们知道生活对他们来说也是有价值的。"

征服富士山对老奶奶来说不是件简单的事情,爬了两天后,老奶奶的腿开始抖起来,浑身一点儿力气也没有。

"我不能放弃,我不是身体疲倦了,而是心里疲倦了。我不能停在这里,我要爬到山顶上。"

凌晨时分,老奶奶终于在富士山的山顶上看见了一轮红日从海面上升起的壮观景象。老奶奶展开双臂,从内心深处涌出一股喜悦之情。老人把第 98 枚徽章别在了背包的上面,这些徽章代表着到目前为止老奶奶所征服过的山峰。

我 请 求

在美国纽约的一个残疾人协会里保存着这样一篇文章，读完这些文字后我对我现在所拥有的一切更为珍视，内心里充满了感激之情。

我请求。

我请求神把我造成一个坚强的人，让我实现所有的心愿。

但是神却把我造成一个孱弱的人，让我明白谦逊之道。

我请求神赋予我健康，让我可做大事。

但是神给了我虚弱，让我去做更有意义的事。

我请求神让我成为富人，让我的生活更为幸福。

但是我收到了贫穷这份礼物，让我成为一个拥有智慧的人。

我请求神赋予我才能，让我能够得到众人的赞赏。

但是我得到了自卑这件礼物，让我理解神存在的必要。

我请求神能给我一切，让我可以享受生活。

但是神给了我生活这件礼物，让我去享受一切。

虽然我没有得到一件我所请求的东西，但是我得到的所有东西都是我需要的。

神并没有因为我的渺小而忽视我，一一聆听了我无声的祈祷。

所有人中我是受到祝福最多的那个。

魔 法 暴 风

在墨西哥的一个职业摔跤场上，有个戴着金色面具参加比赛的职业摔跤手，因为他总是戴着面具出场，人们都很想知道他究竟是谁，但是他从来都不摘下面具。

他有一个"魔法暴风"的绰号，由于他的华丽面具和出色的个人技术，他在观众中非常有人气。

"魔法风暴！魔法风暴！"

观众们高喊着，把欢呼声都送给了他。

就这样过去了 23 年，魔法风暴年纪也大了，不知不觉中

就要告别摔跤界了。他的支持
者非常喜欢这位在每场比赛
都尽力让观众开心的摔跤手，
他们都期待着他摘下面具。

"我已经53岁了，现在我
要和黄金面具一同退出摔跤
场。"

魔法风暴为了支持者们
慢慢地摘下黄金面具。

观众们都屏住呼吸注视
着他，摘下面具的他心怀感激
地对人们说道：

"我是天主教教会的神父
塞尔吉奥·古提艾来。我参加
职业摔跤比赛是为了从经济上帮助孤儿院的孩子们，让他们
能实现自己的梦想和希望。"

静静的观众席中突然爆发出热烈的掌声，掌声持续了很
长很长时间。

墨西哥的塞尔吉奥神父从事了23年的职业摔跤运动，
用挣来的钱收养了3000多名孤儿。

儿童和儿童节

100多年前，领导儿童运动的方政涣先生为了创造一个单词而大伤脑筋。

"能不能有个单词可以表现出对小孩人格上的尊重？"

在当时的韩国还没有儿童这样的词语，大人们看见年幼的小孩会用"小鬼、小孩、小家伙"这样的词来称呼。这些词语包含有与大人不能相提并论的意思，这些词都显得有些肤浅。

"干脆就叫儿童吧！"

儿童这个词就这样诞生了。

1920年的朝鲜处于日本的统治下，不少孩子出去当童工。

在本应该尽情欢笑玩耍、憧憬着未来的年纪里却工作着的童工们只能拿到很少一点儿钱，整天被高强度的劳动压得喘不过气来，受伤更是家常便饭。有感于此，方政涣创造了儿童这个词,1923 年5 月第一次举办了儿童节庆祝活动,当天方政涣还在《东亚日报》上发表了一篇宣言。

第一,把儿童从之前所有的压迫中解放出来,对于儿童要给予人格上的重视。

第二,把儿童从经济困难中解放出来,不允许雇佣14岁以下的儿童作为工人。

第三,创造出能让儿童安静学习和开心玩耍的家庭环境和社会公共设施。

终身为儿童争取利益的方政涣先生的墓碑写有这样的字句:

童心如禅(儿童的心如同禅师一般)
儿童的朋友 方政涣之墓

热心是财产

午后哗哗地下起了阵雨,一个全身淋湿的跛腿老太太站在一个很不起眼的家具店门前。

老太太不像是来买家具的,但是家具店里的年轻店员跑出来说道:

"老奶奶,请进来吧,雨好像还要继续下。"

"不了, 我不是来买家具的, 等一会儿接我的车就要到了。"

但是家具店的主人到底还是让老太太进去了,叫她安心地坐在沙发上等着。

"车的事交给我了,老奶奶你就安心在这儿等吧。"

主人给老太太端上了一杯热水,朝门外张望着。

坐在沙发上的老太太很快就睡着了,主人看见睡着的老太太,悄悄地为她盖上一条毛毯。

不大一会儿,一辆车停在了家具店的门前,司机将熟睡的老太太抱到车内后，开车离去。

看到这种情形，其他人都嘲笑道：

"无论你对这个陌生的老太太怎么热情，她都不是来买家具的。你为什么要白费力气呢？"

"什么，难道热心待人也要分对象么？"

几天后，家具店收到一封钢铁大王——卡耐基寄来的信。

非常感谢您在下雨那天热心地照顾了我的母亲，我决定将我在斯考特兰德的家和我公司的所有家具全放在您的商店里订购。

家具店的主人可能做梦也没想过自己一点点热心就能换来这么大的好运，凭借这个机会他一跃而成为家具业的巨头。

亚历山大大帝的遗言

　　对躺着的亚历山大大帝来说,等待他的只有死亡了。皇帝的病情越来越严重,整个皇室陷入悲痛之中。

　　"快打起精神吧, 像从前那样从座位上站起来号令天下。"

　　"不必担心我,人总有一死。"

　　亚历山大大帝表情平静,心无他物,望着周围的一切。手下人都叫皇帝好好地躺在床上,什么也别想。

　　"对我来说活在这世上睁着眼的时间已所剩不多,我想以最充实的方式去度过这珍贵的时间。"

　　随着亚历山大大帝的病情逐渐恶化,手下人能做的也只有等待死亡了。他们守候在一旁,等待着皇帝留下遗言。

　　但是亚历山大大帝什么遗言也没有留下。

　　最后他把所有人召集在一起,开始费力地说道:

　　"在我死后把我埋葬的时候,要把我的手放在外面,让人

们都可以看见。"

　　手下人都深感疑惑,奇怪掌控天下的皇帝怎么留下这样的遗言。就算是皇帝,也没必要把死人那冰冷、已不成样子的手展示给人们看。

　　亚历山大大帝用低沉的嗓音,慢慢地费力说道:

　　"我只是想让世上的人们知道亚历山大是空着手离开这个世界的。"

青　鸟

　　比利时的诗人兼剧作家莫里斯·梅特林克所写的喜剧《青鸟》讨论的是有关幸福的话题,您知道这个故事吗?这部喜剧还被改编成童话,深受众多少年儿童的喜爱。

　　平安夜,琪尔琪尔和米琪尔由于家里很穷,没有收到一件礼物。气呼呼地进入梦乡的兄妹俩看见一个穿着红色马夹、系着红头巾的女巫来这里寻找青鸟。

　　琪尔琪尔和米琪尔把关在鸟笼里的青鸟拿给女巫看,但是女巫说如果他俩能找到比这个颜色更绿的青鸟,将会赐予他们幸福。

　　兄妹俩为了找到青鸟,在家里狗、猫、光、面包、水、糖、牛奶的精灵陪伴下上路了。

　　他们到记忆的王国、夜晚的宫殿、月亮照射下的森林、墓地、未来王国去寻找,但是没有一个地方有青鸟,虽然他们抓到了很多类似的鸟,但都不是巫婆要的那种。

最后拖着疲惫的身躯回到家里的两个孩子看见家里的鸟正在等着他们。

"哥哥,青鸟好像比昨天要绿一些了。"

"是啊,原来我们要找的青鸟就在这里。"

琪尔琪尔打开鸟笼,把青鸟放飞至天空,对泪眼汪汪的妹妹说:

"没关系,我们可以再找一个青鸟。"

这个故事意味着幸福的青鸟决不在无人知晓的远方,它可能就在我们的身边。

想要一把小提琴

爱尼央求父亲给她买把小提琴,但是囊中羞涩的父亲却买不起小提琴。

当天晚上,父亲给住在俄亥俄州的朋友写了一封信,然后在房子里双膝着地,独自祈祷起来。

"请帮帮我的爱尼吧,让她得到一把小提琴。"

正巧,一直透过房门偷看的爱尼听到了父亲的祈祷,泪水顿时从眼中流了出来。爱尼心里暗自说道:

"父亲,对不起,我再也不缠着你要小提琴了。"

几周后。

住在俄亥俄州的朋友在家里招待了爱尼和他的父亲。

"你就是爱尼呀,听说你小提琴拉得非常棒,你能为叔叔演奏一曲吗?"

叔叔把家里很贵的小提琴递给爱尼,爱尼高兴地拿起小提琴,开始演奏起来。

"这把小提琴和你非常相配呀，你要觉得还行的话就拿走吧。"

　　"真的吗？这个不是很贵吗？"

　　"不，这是在跳蚤市场上只花了 7 美元买的。"

　　那把小提琴陪伴爱尼度过了幸福的童年。直到很久以后爱尼才知道俄亥俄州的叔叔送给她的小提琴价格非常昂贵。

　　步入中年的爱尼有一天看见报纸上登有"为女儿求购便宜小提琴"的一则小广告。

　　爱尼拿出珍藏的小提琴找到登广告的人。

　　"这好像是把非常好的小提琴，我要付多少钱？"

　　爱尼微笑着说：

　　" 7 美元。"

跃 过 小 溪

　　世界著名教育学家裴斯泰洛奇(瑞士,1746~1827)小时候身体单薄,而且十分害羞,以至于别人给他起了个"胆小鬼"的外号。

　　一天,小裴斯泰洛奇和爷爷一起散步,一路上听着小鸟的歌唱。这时,在裴斯泰洛奇的面前出现一条小溪,如果趟过小溪,不仅裤子会弄湿,搞不好还会摔伤在石头上。裴斯泰洛奇心里咯噔了一下。

　　"爷爷,你背我过去吧。"

　　和裴斯泰洛奇手牵着手走路的爷爷突然放开了手,噌地一下跳了过去。

　　"爷爷,我害怕,我怎么办?"

　　独自一人在那里的裴斯泰洛奇急得直跺脚,眼泪直在眼眶里打转。

　　"快跳! 先后退一步再用力一跳,你能跳过去,难道你想继续当胆小鬼吗？你要不跳爷爷就先走了！"

爷爷对裴斯泰洛奇喊完后，佯装先走了。

裴斯泰洛奇独自一人静静地注视着小溪，最终他鼓足勇气从小溪上面跳了过去。

本以为已走远的爷爷这时走过来，把裴斯泰洛奇紧紧抱在怀里说道：

"对，就该这么做，做得好，孩子，从现在起只要是出现在你面前的小溪你都能越过去，只要有决心，所有的事情都能做好。"

汉 斯 救 人

在荷兰海边的一个小村子里,有个小孩叫汉斯。

一天夜里,海上乌云密布,雷声轰鸣,一场暴风雨即将来临。

"有艘船还在海上,快组织救援队,一定要把人救回来。"

居民们听到这个消息,马上都聚集在海边广场上。

救援队乘风破浪,奋力向前。剩下的人各自提着灯笼向海上照去。

一个小时后,雾气散去,救援队的船返回来了。

筋疲力尽的救援队员们瘫倒在沙滩上,大声呼喊:

"人太多了,我们的船没有办法把人都装下,还有一个人留在那里,要快点儿派人把他救回来。"

没人站出来。乘船出去的亲人都回来了,还有谁会愿意去啊？这时,16岁的汉斯喊道:

"我去。"

汉斯的妈妈一把抓住汉斯,将他拦住。

"不行,孩子啊,你爸爸 10 年前遇到海难去世,你哥哥几天前也在海里失踪了,现在对我来说就剩下你,我不能连你也失去。"

"妈妈,即使这样我也要去。"汉斯撇下妈妈上了救援船。

一个小时过去了。

透过浓雾,隐约能见到远处一艘船,汉斯站在船头。

人们大声呼喊起来:

"把人救回来了吗?"

汉斯隔老远兴奋地大声喊道:

"是的,救回来了,请转告我的妈妈,救回的正是我哥哥!"

守 泉 人

从山里流下来的泉水形成了一个小湖。有个老伯每天照看这个湖,人们称他为守泉人。守泉人是个忠厚的人,他每天早上沿着湖边转,把弄脏湖水的垃圾清理掉,并清扫湖底的沉淀物。在湖面上天鹅姿态优美地游来游去,水车不停地转动,有许多观光客都专程过来欣赏这优美的景色。

一天,市议会审查预算,有个议员提出了异议:"每个月要支付守泉人工资,可他都干了些什么啊,这就是浪费。应该马上辞退守泉人,没有必要留着他。"于是,议员们全票通过辞退守泉人。最初几周没有发生什么事情。

但随着秋天的来临,树叶簌簌地落在了湖面上,枯枝掉下来阻住了流淌的水。曾经清澈透底的湖水渐渐变黄,慢慢转动的水车也停止不动,再也不见美丽的天鹅,以前特地来观赏湖水景色的游客也不来了。此时人们才醒悟过来,守泉人做的不起眼的小事实际上发挥了很大的作用。

"没有守泉人的话,湖水不久就会枯竭。"惊慌失措的市议会召开特别会议,又把守泉人找了回来。

于是,湖水又重新焕发了生命力。

守泉人每天又一如既往地做着那平凡而重要的工作,收拾树叶,清理枯枝,照看湖水。

可爱多多龙

日本导演宫崎俊执导的电影《邻居家的多多龙》讲述的是个梦幻般甜蜜美满的故事。11岁的皋月和4岁的梅同爸爸一起搬到了长满橡树的乡下，这是因为妈妈生病住院后，全家人决定在空气清新的地方生活。

一天早晨，姐姐上学，梅在丛林中的羊肠小路上，一下子掉到了巨大的、毛茸茸的多多龙身上。多多龙是至今谁也没见过的大个子。梅骑在有着松软圆滑的身躯、可爱脸蛋上长着圆眼睛的多多龙身上玩耍。后来，他向姐姐炫耀这一切，姐姐不信。

有一天，下了大雨，给父亲送雨伞的皋月也遇到了多多龙，她还用雨伞给被雨淋的多多龙遮雨。多多龙把橡树籽当做礼物送给她。

皋月和梅把种子种到地里日夜守候，看看会发生什么事情。可爱的多多龙们出现了，他们在地上转动，破土而出的幼芽以令人惊讶的速度生长,瞬间覆盖了天空。多多龙拿出陀螺,滴溜溜地转起来,载着孩子们飞向天空。 第二天早上,皋月和梅看到了破土而出的橡树芽。两人高兴地欢呼起来。"是梦!""不是梦!""太好了,太好了,哈哈哈哈。"

似梦非梦中的皋月和梅乘着猫巴士向妈妈所在医院的树顶上飞去。是梦,但又不是梦!

对于皋月和梅来说,多多龙是存在的。不管是谁,心里一定揣着和多多龙相似的东西。

蓝色阳伞

宝石商的女儿阿加塔可以说是想要什么就有什么,金光闪闪的金戒指和昂贵的项链塞满了宝石箱子,漂亮的衣服也挂满了衣柜。但阿加塔一点儿也不高兴,因为她长得十分难看。

"阿加塔呀, 今天你去市场吧, 干活的阿姨生病不能来了。"阿加塔用围巾把脸包得严严实实的就出去了。阿加塔很快买好了面包和肉,快步往家走,一个老奶奶喊住了阿加塔。"孩子,你稍等,我给你看样东西。"老奶奶把蓝色绸缎做的,镶嵌着白色珍珠的漂亮阳伞拿给她看。"如果你用这把阳伞的话,人们就知道你心灵有多美,用它你会过得很幸福。"阿加塔打着阳伞凝视着镜子。镜子里的阿加塔神奇般地变漂亮了。"谢谢老奶奶。"太阳逐渐落下去了,阿加塔再次拿着阳伞去了公园。阿加塔受到了众人的赞美,她拿着蓝色的阳伞高兴地跳起舞来。

突然,在公园里出现了一个驼背人,脸部也是扭曲的。

"滚，马上消失。"人们冲他大喊。阿加塔劝人们别这样，她把蓝色的阳伞递给驼背人。驼背人突然变成了年轻英俊的小伙儿，人们都目瞪口呆。

阿加塔一言不发地离开了公园。一轮圆月照在荷花池上，阿加塔呆呆地看着荷花池里映出的自己的脸庞。此时，有个比打阳伞的时候更漂亮可爱的脸庞正微笑地望着阿加塔呢。

酒　　友

　　在中国有个叫秋的村子里住着个叫守的渔夫。守每天晚上钓鱼时一定要带瓶酒,他喝一口向江里洒一下,看到人们诧异的目光,他就这样回答:"我用酒略微慰劳一下落水身亡的孤魂。"

　　一天晚上,守独自坐在江边喝酒,一个年轻人走了过来。那天一条鱼也没钓到,守很郁闷,那个青年人说话了:"大叔,我去江底把鱼都赶上来。"不大一会儿,好几条胳膊般大小的鱼上钩了。守感到很奇怪,出于感激,想和那个年轻人分享捕获的鱼。那个年轻人客气地说道:"我经常喝大叔送的美酒。"

　　从那以后,他每天来找守,给他赶鱼。守和年轻人日夜把酒言欢,聊得非常投机。这种情况持续了半年。一天深夜,年轻人突然面带悲伤之情说道:"事实上我是个叫王六郎的落水之鬼。明天我的业报就结束了,会有别的鬼来代替我,我要去投胎变成人了,多谢你这段时间陪我。"到了第二天,守冷冷清清地坐在江边，王六郎再次出现了。守吃惊地问这是怎么回事。

　　"今天有个女人和孩子为了来接替我而溺水身亡，我觉得为了我不可以一下子死两个人，所以我把她们推出水面，我决定等下次再投胎转世。"

　　王六郎的这番心意感动了上天。曾是水鬼的王六郎被派到一个叫禹的村子当村子的守护神。成为守护神的王六郎从那以后和渔夫更加亲密，在禹这个村子里做了许多好事。

读者朋友,当你的心变得硬邦邦、脑子里尽是枯燥想法的时候,你该怎么去做?

这个时候你应该让你的心沉浸于喜悦和温暖之中。

能让你的心产生这种变化的101个美丽故事被收进了这本书里。真诚的故事,有关动物的感人故事,有趣而充满爱意的故事,这些故事都在等着你来阅读。

在你读这101个美丽故事的时候,你会一下子感受到当心里播下幸福的种子时所带来的爱和感动。

大家听说过在《彼得·潘》中出现的叮叮铃或住在阿拉丁神灯里的珍吗?他们虽然高矮不同,长相也各异,但都是精灵。除此之外的精灵也很多。有捕食人的可怕的精灵,也有帮忙做家务或给人治病的精灵。

《101个精灵故事》包含着所有有关精灵的故事。

不仅是精灵的种类,精灵喜欢什么,不喜欢什么,吃什么为生等,只要是有关精灵的,在这本书里什么都能知道。好好认识一下这些精灵,交交精灵朋友吧!

什么是机智的人呢?

机智的人是指不管遇到多么艰难的事情,都会以智慧的方式加以解决的人。小朋友们也想拥有机智的心灵和行动,想要成为出色优秀的人吧。那么我们来见见在101个机智故事中登场的有趣而智慧的人们吧。

这本书包含了从古代流传下来的民间故事和伟人们的故事,也有树林里的各种动物们给大家讲的许多有趣和愉快的故事。

读完101个机智故事,不知不觉间机智和智慧就成了大家的朋友了。

那么我们一起在机智的故事世界中开始旅行吧。

小学生最想读的课外读物

走在水上的鸟——水雉、发射强力炮弹的气步甲，从眼睛喷血的尖角蜥蜴，生孩子的红树……

仅仅听名字就觉得很神奇了吧？

听起来像是只在想像中的故事里才会出现的这些动植物，其实是真实地存在于这个世界的。这本书从那些鲜为人知的动植物中，选出了生活方式特殊又神奇的动植物，深入浅出地做了有趣的说明。

读着这本书，你可以更加清楚地了解生活在亚马孙丛林里的奇怪动植物，或只是在动物园见过却不是很了解的动物。

一个一个读下去，您会在不知不觉中产生对大自然的关心和爱。

像宝石那样闪烁的星星们，向我们讲述的美丽故事！

给整个世界撒落美丽光芒的太阳，将红霞铺满之后陷入了梦乡。

于是，开始了夜空中闪烁的星星和星座的世界。

不要出声！静静倾听。星星们开始讲述有趣的故事了！

织女和牛郎悲伤的爱情故事，赫拉克勒斯十二项艰难的冒险，寻找金羊毛的阿尔戈号远征队，救出险境中的安德罗米达公主的珀尔修斯的勇敢精神……

每一个星座都拥有美丽感人的故事。

倾听星座的故事，孩子们的心中也会浸透比星光更为真实的心灵。

笑声可以把我们的生活装点得更加愉快和欢乐，和朋友们在一起的时候，如果说几个有趣的故事，彼此之间的气氛就会变得更为融洽。你难道不想成为一个传播欢笑的趣味故事大王吗？

在本书中，既有能够使朋友们捧腹大笑的幽默笑话，也有许多令人感动的故事；当然，还有许多恐怖故事哦！另外，本书中既有历史上的逸闻趣话，也有许多虚拟世界中的动物故事。如果把本书中的101个故事讲给朋友们听，你一定会体验到笑的巨大力量。

101个故事系列

"花",这一个字中充满了美丽和香气。这本书精□了与花有关的传说和神话、花里所藏着的秘密等10□个美丽而有趣的故事。

苹果树下缔结的王子和公主酸酸甜甜的爱情,给□送了颜色的雪花莲,守着盲人丈夫的篱笆花——木□花,浸透着妈妈对女儿的深切的爱的紫茉莉……

与花相关的一个个故事里都浸透着趣味和感动,□及深切而悲伤的爱情。

悄悄倾听一下花们的耳语吧!

大家的心灵中也会散发出比花更美更浓郁的感□的香气。

在孤独疲惫的时候,能有一个人轻轻抚慰我们的心灵,我们是否就感觉到获得了力量和幸福呀?

现在,这里就有愿意抚慰你心灵的101个朋友。

101个美丽感人的故事,震撼人心,给大家以温暖的感动。

101个朋友,让大家看待这个美丽的世界!

一个人只有身体和心灵同样健康、同样智慧才可以□获得美好的生活。

那么怎样才能成为智慧的人呢?

那就得读很多好书。

增长智慧最好的老师就是书籍呀!

智慧的人在任何危急的情况下,碰上任何艰难的事□情,都可以勇敢机智地解决问题的。因为他拥有可以分□析判断、并下决定的能力。

读一读这本书中的101个故事,你的智慧也会开□始茁壮成长起来的。

小学生最想读的课外读物

Beyond Feelings

A Guide to Critical Thinking

SIXTH EDITION

Vincent Ryan Ruggiero

Professor Emeritus of Humanities
State University of New York, Delhi

Mayfield Publishing Company
Mountain View, California
London • Toronto

To the memory of Howard Trumble,
whose quiet practice of the skills
detailed in this book was an inspiration
to me, to his family, and to all who knew him

Copyright © 2001, 1998, 1995, 1990, 1984 by Mayfield Publishing Company

All rights reserved. No portion of this book may be reproduced in any form or by any means without written permission of the publisher.

Library of Congress Cataloging-in-Publication Data
Ruggiero, Vincent Ryan.
    Beyond feelings : a guide to critical thinking / Vincent Ryan
Ruggiero. —6th ed.
      p. cm.
    Includes bibliographical references and index.
    ISBN 1-7674-1589-2
    1. Critical thinking. I. Title.
BF441.R85 2000   00–037224
153.4'2—dc21   CIP

Manufactured in the United States of America
10 9 8 7 6 5 4 3 2 1

Mayfield Publishing Company
1280 Villa Street
Mountain View, California 94041

Sponsoring editor, Kenneth King; production editor, Julianna Scott Fein; copy-editor, Barbara McGowran; design manager, Glenda King; cover designer, Linda Robertson; manufacturing manager, Randy Hurst. The text was set in 10/13 Palatino by Archetype Book Composition and printed on acid-free 50# Butte des Morts by Banta Book Group.

Cover photo: Robert Mangold. American, born 1937. *Four Color Frame Painting, No. 1,* 1983 (red, green, aqua, and yellow). Acrylic and black pencil on canvas. Four panels, overall: 111 x 150". High Museum of Art, Atlanta, Georgia; Purchase in honor of Karen Andrews, President of the Members Guild of the High Museum of Art, 1994–95, with funds from Alfred Austell Thornton in memory of Leila Austell Thornton and Albert Edward Thornton, Sr., and Sarah Miller Venable and William Hoyt Venable, 1994.141. Photograph by eeva-inkeri, courtesy of PaceWildenstein. © 2000 Robert Mangold/Artists Rights Society (ARS), New York.

Text Credits: p. 166 Editorial, *Atlanta Constitution,* April 14, 1996. Reprinted with permission; p. 167 Editorial, *Washington Times,* March 31, 1996. Reprinted with permission; p. 170 Editorial, *The* (Salt Lake City, Utah) *Desert News,* July 17, 1996. Reprinted with permission; Editorial, *The* (Toledo, Ohio) *Blade,* July 20, 1996. Reprinted with permission; p. 171 Editorial, *The* (Sioux Falls, South Dakota) *Argus-Leader,* July 21, 1996. Reprinted with permission.

Preface

When the first edition of this book appeared in 1975, the dominant intellectual focus was still subjectivity, *feelings*. That focus, the legacy of the 1960s, was originally a necessary reaction to the rationalism and behaviorism that preceded it. It declared, in effect, "People are not robots. They are more than the sum total of their physiology. They have hopes, dreams, emotions. No two humans are alike—each has a special perspective, a unique way of perceiving the world. And any view of humanity that ignores this subjective side is a distortion."

Yet, despite its value, the focus on feelings went too far. Like many other movements, what began as a reaction against an extreme view became an extreme view itself. The result of that extremism was the neglect of thinking. This book was designed to answer that neglect. The introduction to the first edition explained its rationale as follows:

> The emphasis on subjectivity served to correct a dangerous oversimplification. But it is the kind of reaction that cannot be sustained for long without causing an even worse situation—the neglect of thinking. Worse for two reasons. First, because we live in an age of manipulation. Armies of hucksters and demagogues stand ready with the rich resources of psychology to play upon our emotions and subconscious needs to persuade us that superficial is profound, harmful is beneficial, evil is virtuous. And feelings are especially vulnerable to such manipulation.
>
> Secondly, because in virtually every important area of modern life—law, medicine, government, education, science, business, and community affairs—we are beset with serious problems and complex issues that demand careful gathering and weighing of facts and informed opinions, thoughtful consideration of various conclusions or actions, and judicious selection of the best conclusion or most appropriate action. . . .
>
> [Today's college student] has been conditioned not to undervalue subjectivity, but to overvalue it. And so he does not need to have his feelings indulged. Rather, he needs to be taught how to sort out his feelings, decide to what extent they have been shaped by external influences, and evaluate them carefully when they conflict among themselves or with the feelings of others. In short, he needs to be taught to think critically.*

*In 1975, "he" was still accepted as a reference to both sexes.

iii

There is an unfortunate tendency among many to view feeling and thought as mutually exclusive, to force a choice between them. If we focus on one, then in their view we must reject the other. But this is mistaken. Feeling and thought are perfectly complementary. Feeling, being more spontaneous, is an excellent beginning to the development of conclusions. And thought, being more deliberate, provides a way to identify the best and most appropriate feeling. Both are natural.

Thinking, however, is less automatic than feeling. To do it well demands a systematic approach and guided practice. . . .

The general attitude toward thinking has changed considerably since the mid-1970s. The view that critical thinking is an important skill to which education should give prominence is no longer a minority view. Hundreds of voices have joined the chorus calling for the addition of critical thinking objectives to existing courses and even the creation of special courses in thinking. There is little disagreement that the challenges of the new millennium demand minds that can move beyond feelings to clear, impartial, critical problem solving and decision making.

Features of This Edition

This edition of *Beyond Feelings* retains the basic organization of previous editions. The first section explains the psychological, philosophical, and social context in which critical thinking takes place and describes the habits and attitudes that enhance such thinking. The second section helps students recognize and overcome common errors in thinking. The third section provides a step-by-step strategy for dealing with issues.

Within the overall design, however, a number of changes have been made in response to the helpful suggestions of reviewers. Part 1 contains two new chapters: Chapter 6, "What Is Evidence?" and Chapter 7, "What Is Argument?" In addition, the arrangement of Part 2 has been significantly altered. Rather than consisting of a series of chapters, each devoted to a single error in logic, this section now clusters errors according to when they typically occur: *errors of perspective,* which are faulty habits of mind that exist before addressing an issue; *errors of procedure,* which occur in the process of analyzing an issue or developing a line of thought; *errors of expression,* which occur in the course of presenting ideas to others; and *errors of reaction,* which occur after receiving unfavorable criticism or a counterargument. This approach should help students understand logical fallacies and develop more effective strategies for dealing with them.

In almost every chapter, key concepts have been more fully explained and illustrated, and a number of new applications have been added. Also, advice on using the Internet has been added to Chapter 17.

As in the past, I have attempted to follow George Orwell's sage advice: "Never use a foreign phrase, a scientific word or a jargon word if you can think of an everyday English equivalent." This is not always easy. When logicians are taught terms such as *argumentum ad hominem, non sequitur,* and "affirming the consequent," they naturally want to use them. Arguments for doing so urge themselves upon us: for example, "These are the most precise terms. Don't join the ranks of the coddlers and deprive students of them." In weak moments I succumb to this appeal. (Until this edition, for example, I included the term *enthymeme. Mea culpa . . .* there I go again.) But is the precision of such terms the real reason for my wanting to use them? Is it not possible that we professors enjoy parading our knowledge, or that we are reluctant to spare our students the struggle we were forced to undergo ("We suffered, so they should too")? It seems to me that modern culture already provides too many impediments to critical thinking for us to add more.

Is it possible to carry this plain language commitment too far? Yes, and some will think I have done so in avoiding the term *inferences* and speaking instead of conclusions. But I respectfully disagree. Lexicographers point out that the distinction between these terms is extremely subtle, so it seems more reasonable not to devote time to it. Also, I prefer the designation "fact arguments" to "value arguments," but for a somewhat different reason. The word *value* is so associated with relativism that its use in this context can undermine the crucial idea that arguments differ in quality. For many students, the word *value* triggers the thought, "Everyone has a right to his or her values; mine are right for me, and though they may need 'clarification' from time to time, they are never to be questioned." This thought impedes critical thinking.

Acknowledgments

I wish to express my appreciation to all those who contributed to the preparation of this edition. Special thanks to those who reviewed the manuscript: Laura Hamblin, Utah Valley State College; Ron Leonard, University of Nevada, Las Vegas; Debra McGinnis, California State University at Long Beach; and Marshall Osman, University of LaVerne.

I am also grateful to Ken King, Julianna Scott Fein, and Glenda King from Mayfield, who worked on this edition.

Contents

Preface   iii

Introduction   1

PART 1   The Context   3

Chapter 1   Who Are You?   4

    The Influence of Time and Place   4
    The Influence of Mass Culture   5
    The Influence of Psychology   7
    Becoming an Individual   9
    Applications   10

Chapter 2   What Is Critical Thinking?   13

    Mind, Brain, or Both?   14
    Critical Thinking Defined   15
    Characteristics of Critical Thinkers   17
    The Role of Intuition   19
    The Basic Activities in Critical Thinking   20
    Critical Thinking and Writing   21
    Applications   21

Chapter 3   What Is Truth?   23

    Where Does It All Begin?   24
    Imperfect Perception   25

Imperfect Memory   26
Deficient Information   26
Even the Wisest Can Err   27
Truth Is Discovered, Not Created   28
Applications   30

Chapter 4   What Does It Mean to Know?   32

Requirements of Knowing   32
Testing Your Own Knowledge   33
How We Come to Know   35
Why Knowing Is Difficult   36
A Cautionary Tale   38
Is Faith a Form of Knowledge?   39
Obstacles to Knowledge   40
Applications   41

Chapter 5   How Good Are Your Opinions?   44

Opinions Can Be Mistaken   46
Opinions on Moral Issues   46
Even Experts Can Be Wrong   48
Kinds of Error   50
Informed Versus Uninformed Opinion   51
Forming Correct Opinions   52
Applications   53

Chapter 6   What Is Evidence?   57

Kinds of Evidence   58
Evaluating Evidence   63
What Constitutes "Sufficient" Evidence?   64
Applications   65

Chapter 7   What Is Argument?   67

The Parts of an Argument   68
Evaluating Arguments   69
More Difficult Arguments   71
Applications   74

PART 2   The Pitfalls   77

Chapter 8   The Basic Problem: "Mine Is Better"   78

Egocentric People   79
Ethnocentric People   80

Controlling "Mine-Is-Better" Thinking   81
Applications   83

Chapter 9   Errors of Perspective   **86**

Unwarranted Assumptions   86
The Either/Or Outlook   88
Mindless Conformity   89
Absolutism   90
Relativism   90
Bias for or against Change   91
Applications   93

Chapter 10   Errors of Procedure   **97**

Biased Consideration of Evidence   97
Double Standard   98
Hasty Conclusion   98
Overgeneralization and Stereotyping   100
Oversimplification   101
The Post Hoc Fallacy   103
Applications   103

Chapter 11   Errors of Expression   **106**

Shifting the Issue   106
Contradiction   108
Arguing in a Circle   109
Meaningless Statement   109
Mistaken Authority   110
False Analogy   110
Irrational Appeal   111
Applications   113

Chapter 12   Errors of Reaction   **116**

Automatic Rejection   118
Shifting the Burden of Proof   119
"Straw Man"   119
Attacking the Critic   120
Applications   121

Chapter 13   The Errors in Combination   **124**

Errors of Perspective   124
Errors of Procedure   126
Errors of Expression   127
Errors of Reaction   128

Sample Combinations of Errors   129
A Sensible View of Terminology   131
Applications   132

PART 3   A Strategy   137

Chapter 14   Knowing Yourself   138

Critical Thinking Inventory   139
Using Your Inventory   140
Challenge and Reward   141
Applications   141

Chapter 15   Being Observant   144

Observing People   144
Observation in Science and Medicine   145
The Range of Application   146
Becoming More Observant   147
Reflecting on Your Observations   148
Applications   149

Chapter 16   Selecting an Issue   151

The Basic Rule: Less Is More   151
How to Limit an Issue   152
Sample Issue: Pornography   152
Sample Issue: Boxing   154
Sample Issue: Juvenile Crime   154
Applications   157

Chapter 17   Conducting Inquiry   158

Working with Inconclusive Results   158
Where to Look for Information   159
How Much Inquiry Is Enough?   164
Managing Lengthy Material   168
Applications   170

Chapter 18   Forming a Judgment   172

Evaluating Evidence   173
Evaluating Your Sources' Arguments   174
Making Important Distinctions   178
Expressing Judgments   179
Applications   184

Chapter 19   Persuading Others   186
             Guidelines for Persuasion   186
             An Unpersuasive Presentation   196
             A Persuasive Presentation   198
             Applications   199

Notes   *206*

Index   *213*

Introduction

Beyond Feelings is desiged to introduce you to the subject of critical think-ing. The subject is undoubtedly new to you because it is not taught in most elementary and secondary schools. In fact, until fairly recently, it was not taught in most colleges. For the past four decades, the dominant emphasis has been on subjectivity rather than objectivity, on feeling rather than on thought.

Over the past fifteen years, however, a number of studies of America's schools have criticized the neglect of critical thinking, and a growing number of educators and leaders in business, industry, and the professions have urged the development of new courses and teaching materials to overcome that neglect.

It is no exaggeration to say that critical thinking is one of the most important subjects you will study in college regardless of your academic major. The quality of your schoolwork, your efforts in your career, your contributions to community life, your conduct of personal affairs—all will depend on your ability to solve problems and make decisions.

The book has three main sections. The first, "The Context," will help you understand such important concepts as *individuality, thinking, truth, knowledge, opinion, evidence,* and *argument* and to overcome attitudes and ideas that obstruct critical thinking. The second section, "The Pitfalls," will teach you to recognize and avoid the most common errors in think-ing. The third section, "A Strategy," will help you acquire the various skills used in addressing problems and issues. This section includes tips on identifying and overcoming your personal intellectual weaknesses, as well as techniques for becoming more observant, clarifying issues, con-ducting inquiries, evaluating evidence, analyzing other people's views, and making sound judgments.

At the end of each chapter, you will find a number of applications to challenge your critical thinking and exercise your skills. These applications cover problems and issues both timely and timeless.

In brief, *Beyond Feelings* is designed to help you acquire the intellectual skills necessary to solve the exciting problems of today and tomorrow.

PART ONE

The Context

Anyone who wishes to master an activity must first understand its tools and rules. This is as true of critical thinking as it is of golf, carpentry, flying a plane, or brain surgery. In critical thinking, however, the tools are not material objects but concepts, and the rules govern mental rather than physical performance.

This first section explores seven important concepts—*individuality, critical thinking, truth, knowledge, opinion, evidence,* and *argument*—with a separate chapter devoted to each. Most of these concepts are so familiar that you may be inclined to wonder whether there is any point to examining them. The answer is yes, for three reasons. First, much of what is commonly believed about these concepts is mistaken. Second, whoever examines them carefully is always rewarded with fresh insights. Third, the more thorough your knowledge of these concepts, the more proficient you can be in your thinking.

CHAPTER 1

Who Are You?

Suppose someone asked, "Who are you?" It would be simple enough to respond with your name. But if the person wanted to know the entire story about who you are, the question would be more difficult to answer. You'd obviously have to give the details of your height, age, and weight. You'd also have to include all your sentiments and preferences, even the secret ones you'd never shared with anyone—your affection for your loved ones; your desire to please the people you associate with; your dislike of your older sister's husband; your allegiance to your favorite beverage, brand of clothing, and music.

Your attitudes couldn't be overlooked either—your impatience when an issue gets complex, your aversion to certain courses, your fear of high places and dogs and speaking in public. The list would go on. To be complete, it would have to include all your characteristics—not only the physical but also the emotional and intellectual.

To provide all that information would be quite a chore. But suppose the questioner was still curious and asked, "How did you get the way you are?" If your patience were not yet exhausted, chances are you'd answer something like this: "I'm this way because I choose to be, because I've considered other sentiments and preferences and attitudes and have made my selections. The ones I have chosen fit my style and personality best." That answer is natural enough, and in part it's true. But in a larger sense, it's not true. The impact of the world on all of us is much greater than most of us realize.

The Influence of Time and Place

Not only are you a member of a particular species, *Homo sapiens,* but also you exist at a particular moment in the history of that species. Life today is quite different from life thirty years ago, and very different from life in A.D. 1500 or 10,000 B.C. The world's state of progress differs, as does its knowledge and beliefs and values. The opportunities for learning and working and relaxing are not the same, so people's daily thoughts and actions vary.

Variations in place and circumstance also can make a difference. If you're from a large city, the odds are you look at many things differently from someone in the country. A person raised for eighteen years in New York City or Los Angeles who goes to college in a town of three thousand will find the experience difficult. So will a person raised on an isolated farm, but probably for opposite reasons!

If you are an American sports enthusiast, you're probably interested in football, baseball, or basketball. But if you were Asian, you'd be much more familiar with and excited about Ping-Pong or badminton; and if you were English, cricket. If one of your parents were an automobile mechanic, you undoubtedly would know more about cars than the average person. If your other parent were a teacher, you'd tend to have a somewhat different perspective on school and teachers compared with other students.

In much the same way, all the details about the members of your family very likely have some bearing on who you are. Their religion, race, national origin, political affiliation, economic level, and attitudes toward one another all have made some contribution to your identity.

Of course, you may have rejected your parents' beliefs and values. Still, whether you accepted or rejected what your parents tried to teach you, your present views grew out of those teachings. In forming your views you were responding to your upbringing. Given different parents with a different culture and values—growing up, say, in Istanbul rather than Dubuque—your response would necessarily be different. You would, in that sense, not be the same person.

The Influence of Mass Culture

In centuries past, family and teachers were the dominant, and sometimes the only, influence on children. Today, however, the influence exerted by mass culture (the broadcast media, newspapers, magazines, and popular music) often is greater.

By age eighteen the average teenager has spent 11,000 hours in the classroom and 22,000 hours in front of the television set. He or she has done perhaps 13,000 school lessons yet has watched more than 750,000 commercials. By age thirty-five the same person has had fewer than 20,000 school lessons yet has watched approximately 45,000 hours of television and seen close to 2 million commercials.

What effects does mass culture have on us? To answer, we need only consider the formats and devices commonly used in the media. Modern advertising typically bombards the public with slogans and testimonials by celebrities. This approach is designed to appeal to emotions and create artificial needs for products and services. As a result, many people develop the habit of responding emotionally, impulsively, and gullibly to such appeals. They also tend to acquire values very different from those taught in the home and the school. Ads often portray play as more fulfilling than work, self-gratification as more desirable than self-control, and materialism as more meaningful than idealism.

Television programmers use frequent scene shifts and sensory appeals such as car crashes, violence, and sexual encounters to keep audience interest from diminishing. Then they add frequent commercial interruptions. This author has analyzed the attention shifts that television viewers are subjected to. In a dramatic program, for example, attention shifts might include camera angle changes;* shifts in story line from one set of characters (or subplot) to another, or from a present scene to a past one (flashback) or to fantasy; and shifts to "newsbreaks," to commercial breaks, from one commercial to another, and back to the program. Also included might be shifts of attention that occur *within* commercials. I found as many as 78 shifts per hour, excluding the shifts within commercials. The number of shifts within commercials ranged from 6 to 54 and averaged approximately 17 per fifteen-second commercial. The total number of attention shifts came out to over 800 per hour, or over 14 per minute.**

This manipulation has prevented many people from developing a mature attention span. They expect the classroom and the workplace to provide the same constant excitement they get from television. That, of course, is an impossible demand, and when it isn't met they call their teachers boring and their work unfulfilling. Because people seldom have the patience to read books that require them to think, many publishers have replaced serious books with light fare written by celebrities. Sensationalism, even outrageousness, sells, as the successes of authors such as Dennis Rodman, Howard Stern, and Mick "Mankind" Foley attest.

Even when writers of serious books do manage to become published authors, they are often directed to give short, dramatic answers during

*This is typically accomplished by using two or more cameras and switching from one camera to another.

**There are about eleven minutes of commercials per hour, the exact time varying by network and program. Thus, at a rate of 4 per minute, the total number of commercials per hour is 44. This calculates, therefore, to 78 shifts outside commercials plus 748 shifts within commercials (17 shifts per commercial times 44 commercials per hour) for a total of 826.

promotional interviews, sometimes at the expense of accuracy. A man who coaches writers for talk shows offered one client this advice: "If I ask you whether the budget deficit is a good thing or a bad thing, you should not say, 'Well, it stimulates the economy but it passes on a burden.' You have to say, 'It's a great idea!' Or, 'It's a terrible idea!' It doesn't matter which."[1] (Translation—"Don't give a balanced answer. Give an oversimplified one because it will get you noticed.")

Print journalism is also in the grip of sensationalism. As a newspaper editor observed, "Journalists keep trying to find people who are at 1 and at 9 on a scale of 1 to 10 rather than people at 3 to 7 [the more moderate positions] where most people actually are."[2] Another journalist claims, "News is now becoming more opinion than verified fact. Journalists are slipping into entertainment rather than telling us the verified facts we need to know."[3]

Today's politicians manipulate people more offensively than do journalists. Instead of expressing their thoughts, politicians find out what people think and pretend to share their ideas. Many politicians hire people to conduct polls and focus groups to learn what messages will "sell." They even go so far as to test the impact of certain words—that is why we hear so much about "trust," "family," "character," and "values" these days. Political science professor Larry Sabato says that during the Clinton impeachment trial, the president's advisors used the term *private lives* over and over—James Carville used it six times in one four-minute speech—because they knew it could persuade people into believing the president's lying under oath was of no great consequence.[4]

The Influence of Psychology

The social and psychological theories of our time also have an impact on our beliefs. Before the last few decades, people were urged to be self-disciplined, self-critical, and self-effacing. They were urged to practice self-denial, to aspire to self-knowledge, to behave in a manner that ensured they maintain self-respect. Self-centeredness was considered a vice. "Hard work," they were told, "leads to achievement, and that in turn produces satisfaction and self-confidence." By and large, our grandparents internalized those teachings. When they honored them in their behavior, they felt proud; when they dishonored them, they felt ashamed.

Today the theories have been changed—indeed, almost exactly reversed. Self-esteem, which nineteenth-century satirist Ambrose Bierce defined as "an erroneous appraisement," is now considered an imperative. Self-centeredness has been transformed from vice into virtue, and people who devote their lives to helping others, people once considered heroic and saintlike, are now said to be afflicted with "a disease to please." The formula for success and happiness begins with feeling good about ourselves. Students who do poorly in school, workers who don't measure up to the challenges of their jobs, substance abusers, lawbreakers—all are typically diagnosed as deficient in self-esteem.

In addition, just as our grandparents internalized the social and psychological theories of their time, so most contemporary Americans have internalized the message of self-esteem. We hear people speak of it over coffee; we hear it endlessly invoked on talk shows. Challenges to its precepts are usually met with disapproval.

But isn't the theory of self-esteem self-evident? No. A negative perception of our abilities will, of course, handicap our performance. Dr. Maxwell Maltz explains the amazing results one educator had in improving the grades of schoolchildren by changing their self-images. The educator had observed that when the children saw themselves as stupid in a particular subject (or stupid in general), they unconsciously acted to confirm their self-images. They believed they were stupid, so they acted that way. Reasoning that it was their defeatist attitude rather than any lack of ability that was undermining their efforts, the educator set out to change their self-images. He found that when he accomplished that, *they no longer behaved stupidly!* Maltz concludes from this and other examples that our experiences can work a kind of self-hypnotism on us, suggesting a conclusion about ourselves and then urging us to make it come true.[5]

Maltz's research documents that lack of confidence impedes performance, a valuable insight. But such research doesn't explain why the more global concept of self-esteem has become so dominant. The answer to that question lies in the popularization of the work of such humanistic psychologists as Abraham Maslow. Maslow described what he called the hierarchy of human needs in the form of a pyramid, with physiological needs (food and drink) at the foundation. Above them, in ascending order, are safety needs, the need for belongingness and love, the need for esteem and approval, and aesthetic and cognitive needs (knowledge, understanding, etc.). At the pinnacle is the need for self-actualization, or fulfillment of our potential. In Maslow's view, the lower needs must be fulfilled before the higher ones. It's easy to see how the idea that self-esteem must precede achievement was derived from Maslow's theory.

However, other, different theories might have been adopted. A notable one is Austrian psychiatrist Viktor Frankl's, which was advanced at roughly the same time as Maslow's and which was based on both Frankl's professional practice and his experiences in Hitler's concentration camps. Frankl argues that one human need is higher than self-actualization: *self-transcendence,* the need to rise above narrow absorption with self. According to Frankl, "the primordial anthropological fact [is] that being human is being always directed, and pointing to something or someone other than oneself: to a meaning to fulfill or another human being to encounter, a cause to serve or a person to love." A person becomes fully human "by forgetting himself and giving himself, overlooking himself and focusing outward."

Making self-actualization (or happiness) the direct object of our pursuit, in Frankl's view, is ultimately self-defeating; such fulfillment can occur only as "the unintended effect of self-transcendence."[6] The proper perspective on life, Frankl believes, is not what it can give *to* us, but what it expects *from* us; life is daily—even hourly—questioning us, challenging us to accept "the responsibility to find the right answer to its problems and to fulfill the tasks which it constantly sets for [each of us]."[7]

Finding meaning, according to Frankl's theory, involves "perceiving a possibility embedded in reality" and searching for challenging tasks "whose completion might add meaning to [one's] existence." But such perceiving and searching is frustrated by the focus on self: "As long as modern literature confines itself to, and contents itself with, self-expression—not to say self-exhibition—it reflects its authors' sense of futility and absurdity. What is more important, it also creates absurdity. This is understandable in light of the fact that meaning must be discovered, it cannot be invented. Sense cannot be created, but what may well be created is nonsense."[8]

Whether we agree completely with Frankl, one thing is clear: Contemporary American culture would be markedly different if the emphasis over the past several decades had been on Frankl's theory rather than on those of Maslow and the other humanistic psychologists. All of us would have been affected—we can only imagine how profoundly—in our attitudes, values, and beliefs.

Becoming an Individual

What does individuality mean, and to what extent can a person be an individual? In the current popular imagination, individuality means "doing your own thing," responding to life's situations in whatever way seems most natural. The problem with that notion is that it ignores all the shaping forces we have been discussing. It denies the fact that each of us has been channeled and conditioned to a great degree. It pretends there is some inner self untouched by all that we have experienced, all that has happened to us.

The fact is, if you define individuality in the popular way and act on that definition, you'll be behaving like Pavlov's famous dog. Pavlov rang a bell whenever he placed food in front of the dog. After a while, he conditioned the dog to drool when it heard the bell, even though no food was presented. The dog was doing what came naturally to it. But what came naturally was influenced by its experience. The dog was controlled by a force outside itself.

Obviously, individuality must be something more than that. It must involve the habit of developing your own personal responses to people, issues, and situations, rather than mindlessly endorsing the responses you have been conditioned to make. These guidelines will help you achieve individuality:

1. *Treat your first reaction to any person, issue, or situation as tentative.* No matter how appealing it may be, refuse to embrace it until you have examined it.

2. *Decide why you reacted as you did.* Consider whether you borrowed the reaction from someone else—a parent or friend, perhaps, or a celebrity or fictional character on television. If possible, determine what specific experiences conditioned you to react this way.

3. *Think of other possible reactions you might have had to the person, issue, or situation.*

4. *Ask yourself whether one of the other reactions is more appropriate than your first reaction.* And when you answer, resist the influence of your conditioning.

To ensure that you will really be an individual and not merely claim to be one, apply these guidelines throughout your work in this book, as well as in your everyday life.

Applications

Note: One of the best ways to develop your thinking (and writing) skills is to record your observations, questions, and ideas in a journal and then, as time permits, to reflect on what you have recorded—considering the meaning and application of the observations, answering the questions, elaborating on the ideas (and, where appropriate, challenging them), and recording your insights. An inexpensive bound notebook or spiral notebook will serve the purpose. A good approach is to record your initial observations, questions, and ideas on the left side of the page, leaving the right side blank for your later analysis and commentary. The value of this reflective process is so great that you should consider keeping such a journal even if your instructor does not make it a formal part of the course.

1. Do a brief study of attention shifts such as the one described in the chapter. Videotape a half-hour show on a VCR. Then play the tape back twice, the first time counting the number of shifts within the program, excluding commercials, and the second time counting only those within commercials. Complete the necessary arithmetic, and be prepared to share your results in class.

2. Reflect on your findings in application 1. Write several paragraphs discussing the implications of those findings for education, business, and family life.

3. Imagine how different America might be if Frankl's emphasis on self-transcendence (and personal responsibility), rather than Maslow's emphasis on self-actualization and popular culture's emphasis on self-esteem, had been dominant for the past thirty years. List as many ways as you can in which our society might be different today, and comment on whether each would be beneficial or harmful. Be prepared to explain your views in class discussion.

4. Watch one of the music video channels—MTV, VH1, CMT, BET— for at least an hour. Analyze how men and women are depicted in the videos. Note significant details. For example, observe whether men are depicted in power roles more than women, and whether women are portrayed as objects of male desire. Decide what attitudes and values are conveyed. (You may wish to videotape as you are watching so that you can review what you have seen, freeze significant frames for closer analysis, and keep a record of your observations for later reference or class viewing and discussion.)

5. Suppose you asked a friend, "How did you acquire your particular identity—your sentiments and preferences and attitudes?" Then suppose the friend responded, "I'm an individual. No one else influences me. I do my own thing, and I select the sentiments and preferences and attitudes that suit me." How would you explain to your friend what you learned in this chapter?

6. Ask yourself the question, Who am I? Write down ten answers to this on ten separate slips of paper. Use the first three paragraphs of this chapter to help you frame your answers. Arrange the pieces of paper in order of their importance to you. Which self-descriptions are most important to you? Why?

7. Identify the various positive and negative influences that have shaped you. Be sure to include the particular as well as the general and the subtle as well as the obvious influences. Which of those influences have had the greatest effect on you? Explain the effects as precisely as you can.

8. Note your immediate reaction to each of the following statements. Then apply the four guidelines given in this chapter for achieving individuality.
   a. Health care workers should be required to be tested for HIV/AIDS.
   b. Beauty contests and talent competitions for children should be banned.
   c. Extremist groups like the Ku Klux Klan should be allowed to hold rallies on public property or be issued permits to hold parades in city streets.
   d. Freshman composition should be a required course for all students.
   e. Athletes should be tested for anabolic steroid use.
   f. Creationism should be taught in high school biology classes.
   g. Polygamy should be legalized.
   h. The voting age should be lowered to sixteen.
   i. The prison system should give greater emphasis to the punishment of inmates than to their rehabilitation.
   j. Doctors and clinics should be required to notify parents of minors when they prescribe birth control devices for the minors.
   k. A man's self-esteem is severely injured if his wife makes more money than he makes.
   l. Women like being dependent on men.

9. *Group discussion exercise:* Discuss several of the statements in application 8 with two or three of your classmates, applying the four guidelines presented in this chapter for developing individuality. Be prepared to share your group's ideas with the class.

CHAPTER 2

What Is Critical Thinking?

When Arthur was in the first grade, the teacher directed the class to "think." "Now, class," she said, "I know this problem is a little harder than the ones we've been doing, but I'm going to give you a few extra minutes to think about it. Now start thinking."

It was not the first time Arthur had heard the word used. He'd heard it many times at home, but never quite this way. The teacher seemed to be asking for some special activity, something he should know how to start and stop—like his father's car. "Vroom-m-m," he muttered half aloud. Because of his confusion, he was unaware he was making the noise.

"Arthur, please stop making noises and start thinking."

Embarrassed and not knowing quite what to do, he looked down at his desk. Then, out of the corner of his eye, he noticed that the little girl next to him was staring at the ceiling. "Maybe that's the way you start thinking," he guessed. He decided the others had probably learned how to do it last year, that time he was home with the measles. So he stared at the ceiling.

As he progressed through grade school and high school, he heard that same direction hundreds of times. "No, that's not the answer, you're not thinking—now *think!*" And occasionally, he would hear from particularly self-pitying teachers given to talking to themselves aloud: "What did I do to deserve this? Don't they teach them anything in the grades anymore? Don't you people care about ideas? Think, dammit, THINK."

So Arthur learned to feel somewhat guilty about the whole matter. Obviously, this thinking was an important activity that he'd failed to learn. Maybe he lacked the brain power. But he was resourceful enough. He watched the other students and did what they did. Whenever a teacher started in about thinking, he screwed up his face, furrowed his brow, scratched his head, stroked his chin, stared off into space or up at the ceiling, and repeated silently to himself, "Let's see now, I've got to think about that, think, think (I hope he doesn't call on me), think."

Though Arthur didn't know it, that's just what the other students were saying to themselves.

Your experience may have been similar to Arthur's. In other words, many people may have told you simply to think without ever explaining what thinking is and what qualities a good thinker has that a poor thinker lacks. If that is the case, you've got a lot of company. Extensive, effective training in thinking is the exception rather than the rule. This fact and its unfortunate consequences are suggested by the following comments from accomplished observers of the human condition:

> The most interesting and astounding contradiction in life is to me the constant insistence by nearly all people upon "logic," "logical reasoning," "sound reasoning," on the one hand, and on the other their inability to display it, and their unwillingness to accept it when displayed by others.[1]

> Most of our so-called reasoning consists in finding arguments for going on believing as we already do.[2]

> Clear thinking is a very rare thing, but even just plain thinking is almost as rare. Most of us most of the time do not think at all. We believe and we feel, but we do not think.[3]

> Mental indolence is one of the commonest of human traits.[4]

What is this activity that everyone claims is important but few people have mastered? Thinking is a general term covering numerous activities, from daydreaming to reflection and analysis. Here are just some of the synonyms listed in *Roget's Thesaurus* for *think*:

appreciate	consult	fancy	reason
believe	contemplate	imagine	reflect
cerebrate	deliberate	meditate	ruminate
cogitate	digest	muse	speculate
conceive	discuss	ponder	suppose
consider	dream	realize	weigh

All of those are just the *names* that thinking goes under. They really don't explain it. The fact is, after thousands of years of humans' experiencing thought and talking and writing about thinking, it remains in many respects one of the great mysteries of our existence. Still, though much is yet to be learned, a great deal is already known.

Mind, Brain, or Both?

Most modern researchers use the word *mind* synonymously with *brain*, as if the physical organ that resides in the human skull were solely responsible for thinking. This practice conveniently presupposes that a problem that has challenged the greatest thinkers for millennia—the relationship between mind and physical matter—was somehow solved when no one was looking. The problem itself, and the individuals who spent their lives wrestling with it, deserve better.

Neuroscience has provided a number of valuable insights into the cognitive or thinking activities of the brain. It has documented that the left hemisphere of the brain deals mainly with detailed language processing and is associated with analysis and logical thinking, that the right hemisphere deals mainly with sensory images and is associated with intuition and creative thinking, and that the small bundle of nerves that lies between the hemispheres—the *corpus callosum*—integrates the various functions.

The research that produced these insights proved that the brain is *necessary* for thought, but it has not shown that the brain is *sufficient* for thought. In fact, many philosophers claim it can never show that. They argue that the mind and the brain are demonstrably different. Whereas the brain is a physical entity composed of matter and therefore subject to decay, the mind is a *metaphysical* entity. Examine brain cells under the most powerful microscope and you will never see an idea or concept— for example, beauty, government, equality, or love—because ideas and concepts are not matter and so have no physical dimension. Where, then, do these nonmaterial things reside? In the nonmaterial mind.[5]

The late American philosopher William Barrett observed that "history is, fundamentally, the adventure of human consciousness" and "the fundamental history of humankind is the history of mind." In his view, "one of the supreme ironies of modern history" is the fact that science, which owes its very existence to the human mind, has had the audacity to deny the reality of the mind. As he put it, "the offspring denies the parent."[6]

The argument over whether the mind is a reality is not the only issue about the mind that has been hotly debated over the centuries. One especially important issue is whether the mind is *passive,* a "blank slate" on which experience writes, as John Locke held, or *active,* a vehicle by which we take the initiative and exercise our free will, as G. W. Leibnitz argued. This book is based on the latter view.

Critical Thinking Defined

Let's begin by making the important distinction between thinking and feeling. *I feel* and *I think* are sometimes used interchangeably, but that practice causes confusion. Feeling is a subjective response that reflects emotion, sentiment, or desire; it generally occurs spontaneously rather than through a conscious mental act. We don't have to employ our minds to feel angry when we are insulted, afraid when we are threatened, or compassionate when we see a picture of a starving child. The feelings arise automatically.

Feeling is useful in directing our attention to matters we should think about; it also can provide the enthusiasm and commitment necessary to complete arduous mental tasks. However, feeling is never a good substitute for thinking because it is notoriously unreliable. Some feelings are beneficial, honorable, even noble; others are not, as everyday experience demonstrates. We often "feel like" doing things that will harm us—for example, smoking, sunbathing without sunscreen, speaking our mind to our professor or employer, or spending the rent money on lottery tickets.

In contrast, thinking is a conscious mental process performed to solve a problem, make a decision, or gain understanding.* Whereas feeling has no purpose beyond expressing itself, thinking aims beyond itself to knowledge or action. This is not to say that thinking is infallible; in fact, a good part of this book is devoted to exposing errors in thinking and showing you how to avoid them. Yet for all its shortcomings, thinking is the most reliable guide to action we humans possess. To sum up the relationship between feeling and thinking, feelings need to be tested before being trusted, and thinking is the most reasonable and reliable way to test them.

There are two broad categories of thinking: creative and critical. The focus of this book is the latter. The essence of critical thinking is *evaluation.* Critical thinking, therefore, may be defined as the process by which we test claims and arguments and determine which have merit and which do not. In other words, critical thinking is a search for answers, a *quest.* Not surprisingly, one of the most important techniques used in critical thinking is asking probing *questions.* Where the uncritical accept their first thoughts and other people's statements at face value, critical thinkers challenge all ideas in this manner:

Thought	*Question*
Professor Vile cheated me in my composition grade. He weighted some themes more heavily than others.	Did he grade everyone on the same standard? Were the different weightings justified?
Before women entered the work force, there were fewer divorces. That shows that a woman's place is in the home.	How do you know that this factor, and not some other one(s), is responsible for the increase in divorces?

---

*Some informal definitions of thinking include daydreaming. It is excluded from this definition because it is a passive mental state over which we exercise little or no control. It is therefore of little use in evaluating ideas.

A college education isn't worth what you pay for it. Some people never reach a salary level appreciably higher than the level they would have reached without the degree.	Is money the only measure of the worth of an education? What about increased understanding of self and life and increased ability to cope with challenges?

Critical thinking also employs questions to analyze issues. Consider, for example, the subject of values. When it is being discussed, some people say, "Our country has lost its traditional values" and "There would be less crime, especially violent crime, if parents and teachers emphasized moral values." Critical thinking would prompt us to ask:

1. What is the relationship between values and beliefs? Between values and convictions?

2. Are all values *valuable?*

3. How aware is the average person of his or her values? Is it possible that many people deceive themselves about their real values?

4. Where do one's values originate? Within the individual or outside? In thought or in feeling?

5. Does education change a person's values? If so, is this change always for the better?

6. Should parents and teachers attempt to shape children's values?

Characteristics of Critical Thinkers

A number of misconceptions exist about critical thinking. One is that being able to support beliefs with reasons makes one a critical thinker. Virtually everyone has reasons, however weak they may be. The test of critical thinking is whether the reasons are good and sufficient.

Another misconception is that critical thinkers never imitate others in thought or action. If that were the case, then every wacko would be a critical thinker. Critical thinking means making sound decisions, regardless of how common those decisions are.

A third misconception is that critical thinking is synonymous with having a lot of right answers in one's head. There's nothing wrong with having right answers, of course. But critical thinking involves the process of finding answers when they are not so readily available.

Yet another misconception is that critical thinking cannot be learned, that one either "has it" or does not. On the contrary, critical thinking is a matter of habit. The most careless, sloppy thinker can become a critical thinker by developing the characteristics of a critical thinker.

We have already noted one characteristic of critical thinkers—skill in asking appropriate questions. Another is control of one's mental activities.

John Dewey once observed that more of our time than most of us care to admit is spent "trifling with mental pictures, random recollections, pleasant but unfounded hopes, flitting, half-developed impressions."[7] Good thinkers are no exception. However, they have learned better than poor thinkers how to stop that casual, semiconscious drift of images when they wish and how to fix their minds on one specific matter, examine it carefully, and form a judgment about it. They have learned, in other words, *how to take charge of their thoughts,* to use their minds actively as well as passively.

Here are some additional characteristics of critical thinkers, as contrasted with those of uncritical thinkers:

Critical Thinkers…	*Uncritical Thinkers…*
Are honest with themselves, acknowledging what they don't know, recognizing their limitations, and being watchful of their own errors.	Pretend they know more than they do, ignore their limitations, and assume their views are error-free.
Regard problems and controversial issues as exciting challenges.	Regard problems and controversial issues as nuisances or threats to their ego.
Strive for understanding, keep curiosity alive, remain patient with complexity, and are ready to invest time to overcome confusion.	Are impatient with complexity and thus would rather remain confused than make the effort to understand.
Base judgments on evidence rather than personal preferences, deferring judgment whenever evidence is insufficient. They revise judgments when new evidence reveals error.	Base judgments on first impressions and gut reactions. They are unconcerned about the amount or quality of evidence and cling to their views steadfastly.
Are interested in other people's ideas and so are willing to read and listen attentively, even when they tend to disagree with the other person.	Are preoccupied with themselves and their own opinions, and so are unwilling to pay attention to others' views. At the first sign of disagreement, they tend to think, "How can I refute this?"
Recognize that extreme views (whether conservative or liberal) are seldom correct, so they avoid them, practice fairmindedness, and seek a balanced view.	Ignore the need for balance and give preference to views that support their established views.

Practice restraint, controlling their feelings rather than being controlled by them, and thinking before acting.	Tend to follow their feelings and act impulsively.

As the desirable qualities suggest, critical thinking depends on mental discipline. Effective thinkers exert control over their mental life, direct their thoughts rather than being directed by them, and withhold their endorsement of any idea—even their own—until they have tested and confirmed it. John Dewey equated this mental discipline with freedom. That is, he argued that people who do not have it are not free persons but slaves:

> If a man's actions are not guided by thoughtful conclusions, then they are guided by inconsiderate impulse, unbalanced appetite, caprice, or the circumstances of the moment. To cultivate unhindered, unreflective external activity is to foster enslavement, for it leaves the person at the mercy of appetite, sense, and circumstance.[8]

The Role of Intuition

Intuition is commonly defined as immediate perception or comprehension of something; that is, sensing or understanding something *without the use of reasoning*. Some everyday experiences seem to support this definition. You may have met a stranger and instantly "known" that you would be partners for life. When a car salesman told you that the price he was quoting you was his final, rock-bottom price, your intuition may have told you he was lying. On the first day of a particular course, you may have had a strong sense that you would not do well in it.

Some important discoveries seem to have occurred instantaneously. For example, the German chemist Kekule found the solution to a difficult chemical problem that way. He was very tired when he slipped into a daydream. The image of a snake swallowing his tail came to him—and that provided the clue to the structure of the benzene molecule, which is a ring, rather than a chain, of atoms.[9] The German writer Goethe had been experiencing great difficulty organizing a large mass of material for one of his works when he learned of the tragic suicide of a close friend. At that very instant, the plan for organizing his material occurred to him in detail.[10] The English writer Samuel Taylor Coleridge (you may have read his *Rime of the Ancient Mariner* in high school) awoke from a dream with 200–300 lines of a new and complex poem clearly in mind.

Such examples seem to suggest that intuition is very different from reasoning and is not influenced by it. But before accepting that conclusion, consider these facts:

Breathrough ideas favor trained, active minds. It is unusual for someone totally untrained in a subject to make a significant new discovery about it. Thus, if Kekule had been a plumber, Goethe a bookkeeper, and Coleridge a hairdresser, they would probably not have had the particular intuitions credited to them.

Some intuitions eventually prove to be mistaken. That attractive stranger may turn out to be, not your lifelong partner, but a person for whom you develop a strong dislike. The car saleman's final price may have proved to be exactly that. And instead of doing poorly in that course, you may have done well.

It is difficult to make an overall assessment of the quality of our intuitions because we tend to forget the ones that prove mistaken.

These facts have led some scholars to conclude that intuition is simply a consequence of thinking. They would say that something about the stranger appealed to you, something the salesman said or did suggested insincerity, something about the professor frightened you. In each case, they would explain, you made a quick decision—so quick, in fact, that you were unaware that you'd been thinking. In the case of the breakthrough ideas, the scholars would say that when people become engrossed in problems or issues, their unconscious minds often continue working on them long after they have turned their attention elsewhere. Thus, when an insight seems to come "out of nowhere," it is actually a delayed result of thinking.

Which view of intuitions is the correct one? Are they different from and independent of thinking or not? Perhaps, for now, the most prudent answer is sometimes they are and sometimes they are not.

Basic Activities in Critical Thinking

The basic activities in thinking are investigation, interpretation, and judgment, in that order. The following chart summarizes each activity in relation to the other two:

Activity	Definition	Requirements
Investigation	Finding evidence; that is, data that will answer key questions about the issue	The evidence must be both relevant and sufficient.
Interpretation	Deciding what the evidence means	The interpretation must be more reasonable than competing interpretations.
Judgment	Reaching a conclusion about the issue	The conclusion must meet the test of logic.

As we noted previously, irresponsible thinkers first choose their conclusions and then seek out evidence to justify their choices. They fail to realize that the only conclusion worth drawing is one based on a thorough understanding of the problem or issue and its possible solutions or resolutions. Is it acceptable to speculate, guess, and form hunches and hypotheses? Absolutely. Such activities provide a helpful starting point for the thinking process. (Besides, we couldn't avoid doing so even if we tried.) The crucial thing is not to let hunches and hypotheses manipulate our thinking and dictate our conclusion in advance.

Critical Thinking and Writing

Writing may be used for either of two broad purposes: to discover ideas or to communicate them. Most of the writing you have done in school is undoubtedly the latter kind. But the former can be very helpful, not only in sorting out ideas you've already produced but in stimulating the flow of new ideas. For some reason, the very act of writing down one idea seems to generate additional ideas.

Whenever you write to discover ideas, focus on the issue you are examining and record all your thoughts, questions, and assertions. Don't worry about organization or correctness. If ideas come slowly, be patient. If they come suddenly, in a rush, don't try to slow the process down and develop any one of them; simply jot them all down. (There will be time for elaboration and correction later.) Direct your mind's effort, but be sensitive to ideas on the fringes of consciousness. Often they, too, will prove valuable.

If you have done your discovery writing well and have thought critically about the ideas you have produced, the task of writing to communicate will be easier and more enjoyable. You will have many more ideas—carefully evaluated ideas—to develop and organize.

Applications

1. Think back on your previous schooling. How closely has your experience matched Arthur's?

2. Reflect on your powers of concentration. Do you find it difficult to ponder important matters? Are you able to prevent the casual, semiconscious drift of images from interrupting your thoughts? Do you have less control in some situations than in others? Explain.

3. Rate yourself on each of the seven characteristics of good thinkers that are listed on pp. 18 and 19. Which are you strongest in? Which weakest? If your behavior varies from situation to situation, try to determine what kinds of issues or circumstances bring out your best and worst mental qualities.

4. Consider how you approach problems and issues. Is there any pattern to the way you think about a problem or an issue? Does an image come to mind first? Or perhaps a word? What comes next? And what after that? If you can't answer these questions completely, do this exercise: Flip half a dozen pages ahead in this book, pick a sentence at random, read it, and note how your mind deals with it. (Such thinking about your thinking may be a little awkward at first. If it is, try the exercise two or three times.)

5. Read each of the following statements carefully. Then decide what question(s), if any, a good critical thinker would find it appropriate to ask.

   a. Television news sensationalizes its treatment of war because it gives us pictures only of injury, death, and destruction.
   b. My parents were too strict—they wouldn't let me date until I was sixteen.
   c. It's clear to me that Ralph doesn't care for me—he never speaks when we pass in the hall.
   d. From a commercial for a news network: "The news is changing every minute of the day, so you constantly need updating to keep you informed."
   e. The statement of an Alabama public elementary school teacher who had students recite the Lord's Prayer and say grace before meals: "I feel part of my job as a teacher is to instill values children need to have a good life."

CHAPTER 3

What Is Truth?

For hundreds of years, philosophers battled over whether "truth" exists. The argument usually concerned Truth with a capital *T*, a kind of complete record of whatever was, is, or will be, error-proof, beyond doubt and dispute, a final test of the rightness or wrongness of people's ideas and theories.

Those who accepted the existence of this *Truth* believed it was a spiritual reality, not a physical one. That is, it was not a celestial ledger or file drawer—yet it was beyond time and space. It was considered an understanding among the gods, or an idea in the mind of God, or simply the sum total of *Reality*. Could humans ever come to know *Truth*? Some said no, never. Others said yes, but only in the afterlife. Still others said that the wisest and best of humans could catch glimpses of it, and that the rest of humanity could learn about it through these special ones.

Those who rejected this notion of an awesome, all-embracing *Truth* argued that it was an empty notion. How could all reality be summed up that way? More important, what possible evidence could be offered in support of its existence? Many who reasoned this way dismissed the idea of *Truth* as wishful thinking, a kind of philosophical security blanket. A few went further and denied even the existence of *truths* (no capital).

Our age has inherited the whole argument. The focus, however, has changed. It seldom concerns *Truth* anymore. Even if *Truth* does exist, it's of little help to us in our world and our lives because it is beyond human understanding. Even many people of strong and rather conservative religious views no longer consider the question of *Truth* important to the understanding or practice of their faith.

Still, the problem of *truth* (no capital) remains, and the position we take toward this question does have an important bearing on how we conduct our thinking and acting. Unfortunately, there is a good deal of murkiness and confusion about the concept. The rest of this chapter will attempt to shed light on it.

It's fashionable today to believe that truth is relative and subjective. "Everyone creates his or her own truth," the saying goes, "and what is true for you may not be true for me." The meaning of this statement goes far beyond "It's a free country and I can believe what I want." The claim becomes, *whatever a person thinks is true because he or she thinks it*. Not surprisingly, to challenge another person's view on an issue is considered bad taste. "That's my truth you're talking about, Buster. Show a little respect."

The implications of this notion are quite staggering, yet for some reason few people acknowledge them, and fewer still are interested in testing their reasonableness. One implication is that everyone is right and no one is wrong. In fact, no one *can* be wrong. (What an argument that would make against objective tests—true/false, multiple choice, etc: "My answers can't be wrong, professor. They're my truth!") Another is that everyone's perception and memory work flawlessly, with never a blunder, glitch, or gaffe. A third is that no one adopts other people's "truths." The idea of creating truth rules out borrowing—if truth is intensely personal, each person's truth must be unique. Let's examine all these ideas more closely.

Where Does It All Begin?

The idea of creating our own truth without outside influence or assistance may sound reasonable if we focus only on our adulthood. The moment we consider our childhood, however, the idea becomes suspect, because in childhood we were all dependent in every sense: physically, emotionally, and intellectually. What we knew and believed about everything was what others told us. We asked questions—"Why, Mommy?" "Why, Daddy?" Our parents answered them. We accepted those answers and made them the foundation of our belief system, no matter how elaborate it would become in adulthood.

Relativists could, of course, claim that we leave all those early influences behind when we reach adulthood, but that denies the most fundamental principles of psychology. Here is how one writer explained the continuing influence of childhood experience:

> We are told about the world before we see it. We imagine most things before we experience them. And those preconceptions, unless education has made us acutely aware, govern deeply the whole process of perception. They mark out certain objects as familiar or strange, emphasizing the difference, so that the slightly familiar is seen as very familiar, and the somewhat strange as sharply alien. They are aroused by small signs, which may vary from a true index to a vague analogy. Aroused, they flood fresh vision with older images, and project into the world what has been resurrected in memory.[1]

You have heard the old saying, "Seeing is believing." The reverse is equally correct—*believing is seeing*. To a greater or lesser extent, what we regard as our unique perspective bears the imprint of other people's ideas and beliefs.

Imperfect Perception

Is perception flawless? Hardly. For one thing, it is influenced by our desires, interests, and expectations: "From the outset perception is selective and tends to simplify the world around us. Memory continues and hastens the process."[2] For another, even within its limited focus, perception often is flawed. A college student who is positive that the textbook contains a certain statement answers an exam question with perfect confidence. Yet when the student gets the corrected test back and finds the question marked wrong, then hurriedly flips open the book and examines the passage again, he or she may find it says something else entirely.

Moviegoers in the 1930s and 1940s thrilled as Tarzan uttered his famous yell and swung through the treetops to catch the villain. Tell them that Tarzan never made that yell and they'll say, "False, we heard it with our own ears." And yet it's not false. According to one of the men who first played the role of Tarzan, Buster Crabbe, that yell was dubbed into the films in the studio. It was a blend of three voices—a soprano's, a baritone's, and a hog caller's.

At least a dozen times every weekend from September to January, the imperfection of human observation is underlined by that marvel of technology, the instant replay. Is there a football fan anywhere who doesn't occasionally scream, "Bad call," only to be proved wrong a moment later? We can be sure enough to bet a week's wages that the pass receiver's feet came down in bounds or that the running back was down before the ball came loose. And then the replay shows us how erroneous our initial perception was.

The vagaries of perception have long been noted by those who deal with human testimony—notably, trial lawyers, police officers, and psychologists. It is well established that a number of factors can make us see and hear inaccurately. Darkness, cloudy conditions, or distance from what we are witnessing may obscure our vision. We may be distracted at a crucial moment. If we are tired or in the grip of powerful emotions such as fear or anger, our normal perceptiveness may be significantly diminished. Also, perception may be intermingled with interpretation—the expectation that an event will unfold in a certain way may color our perception of the way the event actually unfolds. Loyalty and affection toward the people or things involved may distort our vision as well. If someone we dislike speaks in a loud voice and is animated, we may regard that person as showing off to get attention. But if a friend behaves in the same way, we see him or her as vivacious and extroverted.

Imperfect Memory

Even when our perception is initially flawless, our memory often distorts it. We forget details, and when later attempting to recall what happened, we resort to imagination to fill in the blanks. Though we may at first be aware that such a process of reconstruction is occurring, this awareness soon fades, and we come to believe we are remembering the original perception. As psychologist William James explained:

> The most frequent source of false memory is the accounts we give to others of our experiences. Such acts we almost always make more simple and more interesting than the truth. We quote what we should have said or done rather than what we really said or did; and in the first telling we may be fully aware of the distinction, but [before] long the fiction expels the reality from memory and [replaces it]. We think of what we wish had happened, of possible [interpretations] of acts, and soon we are unable to distinguish between things that actually happened and our own thoughts about what might have occurred. Our wishes, hopes, and sometimes fears are the controlling factor.[3]

As if this weren't enough, memory is vulnerable to contamination from outside the mind. Small children and people with short attention spans are especially susceptible to suggestion, but even college students (of all ages) can be tricked into remembering things that never happened. In one experiment an eminent memory researcher, Elizabeth Loftus, asked the parents of college students to describe some events from their sons' and daughters' childhoods. Then she talked with each student about those events but also *added a fake event or two*. With only slight coaxing, the students "remembered" the fake events, were able to elaborate on the details, and in some cases refused to believe they were fake even when Loftus explained what she had done.[4]

Deficient Information

The quality of a belief depends to a considerable extent on the quality of the information that backs it up. Because it's a big world and reality has many faces, it's easy for us to be misinformed. For example, which way does the water in a sink circle as it goes down the drain—clockwise or counterclockwise? If you're more of an experimenter than a gambler, you'll find a sink, run some water, and find out the truth. The problem is, you can only be half right that way (no matter how much your sink cost). If the sink is north of the equator, the water will circle counterclockwise, and if it's south, clockwise.

Even in more common situations, it's easy to be misinformed. How many drivers take the wrong turn because of faulty directions? How many people get on the wrong bus or train? How many car owners put too much or too little air in their tires on the advice of some service station attendant? And, if misinformation is common enough in such relatively simple matters, how much more common is it in complex matters like law and medicine and government and religion?

It's possible, of course, to devote a lifetime of study to a particular field. But not even those who make that kind of commitment can know everything about their subject. Things keep happening too fast. They occur whether we're watching or not. There's no way to turn them off when we take a coffee break or go to the bathroom. The college student who hasn't been home in three months may be able to picture the neighbor's elm tree vividly, yet it may have been cut down two months ago. The soldier may have total recall of his hometown—every sight and sound and smell—and return home to find half of Main Street sacrificed to urban renewal, the old high school hangout closed, and a new car in his best friend's driveway.

Even the Wisest Can Err

So far, we've established that people can be mistaken in what they perceive and remember and that the information they receive can be faulty or incomplete. But these matters concern individuals. What of *group* judgment—the carefully analyzed observations of the best thinkers, the wisest men and women of the time? Is that record better? Happily, it is. But it, too, leaves a lot to be desired.

All too often, what is taken as truth one day by the most respected minds is proved erroneous the next. You undoubtedly know of some examples. In the early seventeenth century, when Galileo suggested that the sun is the center of our solar system, he was charged with heresy, imprisoned, and pressured to renounce his error. The "truth" of that time, accepted by every scientist worthy of the name, was that the earth was the center of the solar system.

Here are some other examples you may not have heard about in which the "truth" turned out not to be true:

- For a long time surgeons used talc on the rubber gloves they wore while performing surgery. Then they discovered it could be poisonous. So they switched to starch, only to find that it, too, could have a toxic effect on surgical patients.[5]

- Film authorities were certain they were familiar with all the films the late Charlie Chaplin ever made. Then, in 1982, a previously unknown film was discovered in a British screen archive vault.[6]
- For hundreds of years historians believed that, although the people of Pompeii had been trapped by the eruption of Mount Vesuvius in A.D. 79, the people of neighboring Herculaneum had escaped. Then the discovery of eighty bodies (and the hint of hundreds more) under the volcanic ash revealed that many from Herculaneum had also been trapped.[7]
- Your grandparents probably learned that there are eight planets in our solar system. Since Pluto was discovered in 1930, your parents and you learned there are nine. But if the observations of Joseph L. Brady of the University of California prove correct, your children will learn there are *ten*.[8]
- After morphine was used by doctors for some years as a painkiller, it was found to be addictive. The search began for a nonaddictive substitute. What was found to take its place? *Heroin*.[9]

Truth Is Discovered, Not Created

Let's review what our evaluation has revealed. First, our ideas and beliefs are unavoidably influenced by other people's, particularly in childhood. Second, perception and memory are imperfect. Third, our information can be inaccurate or incomplete. Add to this the fact, noted in Chapter 2, that some people's thinking skills are woefully meager and/or ineffectively used, and the idea that "everyone creates his or her own truth" becomes laughable. We do create something, all right, but it is not truth. It is *beliefs*, ideas that we accept as true but that could easily be false. What, then, is the most reasonable view of truth?

The truth about something is *what is so* about it—the facts in their exact arrangement and proportions. Did time run out before the basketball player got the shot off? How does gravity work? Who stole your hubcaps? Are there time/space limits to the universe? Who started the argument between you and your neighbor last weekend? Have you been working up to your potential in this course? To look for the truth in any of these matters is to look for the correct answer, the one that expresses the full reality. Our beliefs and assertions are true when they correspond to that reality and false when they do not.

Truth is apprehended by *discovery,* a process that favors the curious and the diligent. Truth does not depend on our acknowledgment of it, nor is it in any way altered by our ignorance or transformed by our wishful thinking. King Tut's tomb did not spring into existence when archaeologists dug it up; it was there waiting to be discovered. Art forgeries are not genuine when people are fooled and fake when the deception is revealed. Cigarette smoking is not rendered harmless to our health because we would prefer it so.

Much of the confusion about truth arises from complex situations in which the truth is difficult to ascertain or express. Consider a question like, Are there really UFOs that are piloted by extraterrestrial beings? Although the question is often hotly debated, and people make assertions that purport to express the truth, there is not yet sufficient evidence to say we know the truth about UFOs. That, however, doesn't mean there is no truth about them or that people who affirm their existence and people who deny it are equally correct. It means that whatever the truth is, we do not yet possess it.

Similar difficulty arises from many psychological and philosophical questions—for example: Why are some people heterosexual and others homosexual? Is the cause of criminality genetic or environmental or a combination of the two? Are humans inherently violent? Is there an afterlife? What constitutes success? The answers to these questions, and to many of the issues you will encounter in the applications in this book, will often be incomplete or tentative. Yet that fact should not shake your conviction that there are truths to be discovered.

During the Senate hearings on Clarence Thomas's candidacy for the Supreme Court, Anita Hill's charge of sexual harassment was the focus of national debate. Was Thomas guilty, as she claimed, or innocent, as he maintained? Tens of thousands of editorials, letters to editors, articles, and books were written about the case, and hundreds of hours of television air time were devoted to analysis of the evidence. Many people believed him a villain; many others saw him as a victim of false accusation; still others couldn't make up their minds. But to my knowledge, no one advanced the argument that *both stories were true*—that Clarence Thomas was at the same time guilty and innocent of the charge. If anyone had, he or she would have been attacked by both camps for talking nonsense and trivializing an important issue. However fashionable it may be to speak of "my truth" and "your truth," on significant issues like the Thomas case, people want to know *the* truth, what really happened.

Having the right frame of mind can make your pursuit of the truth less burdensome and give it the sense of adventure that the great thinkers in history experienced. A good way to begin is to keep the following thought in mind: "I know I've got limitations and can easily be mistaken. And surely I'll never find all the answers I'd like to. But I can observe a little more accurately, weigh things a little more thoroughly, and make up my mind a little more carefully. If I do so, I'll be a little closer to the truth."

That's far different from saying, "Everyone makes his or her own truth" or "It all depends on how you look at it." And it is much more reasonable.

Applications

1. Think of a recent situation in which someone referred inappropriately to "my truth." Write two or three paragraphs, in your own words, explaining to that person what you learned in this chapter.

2. A central question in sociology is, How does society evolve? Three well-known individuals gave very different answers. Auguste Comte (1798–1857) suggested that it involved three stages: religious, metaphysical, and scientific. Herbert Spencer (1820–1903) claimed that it followed Darwinian "natural selection," in which only the fittest survive. Karl Marx (1818–1883) argued that it occurred through class conflict as a result of economic exploitation. Would belief in relativism—the idea that everyone creates his or her own truth—increase or decrease someone's motivation to analyze these three viewpoints and pursue the question of society's evolution? Explain your response.

3. Read each of the following passages, decide how reasonable it is, and explain your thinking:
   a. People who believe that "everyone creates his or her own truth" should never argue with anyone about anything. If they do, they are being inconsistent.
   b. Motivation to do anything depends on the belief that it has not yet been done. Everyone who loses something precious, say a diamond ring, will search diligently and even desperately until it is found. But only a fool would continue searching for it *after* it was found. It is no different with other kinds of searches, such as the search for truth. Once we think we have it, we stop looking.

4. For years grade school students faced this question on their science tests: "True or False—The famous rings of the planet Saturn are composed of solid material." If the students marked "true," they lost credit, because the "truth" was that Saturn's rings were composed of gas or dust. Then, in 1973, radar probes revealed that all those wrong answers had been right. Saturn's rings are, in fact, composed of solid matter.[10] This confusing case seems to suggest *that the truth changed.* Did it really? Explain.

5. The scene is a school security office, where two students are being questioned. A few minutes earlier, they were engaged in a fistfight in the cafeteria. The campus police ask them again and again how the fight started. The stories conflict. Because each student seems genuinely convinced that the other one was the aggressor, and there were no witnesses, the campus police have no hope of discovering the truth. But is there a truth to discover? Or are there two truths, one for each student's story? What light does the chapter shed on these questions?

6. A strange phenomenon that affects a tiny number of the world's inhabitants has interested psychologists for some time. It occurs during what Norwegians call the "murky time," the two months each year during which areas above the Arctic Circle experience almost unrelieved darkness. The effects on people have been discovered to be unfortunate, and even dangerous. At worst, people experience severe tenseness, restlessness, fear, and a preoccupation with thoughts of death and even suicide. At best, they experience an inability to concentrate, fatigue, a lack of enthusiasm for anything, suspicion, and jealousy. Part of the cause is seen as lack of sleep. Accustomed to day and night, people

become confused by constant darkness.[11] This phenomenon poses an interesting test of truth. Would it be proper to say the phenomenon was true before it was recognized and acknowledged by psychologists? Or did it become true only when they became aware of it? And what of your relationship to the phenomenon? Before you became aware of it for the first time, whether reading it here or elsewhere, it was not "true to you." But did that make it any less true? Explain in light of this chapter.

7. Evaluate the following dialogues in light of what you learned in this chapter. If you lack sufficient knowledge to judge the issue, do some research.

   a. *Martha:* I don't care what the courts say about abortion—I'm convinced it's murder because the fetus is a human being.
   Marian: If you want to believe that, fine. Just don't impose your beliefs on others and prevent them from exercising their rights.
   Martha: You don't seem to understand. It's not just a fetus in my uterus that's human but the fetus in the uterus of every pregnant woman.
   Marian: Nonsense. You have no right to classify what exists in someone else's uterus. That's her business. You should mind your own business.

   b. *Barbi:* Television shows about suicide should not be aired.
   Ken: Why?
   Barbi: Because they cause people to commit suicide.
   Ken: That's ridiculous. How can a drama or documentary that shows the tragedy of suicide cause people to commit suicide?
   Barbi: I don't know how it happens. Maybe some people have thoughts of suicide already and the show reinforces them. Or maybe they focus on the act of suicide and lose sight of the tragedy. All I know is that attempted suicides increase after the airing of such shows.

   c. *Mabel:* I notice that when you get a newspaper you immediately turn to the astrology column. Do you really believe that nonsense?
   Alphonse: It's not nonsense. The planets exercise a powerful influence on our lives; their positions in the heavens at the time of our birth can shape our destiny.
   Mabel: I can't believe I'm hearing such slop from a science major.
   Alphonse: What you fail to understand is that astrology is science, one of the most ancient sciences at that.

   d. *Jake:* What did you think of the chapter "What Is Truth?"
   Rocky: It's stupid.
   Jake: What do you mean?
   Rocky: It contradicts Chapter 1.
   Jake: I didn't get that impression. Where's the contradiction?
   Rocky: In Chapter 1 the author says that we should strive to be individuals and think for ourselves. Now he says that his idea about truth is OK and ours isn't and that we should follow his. That's a contradiction.

8. *Group discussion exercise:* How many times have you been certain something was true, only to find out later that it was not? Discuss those experiences with two or three classmates. Be prepared to share the most dramatic and interesting experiences with the rest of the class.

CHAPTER 4

What Does It Mean to Know?

Sally looks up from her composition and asks her roommates, "How do you spell *embarrass?*"

Nancy says, "I'm not sure. I think it has a double *r* and a double *s*. Oh, I really don't know."

Marie smiles her smug smile. "I guess spelling isn't your cup of tea, Nancy. The correct spelling is e-m-b-a-r-a-s-s. Only one *r*."

By this time Sally has already opened her dictionary. "Might as well check to be sure," she says. "Let's see, *embargo, embark* . . . here it is, *embarrass*. Double *r* and double *s*. You were right, Nancy."

Let's consider what happened more closely. Marie *knew* the answer, but she was wrong. Nancy *didn't know,* but she was right. Confusing. What kind of thing can this "knowing" be? When you're doing it, you're not doing it. And when you aren't, you are.

Fortunately, it only appears to be that way. The confusion arises because the feelings that accompany knowing can be present when we don't know. Marie had those feelings. She no longer wondered or experienced any confusion; she was sure of the answer. Yet she was mistaken.

Requirements of Knowing

Nancy was in a better position than Marie because she answered correctly. Yet she didn't *know* either, for knowing involves more than having the right answer. It also involves *the realization that you have it.*

The issue, of course, may not always be as simple as the spelling of a word. It may require understanding numerous details or complex principles or steps in a process. (It may also involve a skill—knowing *how to do* something. But that is a slightly different use of the word than concerns us here.)

Knowing usually implies something else, too—the ability to express what is known and how we came to know it. This, however, is not *always* so. We may not be able to express our knowledge in words. The best we may be able to say is "I just know, that's all" or "I know because I know." Yet these replies are feeble and hardly satisfy those who wish to verify our knowledge or acquire it.

Testing Your Own Knowledge

Following are some items of "common knowledge." Determine how many you already know, and then decide, if possible, how you came to know each. Complete this informal inventory before continuing with the chapter.

1. Women are nurturing but men are not.
2. African Americans had little or no part in settling the American West.
3. Expressing anger has the effect of reducing it and making us feel better.
4. The Puritans were "prim, proper, and prudish prigs."
5. Before Columbus arrived in the New World, Native Americans lived in peace with one another and in respectful harmony with the environment.
6. Alfred Kinsey's research on human sexuality is scrupulously scholarly and objective.
7. Employers import unskilled labor from other countries to save money.
8. The practice of slavery originated in colonial America.

It would be surprising if you did not "know" most of these items. After all, many writers have written about them, and they are widely accepted as conventional wisdom. But let's look a little more closely at each of them.

1. Barbara Risman became curious about this idea and decided to study it further. Her findings challenged the conventional wisdom. Apparently, men who are responsible for caring for children or elderly parents display the same nurturing traits usually associated with women. She concluded that these traits are as dependent on one's role in life as on one's sex.[1]
2. The facts contradict what is "known." For example, 25 percent of the cowboys in Texas cattle drives were African American, as were 60 percent of original settlers of Los Angeles.[2] The reason these facts are not more widely known is probably because scholarly omission of information about African Americans from the history books.

3. Conventional wisdom is again wrong. After reviewing the evidence about anger, Carol Tavris concludes: "The psychological rationales for ventilating anger do not stand up under experimental scrutiny. The weight of the evidence indicates precisely the opposite: expressing anger makes you angrier, solidifies an angry attitude, and establishes a hostile habit. If you keep quiet about momentary irritations and distract yourself with pleasant activity until your fury simmers down, chances are you will feel better, and feel better faster, than if you let yourself go in a shouting match."[3]

4. Although the Puritans did hold that sex is rightly reserved for marriage, they did not hesitate to talk openly about the subject and were not prudish *within* marriage. The problem seems to be that people confuse the Puritans with the Victorians.[4]

5. This is pure myth. Few tribes were completely peaceful, and many not only were warlike but slaughtered women and children and tortured their captives. Some tribes also offered human sacrifices, murdered the elderly, and practiced cannibalism. As to their alleged harmonious respect for nature, many tribes deforested the land and wantonly killed whole herds of animals.[5]

6. Alfred Kinsey's work on human sexuality has been regarded as objective, scholarly, and definitive for almost half a century. In fact, it has become a foundation of psychotherapy, education, and even religion. Amazingly, in all that time no one read it critically until Judith A. Reisman and Edward W. Eichel did so. They document that Kinsey approached his work with a firm bias that significantly influenced his conclusions. He sought to establish that exclusive heterosexuality is abnormal and results merely from conditioning and inhibition; that sex between a man and a woman is no more natural than sex between two men, two women, a man and a child, or a man and an animal; and that bisexuality should be considered the norm for human sexuality. When Abraham Maslow demonstrated to Kinsey that his approach was unscientific, Kinsey simply ignored him. Kinsey went on to assert that incest can be satisfying and enriching and that children are upset by adult sexual advances solely because of the prudishness of parents and legal authorities. The authors also allege that in his research Kinsey employed a group of nine sex offenders to manually and orally stimulate to orgasm several hundred infants and children.[6]

7. The fact is that in many cases imported labor costs more money than domestic labor when the cost of transporting the workers is included in the calculation. For example, Indian workers were chosen over local Africans to build a railroad in East Africa. Similarly, Chinese workers were chosen over colonial Malayans. In both cases, the total cost of using imported workers was greater, *but the cost per unit of work was lower because the imported workers produced more.* In these and many other cases, the principal reason for choosing foreign over domestic labor is that the foreign workers are "more diligent, reliable, skilled, or careful."[7]

8. This notion is also mistaken. Slavery is thousands of years old, pre-dating Islam, Buddhism, and Christianity. It was practiced by the Venetians, Greeks, Jews, Chinese, Indians, and Egyptians, among others. Native American tribes enslaved one another long before the time of Columbus. The distinction enjoyed by the Americas is not having introduced slavery, but having *abolished* it. Slavery was *outlawed* in the Western Hemisphere many decades before it was abolished in Africa, Asia, and the Middle East.[8]

The more of the eight items you "knew," and the surer you were of your "knowledge," the more troubling you are likely to find these facts. You may, in fact, be thinking, "Wait a minute, there must be some mistake. Who are these people Ruggiero is quoting? Are they genuine scholars? I'm skeptical of the whole lot of them." That is understandable, because the feelings associated with knowing are often powerful. Yet it is a reaction critical thinkers keep on a short leash. The ancient Greek philosopher Epictetus's warning is relevant: "Get rid of self-conceit. For it is impossible for anyone to begin to learn that which he thinks he already knows."

Are you still troubled by our debunking of the conventional wisdom? Then consider that for centuries, conventional wisdom also held that heavier objects fall more rapidly than lighter ones and that the heart and not the brain was the seat of consciousness.[9] It also rejected the idea that machines could ever fly, enable people to communicate with one another across town, or create pictures of the interior of the human body. That such "wisdom" is really shortsightedness is plain to us only because some individuals were willing to ask, Is it possible that what I and other people think we know isn't really so? This little question is one of the most useful tools in critical thinking.

How We Come to Know

We can achieve knowledge either actively or passively. We achieve it actively by direct experience, by testing and proving an idea (as in a scientific experiment), or by reasoning. When we do it by reasoning, we analyze a problem, consider all the facts and possible interpretations, and draw the logical conclusion.

We achieve knowledge passively by being told by someone else. Most of the learning that takes place in the classroom and the kind that happens when we watch TV news reports or read newspapers or magazines is passive. Conditioned as we are to passive learning, it's not surprising that we depend on it in our everyday communication with friends and co-workers.

Unfortunately, passive learning has a serious defect. It makes us tend to accept uncritically what we are told even when what we are told is little more than hearsay and rumor.

Did you ever play the game Rumor (or Telephone)? It begins when one person writes down a message but doesn't show it to anyone. Then the person whispers it, word for word, to another person. That person, in turn, whispers it to still another, and so on, through all the people playing the game. The last person writes down the message word for word as he or she hears it. Then the two written statements are compared. Typically, the original message has changed, often dramatically, in passing from person to person.

That's what happens in daily life. No two words have precisely the same shades of meaning. Therefore, the simple fact that people repeat a story in their own words rather than in exact quotation changes the story. Then, too, most people listen imperfectly. And many enjoy adding their own creative touch to a story, trying to improve on it, stamping it with their own personal style. This tendency may be conscious or unconscious. Yet the effect is the same in either case—those who hear it think they know.

This process is not limited to everyday exchanges among people. It is also found among scholars and authors: "A statement of opinion by one writer may be re-stated as a fact by another, who may in turn be quoted as an authority by yet another; and this process may continue indefinitely, unless it occurs to someone to question the facts on which the original writer based his opinion or to challenge the interpretation he placed upon those facts."[10]

Why Knowing Is Difficult

One reason knowing is difficult is that old unanswered questions continue to resist solution, questions like What causes cancer? What approach to education is best for children? and How can we prevent crime without compromising individual rights?

Another reason is that everyday situations arise for which there are no precedents. When the brain procedure known as frontal lobotomy was developed to calm raging violence in people, it raised the question of the morality of a "cure" that robbed the patient of human sensibilities. When the heart transplant and the artificial heart became realities, the issue of which patients should be given priority was created, as well as the question of how donors were to be obtained. When smoking was definitely determined to be a causative factor in numerous fatal diseases, we were forced to examine the wisdom of allowing cigarette commercials to mislead TV viewers and entice them into harming themselves. More recently, when smoking was shown to harm the nonsmoker as well as the smoker, a debate arose concerning the rights of smokers and nonsmokers in public places.

Still another reason knowing is difficult is that, as one generation succeeds another, knowledge is often forgotten or unwisely rejected. For example, the ancient Greeks knew that whales have lungs instead of gills and are therefore mammals. Subsequently, however, the Romans regarded whales as fish, a false notion that persisted in Western minds until the seventeenth century. In that century one man suggested that whales are really mammals, and another later established it as fact. The West rediscovered an item of knowledge.[11]

In our time the ideas of "sin" and "guilt" have come to be regarded as useless and even harmful holdovers from Puritan times. The "new morality" has urged people to put aside such old-fashioned notions as obstacles to happiness and fulfillment. Then Karl Menninger, one of America's leading psychiatrists, wrote a book called *Whatever Became of Sin?* in which he argues that the notions of "sin" and "guilt" are good and necessary in civilized society.[12] He says, in other words, that our age rejected those concepts too quickly and quite unwisely.

Knowledge is often thought of as dead matter stored on dusty shelves in dull libraries. Unfortunately, the hushed atmosphere of a library can suggest a funeral chapel or a cemetery. But the appearance is deceiving. The ideas on those shelves are very much alive—and often fighting furiously with one another. Consider the following cases.

The idea that Columbus was the first person from Europe, Africa, or Asia to land on the shores of North or South America hangs on tenaciously. The opposite idea challenges this again and again. (The evidence against the Columbus theory continues to mount: the discovery of ancient Japanese pottery in Ecuador, traces of visits by seafarers from Sidon in 541 B.C. as well as by the Greeks and Hebrews in A.D. 200 and by the Vikings in A.D. 874.[13] The most recent evidence suggests that the Chinese may have discovered America by 2500 B.C.)[14]

The idea that a history of slavery and deprivation has caused African Americans to have less self-esteem than whites was well established. Then it was challenged by two University of Connecticut sociologists, Jerold Heiss and Susan Owens. Their studies indicate that the self-esteem of middle-class African Americans is almost identical to that of middle-class whites and that the self-esteem of lower-class African Americans is *higher* than that of lower-class whites.[15]

The notion that when the youngest child leaves home, middle-aged parents, especially mothers, become deeply depressed and feel that life is over for them has many believers. Yet at least one study attacks that notion. It shows that many, perhaps most, parents are not depressed at all; rather, they look forward to a simpler, less demanding life.[16]

Similarly, until recently, most scientists accepted that senility is a result of the physical deterioration of the brain and is both progressive and irreversible. Then experimenters in an Alabama veterans' hospital found that in many cases the symptoms of senility—confusion, disorientation, and withdrawal from reality—can be halted and even reversed by "a simple program of keeping the aged constantly in touch with the surrounding environment."[17]

Books and articles referring to athletes' "second wind" abound. Yet Nyles Humphrey and Robert Ruhling of the University of Utah have presented evidence that there really is no second wind and that the sensation experienced by many athletes is merely psychological.[18]

A Cautionary Tale

Even authorities who have the most sophisticated measurement tools at their disposal fail to achieve certainty. Consider, for example, the challenge to anthropologists posed by the Tasaday tribe. When discovered on the Philippine island of Mindanao in the late 1960s, the Tasaday were living a Stone Age existence—inhabiting caves in the deep jungle, ignorant of agriculture, subsisting by hunting and gathering. Manuel Elizaldo, an associate of then dictator Ferdinand Marcos, quickly became their protector, mentor, and go-between with a fascinated world. A number of anthropologists and other experts visited the tribe and studied their artifacts, language, and social structure. Except for a few skeptics, most scholars judged them to be authentic Stone Age people. Prestigious publications like the *National Geographic* wrote about the Tasaday and marveled at the fact that they were such an innocent, gentle people with no words in their language for "weapon," "war," or "hostility."

In 1986, after the Marcos regime collapsed, a Swiss journalist visited the Tasaday and found them living in houses. They reportedly admitted to him that their story was an elaborate hoax perpetrated by Elizaldo. He supposedly told them when to go to the caves and put on the Stone Age act for visiting journalists and scholars. Elizaldo has denied the charge and has had the continuing support of many scientists. Douglas Yen, an ethnobiologist and early Tasaday researcher, originally sought to link the group to neighboring farming tribes, but he now believes the Stone Age circumstances were genuine. (He cites a case in which little children were shown cultivated rice and displayed amazement.) Carol Molony, a linguist and another early Tasaday scholar, is also a believer. She argues that the tribe, children as well as adults, would have to have been superb actors to eliminate all agricultural metaphors from their speech. A local priest and former skeptic, Fr. Sean McDonagh, also believes the Tasaday to be authentic and says neighboring tribes do too.

One continuing element of dispute concerns the authenticity of Tasaday tools. Zeus Salazar, a Philippine anthropologist, maintains that the loose straps attaching stones to handles suggest a poor attempt to fake Stone Age methods. Yet archaeologist Ian Glover says such looseness has been noted in authentic Stone Age implements. The Tasaday's own statements have not simplified the puzzle. They told NBC and Philippine television that their original story was true and then told ABC and British television that it was false.

How likely is it that any outside observer *knows* the real story about the Tasaday, in all its complexity? Not very. That is why in this and similarly difficult cases, responsible people do not claim to *know* what happened. Instead, they speak of what is most *plausible* to believe happened, in light of the evidence. That is how anthropologist Thomas Headland, who exhaustively researched the Tasaday case, speaks of it. He suggests that there was probably no hoax but that there were gross exaggerations and false media reports, as well as some self-fulfilling expectations by anthropologists. It is likely, he believes, that the Tasaday were once members of the neighboring farming tribes who fled several hundred years ago (perhaps to avoid slave traders) and who hid in the forest for so many generations that they not only regressed to a Stone Age culture but lost all memory of their more advanced state.[19]

Is Faith a Form of Knowledge?

Some readers, particularly religious conservatives, may wonder whether what has been said thus far about knowledge represents a denunciation of faith. Their concern is understandable, given the number of intellectuals in this and previous centuries who have dismissed religion as mere superstition. But no such denunciation is intended here. The relationship between knowledge and religious faith is both complex and subtle. The term *religious faith* by definition suggests belief in something that cannot be proved. This is not to say that what is believed is not true, but only that *its truth cannot be demonstrated conclusively.* Jews (and many others) believe that God gave Moses the Ten Commandments, Muslims believe that Muhammad is Allah's prophet, and Christians believe that Jesus Christ is the Son of God. Science is simply not applicable to these beliefs. Philosophy can offer complementary arguments for or against them but cannot prove or disprove them.

Mortimer Adler, a distinguished philosopher, offers a very useful insight into the nature of faith:

> What is usually called a "leap of faith" is needed to carry anyone across the chasm [between philosophy and religion]. But the leap of faith is usually misunderstood as being a progress from having insufficient reasons for affirming God's existence to a state of greater certitude in that affirmation. That is not the case. The leap of faith consists in going from

the conclusion of a merely philosophical theology to a religious belief in a God that has revealed himself as a loving, just and merciful Creator of the cosmos, a God to be loved, worshiped and prayed to.[20]

A related concern of religious conservatives may be whether they are compromising their faith by embracing the philosophical position expressed in this chapter. Each of us must, of course, answer this question for him- or herself. Before deciding, however, we would do well to consider the argument advanced by Mark Noll, a leading evangelical scholar. In spurning philosophical investigation, he says, evangelicals not only have removed themselves from the discussion of issues vital to all people but also have lost touch with "the habits of mind that for nearly two centuries defined the evangelical experience in America." In his view, that has proved to be a tragic mistake.[21]

Obstacles to Knowledge

Before discussing how knowledge is best sought, let's consider two habits that *impede* knowledge: assuming and guessing. *Assuming* is taking something for granted—that is, arbitrarily accepting as true something that has not been proved or that may reasonably be disputed. Because assuming is generally an unconscious activity, we are often unaware of our assumptions and their influence on us.* The main negative effect of unrecognized assumptions is that they stifle the curiosity that leads to knowledge.

Many people, for example, never speculate about the daily life of fish. They may occasionally stop at the pet store in the mall and stare at the tank of tropical fish. But they never display curiosity about the social roles and relationships of fish communities because they assume fish have no such roles and relationships. Yet the fact is, in the words of underwater sociologist C. Lavett Smith, "There are fish equivalents of barbers, policemen, and farmers. Some are always on the move and others are sedentary. Some work at night and some by day."[22]

Guessing is offering a judgment on a hunch or taking a chance on an answer without any confidence that it is correct. It's a common, everyday activity. For students who don't do their studying for exams, it's a last-ditch survival technique. For an example of guessing, though, let's take a more pleasant subject—drinking beer. Some time ago a professor of behavioral science at a California college conducted a beer taste test among his students. The issue was whether they could really tell a good beer from a bad one or their favorite from others. Many students would guess they could, and a number of participants in the test actually guessed that

---

*It is, of course, possible to raise assumptions to the conscious level and express them. Most scientific references to assumptions are made in this context.

way. However, the test showed that when the labels were removed from the cans, not one student could identify a single brand.[23]

Because assuming stifles curiosity and guessing denies the importance of evidence, neither is likely to lead to knowledge. The most reliable approach is to be cautious in asserting that you know something. Be conservative in your level of assertion—whenever you are less than certain, speak about possibilities and probabilities. Say "I think" or "It seems to me" rather than "I know." Most important, be honest to yourself and others about your ignorance. To admit you don't know something shows good sense, restraint, and intellectual honesty. These are not weaknesses but strengths. The admission of ignorance is the essential first step toward knowledge.

Does this mean you should be wishy-washy and hedge everything you say with maybes and perhapses? Does it mean that to be a critical thinker you must forsake convictions? The answer to both questions is an emphatic *no!* It means only that you should value firm, bold statements so much that you reserve them for occasions when the evidence permits. Similarly, you should value convictions so highly that you embrace them only when you have sufficient knowledge to do so and modify them whenever intellectual honesty requires.

Applications

1. Consider this statement by the ancient Greek philosopher Epictetus: "Appearances to the mind are of four kinds. Things are either what they appear to be; or they neither are nor appear to be; or they are and do not appear to be; or they are not and yet appear to be. Rightly to aim in all these cases is the wise man's task." Does this reinforce or challenge what you learned in this chapter? Explain.

2. Read the following comment by Robert Lichter, director of the Center for Media and Public Affairs: "But over time, when journalists decide that something is or isn't newsworthy, it really determines to a great degree whether that becomes an issue on which the general public can have an impact. A good example of that is Paula Jones [the young Arkansan woman who accused then governor Bill Clinton of sexual harassment]. Almost three years ago, she made these charges publicly, and the mainstream media just didn't want to hear them. The only thing that changed is that journalists changed their minds. The news hasn't changed. The facts haven't changed. But the attitudes of the mainstream media have changed. So all of a sudden this [Paula Jones] is a big story. . . . The problem is, some journalists got to feel they were too good for the news."[24] What implications does this idea have for the subject of this chapter? Explain your answer.

3. In each of the following cases, someone believes he or she knows something. In light of what you learned in this chapter, discuss whether the person really does.
    a. Ted reads in the morning newspaper that a close friend of his has been arrested and charged with burglarizing a number of stores. Ted is

shocked. "It's impossible. The police have made a mistake," he tells his mother. "Bob and I have been as close as brothers. I just know he's not guilty."

b. *Ralph:* Here, Harry, try my deodorant. It really stops wetness.

Harry: No, thanks. I'm suspicious of antiperspirants. It seems to me that anything designed to block a normal body function may do a lot of harm. I wouldn't be surprised if it caused cancer.

Ralph: Don't be foolish. I know it doesn't cause cancer. Products like these are carefully tested before they're allowed to be sold. If it caused cancer, it would be banned.

c. *Jane:* I just read there's some evidence that aspirin can prevent heart attacks.

Jenny: That's a lot of nonsense. I know it can't. My uncle took lots of aspirin and he died of a heart attack last year.

4. "Man Is Released in Wrong Rape Charges," "Traditional Idea Debunked," "Ex-Aide Admits Lying About Lawmakers"—daily newspapers contain numerous stories like these, stories showing how what was "known" a week, a month, or years ago has been found to be false. Find at least three examples of such stories in current or recent newspapers.

5. "It ain't what a man doesn't know that makes him a fool, but what he does know that ain't so," wrote Josh Billings, the nineteenth-century American humorist. Recall as many occasions as you can in which your own experience confirmed his observation.

6. A court case pitting the U.S. government against the American Indian Movement was conducted quietly in South Dakota in late 1982. The government sought to end the Native American group's twenty-month occupation of public land in the Black Hills National Forest. The group claimed that the area was a holy land to them—their birthplace, the graveyard of their ancestors, and the center of their universe—and therefore should be turned into a permanent, religion-based Native American community.[25] The government maintained that the group had no legal claim to the land. What factors do you think should be considered in a case like this, and what solution would best serve the interests of justice? In answering, be sure to distinguish carefully between what you know and what you assume, guess, or speculate. If your knowledge is very limited, you may wish to do some research.

7. The Equal Rights Amendment (ERA) failed to gain ratification by enough states to be passed into law. Its opponents believe that wisdom prevailed. Its sponsors, however, attribute its defeat to apathy and ignorance. What is your position? Do you believe the ERA is a worthy addition to the U.S. Constitution? In answering, be sure to distinguish carefully between what you know and what you assume, guess, or speculate. If your knowledge is very limited, you may wish to do some research.

8. In recent years there has been much discussion of the insanity plea as a legal defense. Many believe it should be abolished, but many others regard it as an essential part of any reasonable criminal justice system. What is your position? In answering, be sure to distinguish carefully between what you know and what you assume, guess, or speculate. If your knowledge is very limited, you may wish to do some research.

9. *Group discussion exercise:* Decide if you know whether each of the following statements is accurate. Discuss your decisions with two or three classmates. Be sure to distinguish knowing from guessing or assuming.

    a. Most criminals come from lower economic backgrounds.

    b. African Americans are victims of crimes more often than are whites.

    c. The U.S. Constitution guarantees every citizen the right to own a handgun.

    d. Violence in the media is responsible for real-life violence.

CHAPTER 5

How Good Are Your Opinions?

> To me truth is precious. . . . I should rather be right and stand alone than to run with the multitude and be wrong. . . . The holding of the views herein set forth has already won for me the scorn and contempt and ridicule of some of my fellow men. I am looked upon as being odd, strange, peculiar. . . . But truth is truth and though all the world reject it and turn against me, I will cling to truth still.[1]

Stirring words, those. You can envision their author bravely facing legions of reactionaries intent on imposing their narrow dogmas on him. In the background you can almost hear a chorus singing "Stout-Hearted Men." Stand tall, brave hero. Never give in!

But wait a minute. Just who is the author? And what exactly is the opinion he is valiantly defending? His name is Charles Silvester de Fort. The quotation is from a booklet he wrote in 1931. And the opinion is—are you ready for this?—*that the earth is flat.*

People have always taken their opinions seriously, but today many people embrace their opinions with extraordinary passion. "I have a right to my opinion" and "Everyone's entitled to his or her opinion" are common expressions. Question another person's opinion and you're likely to hear, "Well, that's my O-P-I-N-I-O-N." The unspoken message is "Case closed."

Is that a reasonable view? Is it inappropriate to challenge the opinions of others? The answer depends on the kind of issue involved. If it is a *matter of taste,* then the standard is the undemanding one of personal preference. If Agnes finds Reginald handsome and Sally disagrees, there's really no basis for a meaningful dispute. Ditto if Ralph drools over an orange Camaro with brass wire hubcaps and purple upholstery and Carla is repulsed by it. Some people put catsup on hot dogs, while others prefer mustard or relish, and perhaps at this very moment someone, somewhere, is slathering a hot dog with mayonnaise or blueberries or pureed brussels sprouts. So what? *Vive la différence!*

However, consider this very different use of the term *opinion*. A newspaper reports that the Supreme Court has delivered its opinion in a controversial case. Obviously, the justices did not state their personal preferences, their mere likes and dislikes. They stated their *considered judgment*, painstakingly arrived at after thorough inquiry and deliberation.

In the context of critical thinking, the term *opinion* refers to expressions of judgment rather than to expressions of taste.* In some cases, unfortunately, it is not clear whether someone is expressing taste or judgment. A friend might say to you, as you leave a movie theater, "That was a wonderful film," which could mean "I liked it" or "It meets a very high standard of cinematography." Is she is merely saying she liked it, and you didn't, the disagreement would be over personal taste, which is pointless to debate. However, if she is making an aesthetic judgment, you could reasonably challenge her, citing specific film standards the movie failed to meet.

Is everyone entitled to his or her opinion? In a free country this is not only permitted but guaranteed. In Great Britain, for example, there is still a Flat Earth Society. As the name implies, the members of this organization believe that the earth is not spherical but flat. In this country, too, each of us is free to take as bizarre a position as we please about any matter we choose. When the telephone operator announces, "That'll be ninety-five cents for the first three minutes," you may respond, "No, it won't—it'll be twenty-eight cents." When the service station attendant notifies you, "Your oil is down a quart," you may reply, "Wrong—it's up three."

Being free to hold an opinion and express it does not, of course, guarantee favorable consequences. The operator may hang up on you, and the service station attendant may threaten to beat you up.

Acting on our opinions carries even less assurance. Consider the case of the California couple who took their eleven-year-old diabetic son to a faith healer. Secure in their opinion that the man had cured the boy, they threw away his insulin. Three days later, the boy died. The parents remained unshaken in their belief, expressing the opinion that God would raise the boy from the dead. The police arrested them, charging them with manslaughter.[2] The law in such matters is both clear and reasonable: We are free to act on our opinions only so long as, in doing so, we do not harm others.

---

*Judgment and taste may, of course, be present in the mind without being expressed. And though we can evaluate our own judgments whether they are expressed or not, we can evaluate other people's judgments only when they are expressed. Hence, our definition specifies expressed judgments.

Opinions Can Be Mistaken

We may be tempted to conclude that if we are free to have an opinion, it must be correct. That, however, is not the case. Free societies are based on the wise observation that people have an inalienable right to think their own thoughts and make their own choices. But this fact in no way suggests that the thoughts they think and the choices they make will be reasonable. It is a fundamental principle of critical thinking that ideas are seldom of equal quality. Solutions to problems vary from the practical to the impractical, beliefs from the well-founded to the ill-founded, arguments from the logical to the illogical, and opinions from the informed to the uninformed. Critical thinking serves to separate the more worthy from the less and, ultimately, to identify the best.

Evidence that opinions can be mistaken is all around us. The weekend drinker often has the opinion that as long as he doesn't drink during the week, he is not an alcoholic. The person who continues driving her gas guzzler with the needle on Empty may have the opinion that the problem being signaled can wait for another fifty miles. The student who quits school at age sixteen may have the opinion that an early entry into the job market ultimately improves job security. Yet, however deeply and sincerely such opinions are held, they are wrong.

Research shows that people can be mistaken even when they are making a special effort to judge objectively. Sometimes their errors are caused by considerations so subtle that they are unaware of them. For example, before Taster's Choice coffee was introduced, it was tested and sampled with three different labels—brown, yellow, and red. People who sampled the coffee in the container with the brown label reported that it was too strong and kept them awake at night. Those who sampled the yellow-labeled coffee found it weak and watery. Those who sampled the red-labeled coffee judged it to be just the right strength and delicious. All this even though the coffee in all the jars was exactly the same. *The people had been subconsciously influenced by the color of the label.*[3]

Opinions on Moral Issues

The notion that everyone is entitled to his or her opinion is especially strong in the area of morality. Questions of right and wrong are presumed to be completely subjective and personal. According to this belief, if you believe a particular behavior is immoral and I believe it is moral, even noble, we are both right. Your view is "right for you" and mine is "right for me."

This popular perspective may seem eminently sensible and broad minded, but it is utterly shallow. Almost every day, situations arise that require reasonable people to violate it. Have you ever heard anyone claim that burglary, spousal abuse, or rape is morally acceptable for those who believe it is? When someone is convicted of child molesting, do citizens parade in front of the courthouse with banners proclaiming, "Pedophilia may be wrong for us, but it was right for him"? If your instructor discovers you cheating on an examination, will she accept your explanation that you believe the end justifies the means? If a Breathalyzer test reveals that your classmate was driving with a blood-alcohol level higher than his grade point average, will the police officer commend him for living by his moral conviction?

Virtually every professional organization and every corporation has a code of ethics that specifies the behaviors that are required or forbidden. Every country has a body of laws with prescribed penalties for violators. There are even international laws that govern affairs among countries. All these codes and legal systems don't appear out of thin air. They are the products of moral judgment, the same mental activity individuals use in deciding everyday issues of right and wrong. And they are subject to the same limitiations and imperfections. Opinions about moral issues, like other opinions, may be correct or incorrect.

Are there criteria we can use to increase the chance that our moral judgments will be correct? Definitely. The most important ones are obligations, ideals, and consequences.*

- *Obligations:* Obligations are restrictions on behavior, demands that we do or avoid doing something. The most obvious kinds of obligations are formal agreements such as contracts. Others include professional and business obligations, and obligations of friendship and citizenship. When two or more conflict, the most important one should take precedence.

- *Ideals:* In the general sense, ideals are notions of excellence, goals that bring greater harmony within ourselves and with others. In ethics they are also specific concepts that help us maintain respect for persons. Some noteworthy examples of ideals are honesty, integrity, justice, and fairness. When two or more ideals conflict in a given situation, the most important one should be given precedence.

- *Consequences:* Consequences are the beneficial and/or harmful results of an action that affect both the person performing that action and others. Any examination of consequences should consider the various kinds: personal and societal; physical and emotional; immediate and eventual; intended and unintended; obvious and subtle;

---

*Space limitations do not permit more than a brief explanation of moral judgment. For a fuller discussion, see the companion book by the same author, *Thinking Critically About Ethical Issues* (Mountain View, Calif.: Mayfield, 1997).

possible, probable, and certain. Actions that achieve beneficial consequences should be preferred over those that do harm. Whenever the consequences are mixed (some beneficial, others harmful), the preferred action is the one that achieves the greater good or the lesser evil.

Even Experts Can Be Wrong

History records numerous occasions when the expert opinion has been the wrong opinion. In ancient times the standard medical opinion was that headaches were caused by demons inside the skull. The accepted treatment ranged from opening the skull to release the demons to giving medicines derived from cow's brain and goat dung. (Some Native American tribes preferred beaver testicles.)[4]

When the idea of inoculating people against diseases such as smallpox first arrived in the colonies in the early 1700s, most authorities regarded it as nonsense. Among them were Benjamin Franklin and a number of the men who later founded Harvard Medical School. Against the authorities stood a relatively unknown man who didn't even have a medical degree, Zabdiel Boylston. Whose opinion was proved right? Not the experts' but Zabdiel Boylston's.[5]

In 1890 a Nobel Prize–winning bacteriologist, Dr. Robert Koch, reported that he had found a substance that would cure tuberculosis. When it was injected into patients, though, it was found to cause further illness and even death.

In 1904 psychologist G. Stanley Hall expressed his professional opinion that when women engage in strenuous mental activity, particularly with men, they experience a loss of mammary function and interest in motherhood, as well as decreased fertility. If they subsequently have children, the children will tend to be sickly.[6] Today this idea is laughable.

Between 1919 and 1922 the Metropolitan Museum of Art in New York City bought seventeen gold vessels that experts determined were authentic treasures from a 3500-year-old Egyptian tomb. In 1982 the vessels were discovered to be twentieth-century fakes.[7]

In 1928 a drug called thorotrast was developed and used to outline certain organs of the body so that clearer X rays could be taken. Nineteen years later, doctors learned that even small doses of the drug caused cancer.

In 1959 a sedative called thalidomide was placed on the market. Many physicians prescribed it for pregnant women. Then, when a large number of babies were born deformed, medical authorities realized that thalidomide was to blame.

In 1973, using refined radar mapping techniques, scientists decided that their earlier claims about the surface of Venus were wrong. It was not smooth, as they had thought, but pockmarked with craters.[8]

In the 1980s and 1990s, one of the hottest topics in the publishing and seminar industries was co-dependency. Anyone related to an alcoholic or drug addict was considered to be a contributor to the problem, chiefly by unconsciously encouraging the person's habit or "enabling" the person to indulge it. Soon the idea of co-dependency became the diagnosis of choice for any situation characterized by out-of-control behavior. Co-dependents were urged to buy books, attend seminars, and join their troubled family member in counseling. Then one curious researcher, Edith Gomberg, examined the scientific research base on which the movement was founded. She found . . . zip, *nada,* nothing. In her words, "There are no surveys, no clinical research, no evaluations; only descriptive, impressionistic statements."[9]

For most of the twentieth century, the universally accepted scientific opinion was that stomach ulcers are caused by excess stomach acid generated by stress. Then Barry Marshall demonstrated that ulcers are caused by bacteria and can be cured with antibiotics.

Remember the brontosaurus with his head stretching to the treetops in *Jurassic Park?* That scene reflected the traditional scientific opinion that the big dinosaurs dined on leaves thirty or more feet off the ground. In 1999, however, Michael Parrish, a northern Illinois researcher, experimented with a computer model of the neck bones of large dinosaurs and discovered that they could never have lifted their heads above the level of their bodies. If they had, their neck vertebrae would have collapsed. They couldn't have stood on their hind legs either, because the demands on their blood pressure would have been excessive.[10]

For years physicians told us that fiber lowers cholesterol and protects against colon cancer. Eventually, medical research established that it doesn't lower cholesterol. Then researchers demonstrated that it doesn't protect against colon cancer.[11]

To this day, many experts are convinced that the cause of crime is a bad social environment and that the solution is to pour millions of dollars into poor neighborhoods for a variety of social programs. Other experts are equally convinced that the cause of crime is an emotional disorder that can be cured only by psychological counseling. But a leading researcher, Stanton Samenow, disputes both views. Samenow argues that "bad neighborhoods, inadequate parents, television, schools, drugs, or unemployment" are not the cause of crime—criminals themselves are. They break the law not because conditions force them to but because they choose to, and they *choose* to because they consider themselves special and therefore above the law. In Samenow's view, the key to criminals' rehabilitation is for them to accept responsibility for their behavior.[12]

It is impossible to know what expert opinions of our time will be overturned by researchers in the future. But we can be sure that some will be. And they may well be views that today seem unassailable.

Kinds of Error

Opinion can be corrupted by any one of four broad kinds of error.* These classifications, with examples added for clarification, are:

1. Errors or tendencies to error common among all people by virtue of their being human (for example, the tendency to perceive selectively or rush to judgment or oversimplify complex realities)

2. Errors or tendencies to error associated with one's individual habits of mind or personal attitudes, beliefs, or theories (for example, the habit of thinking the worst of members of a race or religion against which one harbors prejudice)

3. Errors that come from human communication and the limitations of language (for example, the practice of expressing a thought or feeling inadequately and leading others to form a mistaken impression)

4. Errors in the general fashion of an age (for example, the tendency in our grandparents' day to accept authority unquestioningly or the tendency in ours to recognize no authority but oneself)

Some people, of course, are more prone to errors than others. English philosopher John Locke observed that these people fall into three groups:

> Those who seldom reason at all, but think and act as those around them do—parents, neighbors, the clergy, or anyone else they admire and respect. Such people want to avoid the difficulty that accompanies thinking for themselves.
>
> Those who are determined to let passion rather than reason govern their lives. Those people are influenced only by reasoning that supports their prejudices.
>
> Those who sincerely follow reason, but lack sound, overall good sense, and so do not look at all sides of an issue. They tend to talk with one type of person, read one type of book, and so are exposed to only one viewpoint.[13]

To Locke's list we should add one more type: those people who never bother to reexamine an opinion once it has been formed. These people are often the most error prone of all, for they forfeit all opportunity to correct mistaken opinions when new evidence arises.

---

*The classifications noted here are adaptations of Francis Bacon's well-known "Idols," *Novum Organum,* Book I (1620).

Informed Versus Uninformed Opinion

If experts can, like the rest of us, be wrong, why are their opinions more highly valued than those of nonexperts? In light of the examples we have considered, we might conclude that it is a waste of time to consult the experts. Let's look at some situations and see if this conclusion is reasonable.

What are the effects of hashish on those who smoke it? We could ask the opinion of a smoker or take a poll of a large number of smokers. But it would be more prudent to obtain the opinion of one or more *trained* observers, research scientists who have conducted studies of the effects of hashish smoking. (At least one such group, a team of army doctors, has found that heavy use of hashish leads to severe lung damage. Also, if the smoker is predisposed to schizophrenia, it can cause long-lasting episodes of that disorder.[14])

A giant quasar is positioned on what may be the edge of our universe, 10 billion light-years away from us.[15] (To calculate the distance in miles, just multiply the speed of light, 186,000 miles per second, by the number of seconds in a day, 86,400; next multiply that answer by the number of days in a year, 365; finally, multiply that answer by 10,000,000,000.) The pinpoint of light viewed by astronomers has been streaking through space for all those years and has just reached us. The quasar may very well have *ceased to exist* millions and millions of years ago. Did it? It may take millions and millions of years before we can say. If we wanted to find out more about this quasar or about quasars in general, we could stop someone on a street corner and ask about it, and that person would be free to offer an opinion. But it would be more sensible to ask an astronomer.

Can whales communicate with one another? If so, how far can they transmit messages? Would our auto mechanic have an opinion on this matter? Perhaps. And so might our grocer, dentist, and banker. But no matter how intelligent these people are, chances are their opinions about whales are not very well informed. The people whose opinions would be valuable would be those who have done some research with whales. (They would tell us that the humpback whales can make a variety of sounds. In addition to clicking noises, they make creaking and banging and squeaking noises. They've been found to make these sounds for as long as several minutes at a time, at an intensity of 100 to 110 decibels, and for a distance of 25,000 miles.[16])

Similar examples could be cited from every field of knowledge: from antique collecting to ethics, from art to criminology. All would support the same view: that by examining the opinions of informed people before making up our minds, we broaden our perspective, see details we might not see by ourselves, consider facts we would otherwise be unaware of, and lessen our chances of error. (It is foolish to look for *guarantees* of correctness—there are none.) No one can know everything about everything; there is simply not enough time to learn. Consulting those who have given their special attention to the field of knowledge in question is therefore a mark not of dependence or irresponsibility, but of efficiency and good sense.

To be considered informed, an opinion must be based on something more substantial than its familiarity to us or the length of time we have held it or our presumed right to think whatever we wish. It must be based on careful consideration of the evidence. And when we express an opinion in formal speaking or writing, we should support it adequately. Authors Ray Marshall and Marc Tucker, for example, assert that the reason teaching in the United States has not been a highly respected profession is the fact that most schoolteachers traditionally have been women. To support this contention, they traced the relevant historical development, citing administrative directives and statements of philosophy, presenting hiring patterns (from 59 percent women in 1870 to 86 percent in 1920), detailing significant shifts in curricula, contrasting male and female salary statistics, and demonstrating the relative powerlessness of women to negotiate professional-level salaries and working conditions.[17]

As this example illustrates, in most responsible expressions of opinion, the statement of opinion takes up only a sentence or two, while the supporting details fill paragraphs, pages, and even entire chapters.

Forming Correct Opinions

One of the things that makes human beings vastly more complex and interesting than cows or trees is their ability to form opinions. Forming opinions is natural. Even if we wanted to stop doing so, we couldn't. Nor should we want to. This ability has two sides, however. It can either lift us to wisdom or mire us in shallowness or even absurdity. Here are some tips that can help you improve the quality of your opinions:

1. *Understand how opinions are formed.* Like every other human being, you are constantly perceiving—that is, receiving data through your senses. Also like everyone else, you have a natural drive to discover meaning in your perceptions. That drive can be enhanced or suppressed, but it can never be entirely lost. In practical terms, this means that you cannot help producing opinions about what you see and hear *whether or not you take control of the process.* When you are not in control, your mental system operates in the uncritical default mode. Here is how that uncritical mode compares with the conscious and more conscientious *critical* thinking mode:

Uncritical Default Mode	*Critical Thinking Mode*
Perceive	Perceive
Let an opinion "come to mind"	Investigate the issue
Focus on information that supports the opinion	Consider alternative opinions
Embrace the opinion	Decide which opinion is most reasonable

2. *Resist the temptation to treat your opinions as facts.* This temptation can be powerful. Once you've formed an opinion, it is natural to bond with it, much as a parent bonds with a baby. The more you call it to mind and express it to others, the stronger the bond becomes. To question its legitimacy soon becomes unthinkable. Nevertheless, you can be sure that some of your opinions have been uncritically formed and therefore need to be challenged. The problem is that you can't be sure which ones those are. The prudent approach is to question any opinion, even a cherished one, the moment evidence arises that suggests it is based on habit, impulse, whim, personal preference, or the influence of fashionable ideas rather than reality.

3. *Monitor your thoughts to prevent the uncritical default mode from taking charge.* Whenever you begin forming impressions of a person, place, or situation, follow the advice of the ancient Greek philosopher Epictetus: "Be not swept off your feet by the vividness of the impression, but say, 'Impression, wait for me a little. Let me see what you are and what you represent. Let me try [test] you.'" This approach will prevent your impressions from hardening into opinions before you determine their reasonableness.

What benefit will you receive from following these three steps? You will gain control of your opinions, and that is a considerable advantage over having them control you.

Applications

1. Imagine that you are the senior librarian for your college. A faculty member sends you the following list of recommended magazines, with a brief description of each quoted from a standard guide, *Magazines for Libraries*, by Bill Katz and Linda Sternberg Katz:[18]

   a. *The Nation.* "This is the foremost liberal/left-wing journal, and the standard by which all other liberal publications should be judged . . . unabashedly partisan. . . . "

   b. *Human Events.* "The editor makes no claims about impartiality. . . . The editorial tone is decidedly conservative, particularly when discussing Congress."

   c. *Free Inquiry: A Secular Humanist Magazine.* "The articles in this journal strongly reflect the position of CODESH [the Council for Democratic and

Secular Humanism] and tend to be more anti–organized religion than positively secular humanist."

d. *Paidika: The Journal of Paedophilia.* "*Paidika* is a journal intended for academics studying human sexuality as well as for pedophiles and pederasts discovering a history and an identity."

Explain which magazines you would subscribe to for the library, which you would not, and which you would need more information about before you decided. If you would need more information, explain what it would be and how you would obtain it. (*Note:* Your library may have a copy of *Magazines for Libraries.*)

2. Which of the following individuals is likely to be most successful at persuading the public to buy a certain brand of running shoes? Explain your reasoning.
   a. an experienced trainer
   b. an Olympic running champion
   c. a podiatrist
   d. a physician in general practice
   e. the surgeon general of the United States

3. Of the individuals listed in application 2, who is likely to be the most knowledgeable source of information on running shoes?

4. What factors might possibly compromise the endorsements of the various people listed in application 2? Which one is likely to be the most reliable source of information? Explain the reasoning underlying each answer.

5. When this author uses the word *opinion,* his major emphasis is on which of the following? Explain your reasoning.
   a. a statement of preference
   b. a considered judgment
   c. a view or belief casually arrived at
   d. a bigoted position
   e. an unsupportable position
   f. all of the above
   g. none of the above

6. Which of the following would this author be likely to rate as most important in forming a reliable opinion? Explain your reasoning.
   a. Seek reasons to support your opinions.
   b. Distinguish between input from experts and input from others.
   c. Reject others' opinions.
   d. Subject opinions to ongoing reexamination based on new evidence.

7. A high school junior invited his thirty-five-year-old neighbor, the mother of four children, to his prom. The woman was married, and her husband approved of the date. However, the school board ruled that the boy would be denied admission to the dance if he took her.[19] What is your opinion of the board's decision?

8. Read the following dialogue carefully. Then decide whether anything said violates the ideas in the chapter. Identify any erroneous notions, and explain in your own words how they are in error.
   Fred: There was this discussion in class today that really bugged me.
   Art: Yeah? What was it about?

Fred: Teenage sex. The question was whether having sex whenever we please with whomever we please is harmful to teenagers. Some people said yes. Others said it depends on the circumstances.
Art: What did you say?
Fred: I said it doesn't do any harm to anybody, that parents use that story to scare us. Then the teacher asked me what evidence I had to back up my idea.
Art: What did you tell him?
Fred: I said I didn't need any evidence because it's my *opinion.* Sex is a personal matter, I said, and I've got a right to think anything I want about it. My opinions are as good as anybody else's.

9. Think of an instance in which you or someone you know formed an opinion that later proved incorrect. State the opinion and explain in what way it was incorrect.

10. Each of the following questions reflects a controversial issue—that is, an issue that tends to excite strong disagreement among people. State and support your opinion about each issue, applying what you learned in this chapter.

    a. In divorce cases, what guidelines should the courts use in deciding which parent gets custody of the children?

    b. Until what age should children be spanked (if indeed they should be spanked at all)?

    c. Should the minimum drinking age be sixteen in all states?

    d. In what situation, if any, should the United States make the first strike with nuclear weapons?

    e. Do evil spirits exist? If so, can they influence people's actions?

    f. Does the end ever justify the means?

    g. Does attending class regularly increase one's chances for academic success?

    h. Were teachers more respected fifty years ago than they are today?

    i. Does binge drinking on weekends constitute alcoholism?

    j. Is antisocial behavior increasing, or are the media just doing a better job of reporting it?

11. Read the following dialogue carefully. Then determine which opinion of the issue is more reasonable. Be sure to base your decision on evidence rather than mere preference.

Background note: A Rochester, New York, lawyer issued a court challenge to the practice of charging women half price for drinks during "ladies' nights" at bars. He argued that the practice is a form of sex discrimination against men.[20]

Henrietta: That lawyer must be making a joke against feminism. He can't be serious.
Burt: Why not? It's clearly a case of discrimination.
Henrietta: Look, we both know why ladies' nights are scheduled in bars: as a gimmick to attract customers. The women flock to the bars to get cheap drinks, and the men flock there because the women are there. It's no different from other gimmicks, such as mud-wrestling contests and "two for the price of one" cocktail hours.
Burt: Sorry, Hank. It's very different from two-for-one cocktail hours, where a person of either sex can buy a cocktail at the same price. Ladies' nights set a double standard based on sex and that's sex discrimination, pure and simple.

Henrietta: So now you're a great foe of discrimination. How come you're not complaining that men haven't got an equal opportunity to participate half naked in mud-wrestling contests? And why aren't you protesting the fact that women are paid less for doing the same jobs men do? You're a phony, Burt, and you make me sick.

Burt: Name calling is not a sign of a strong intellect. And why you should get so emotional over some lawyer's protest, I can't imagine. I guess it goes to show that women are more emotional than men.

CHAPTER 6

What Is Evidence?

To state an opinion is to tell others what we think about something; to present evidence is to *show* others that what we think makes sense. Being shown is much more interesting and impressive than being told—we've all known this since grade school. Why, then, does so much writing and speaking consist of piling one opinion on another, with little or no evidence offered in support of any of them? As we saw in Chapter 5, one reason is that the human mind is a veritable opinion factory, so most people have an abundance of opinions to share. Another reason is that people tend to remember their opinions and forget the process by which they got them, much as students remember their final grade in a course long after they have forgotten the tests and homework grades that it comprises.

A third, and in some ways more significant, reason is that sometimes there is little or no evidence to remember—in other words, the opinion is based on nothing substantial. For example, in early 1999 many people held the opinion that William Jefferson Clinton's lying under oath did not "rise to the level of an impeachable offense." When asked to explain why they thought that, some people repeated the assertion in identical or similar words: "He shouldn't be removed from office for what he did," "It's between him and Hillary." Or they offered related opinions: "It's a right-wing conspiracy," "Independent counsel Kenneth Starr is on a witch-hunt." Though it is impossible to be *certain* why they thought as they did, the fact that they expressed the opinion in the very same words incessantly repeated by a half dozen White House advisors and innumerable other Clinton supporters suggests that they simply borrowed the opinion without evaluating it.*

---

*The fact that many people embraced this opinion without much evidence does not mean that no evidence could be marshalled for the view. Other supporters of President Clinton responded more substantively.

We can all identify with those people. More often than most of us would care to admit, when called on to support our opinions, we manage to produce only the flimsiest of evidence. We may soothe ourselves with the notion that a thick folder of evidence lies misfiled in our minds, but the very real possibility remains that flimsy evidence was all we ever had. Critical thinkers are tempted to commit the same self-deception that plagues others, but they have learned the value of resisting that temptation. More importantly, they have developed the habit of checking the quality and quantity of the evidence before forming an opinion. Also, before *expressing* an opinion, they review their evidence. The extra time this takes is more than compensated by the confidence that comes from knowing what they are talking about.

Kinds of Evidence

To evaluate your own and other people's opinions, you will need to understand the various kinds of evidence. This entails knowing the value and limitations of each kind, as well as the appropriate questions to ask. The most important kinds of evidence are *personal experience, unpublished report, published report, eyewitness testimony, celebrity testimony, expert opinion, experiment, statistics, survey, formal observation,* and *research review.*

PERSONAL EXPERIENCE

This is the one kind of evidence we don't have to go to the library or the Internet to get. We carry it with us in our minds. For this reason, it tends to exert a greater influence than other kinds of evidence. The individuals we've met, the situations we've been in, the things that have happened to us seem more authentic and meaningful than what we have merely heard or read. We are confident about our personal experience. Unfortunately, this confidence can cause us to attach greater significance and universality to particular events than they deserve. If we ride in a New York City taxicab on one occasion, we may think we are acquanted with New York City taxicab drivers. If we have a Korean friend, we may feel that we know Koreans in general or even Asians in general. However, it takes more than one or a few examples to support a generalization; for sweeping generalizations, even a dozen may not be enough.

To evaluate personal experience—your own or other people's—ask: Are the events typical or unique? Are they sufficient in number and kind to support the conclusion? Remember that the vividness and dramatic quality of an anecdote cannot compensate for its limitedness.

UNPUBLISHED REPORT

Unpublished reports are stories we hear from other people, often referred to as gossip or hearsay. The biggest problem with such reports is that it is difficult to confirm them. In many cases, we don't know whether the stories are secondhand or third-, fourth-, or *fiftieth*-hand. And stories have a way of changing as they are passed from person to person. The people who repeat them may not be dishonest; they may, in fact, try to be accurate but then inadvertently leave out some words, add others, or change the details or order of events.

To evaluate an unpublished report, ask: Where did the story originate? How can I confirm that the version I heard is accurate?

PUBLISHED REPORT

This kind of evidence is found in a wide variety of published or broadcast works, from scholarly books, professional journals, and encyclopedia articles, to magazine or newspaper articles, news broadcasts, and radio or television commentaries. In scholarly works the sources of the material are usually carefully documented in footnotes and bibliographic citations. In nonscholarly works, the documentation may be informal, fragmentary, or in some cases, nonexistent. Even when the source is not cited, we can assess the author's and publisher's reliability. Facts and opinions are often mingled in contemporary publications, particularly nonscholarly ones, so careful reading may be necessary to reveal which statements constitute evidence and which should *themselves* be supported with evidence.

To evaluate a published report, ask: Does the report cite the sources of all important items of information? (If so, you may wish to check them.) Does the author have a reputation for careful reporting? Does the publisher or broadcaster have a reputation for reliability? Which statements in the published report constitute evidence, and which should themselves be supported with evidence? (Another way to ask this question is, Which statements might a thoughtful person challenge? Does the author answer the challenges satisfactorily?)

EYEWITNESS TESTIMONY

Because eyewitness testimony is commonly considered to be the most reliable kind of evidence, you may be surprised to find that it is sometimes badly flawed for any one of several reasons. The external conditions may not have been optimal—for example, the incident may have occurred late on a foggy night and the eyewitness may have been some distance away.

The eyewitness may have been tired or under the influence of alcohol or drugs; his or her observation may also have been distorted by preconceptions or expectations. Finally, the person's memory of what occurred may have been confused by subsequent events. Such confusion can be a special problem when considerable time has elapsed between the event and the testimony.

To evaluate eyewitness testimony, ask: What circumstances surrounding the event, including the eyewitness' state of mind, could have distorted his or her perception? (If any such distortion was likely, try to determine whether it actually occurred.) What circumstances since the event—for example, the publication of other accounts of the event—could have affected the eyewitness's recollection?

CELEBRITY TESTIMONY

Increasingly, celebrities are seen endorsing products and services in commercials and "infomercials." In addition, when they appear as guests on radio and television talk shows, they are encouraged to state their personal views about whatever happens to be in the news at the time. On any given day you may hear singers, actors, and athletes discussing religion, criminal justice, education, economics, international relations, campaign finance reform, and psychology, among other topics. For example, a TV host once asked an actor, "How big a factor in human life do you believe is chance in the universe?"

Your respect for celebrities as entertainers may lead you to assume that they know what they are talking about in interviews. This assumption is often mistaken. They may be very well informed. Or they may have been caught unaware by the host's question and, not wanting to seem ignorant, uttered whatever happened to come to mind. Some may be so impressed with their own importance that they imagine whatever they say is profound for no other reason than that they say it! In the case of testimonials for products or services, the celebrities may have been paid to read words about products that they know little or nothing about.

To evaluate celebrity testimony, ask: In the case of advertisements or "infomercials," is the celebrity a paid spokesperson? (This is often indicated in small print at the end of the ad.) In the case of talk show comments, does the celebrity offer any support for his or her views—for example, citing research conducted by more qualified people? Also, does the host ask for such support? If the discussion consists of little more than a series of assertions expressing the celebrity's unsupported opinion, you would do well to discount it no matter now much you may admire the person.

EXPERT OPINION

As you might expect, expert opinion is generally more reliable than most of the varieties of evidence we have considered so far. The advantage it enjoys over personal experience is that it can usually address the crucial question of what is typical and what is not. Nevertheless, not even expert opinion is consistently reliable. The most significant reason for unreliability is that knowledge in virtually every field is rapidly expanding. A century ago it was possible to gain expertise in more than one discipline. Today's scholars typically have expertise in *a single narrow aspect of one discipline* and may have difficulty keeping abreast of significant developments in that one. Unfortunately, some people can't resist the temptation to think of themselves as experts in everything. A well-known astronomer, for example, used to write articles in popular magazines and offer his opinions on ethics, anthropology, and theology.

To evaluate expert opinion, ask: Does the person have, in addition to credentials in the broad field in question, *specific* expertise in the particular issue under discussion? This is not always easy to ascertain by those outside the field, but one good indication is that the person does not just state his or her opinion but also supports it with references to current research. Also ask whether the expert was paid. The acceptance of money does not necessarily taint expert opinion, but it may raise questions about the person's objectivity. Finally, ask whether other authorities agree or disagree with the expert's view.

EXPERIMENT

There are two broad types of experiment. The *laboratory* experiment enables researchers to vary the conditions and thereby identify causes and effects more precisely. One disadvantage of the laboratory experiment, however, is its artificiality. The *field* experiment has the advantage of occurring in a natural setting, but the presence of the researchers can influence the subjects and distort the findings.

To evaluate experimental evidence, ask: For a laboratory experiment, has it been replicated by other researchers? For a field experiment, have other researchers independently confirmed the findings? If replication or confirmation has been unsuccessfully attempted, it is best to postpone your acceptance of the experimental findings.

STATISTICS

In the broad sense, the term *statistics* applies to any information that can be quantified; for example, the changes in average temperature over a period of time to determine whether the phenomenon of global warming is occurring. The term *statistics* may also be used more narrowly to mean quantifiable information about a group that is obtained by contacting, or otherwise accounting for, every individual in the group. The U.S. Census is one example of statistics in this sense. Others are the voting records of U.S. senators, the percentage of automobile fatalities involving drunk driving, the fluctuations in immigration patterns over the past century, the percentage of unwed mothers who come from one-parent homes, and the comparative education and income levels of various racial-ethnic groups.

When evaluating statistical information, ask: What is the source of the statistics? Is the source reliable? How old are the data? Have any important factors changed since the data were collected?

SURVEY

Surveys are among the most common tools used by professionals, particularly in the social sciences. Since the data obtained from surveys are quantifiable, surveys are often included under the broad heading of "statistics." However, we are considering them to highlight one distinguishing characteristic: surveys typically obtain data by contacting, not every individual in the group (known as a population), but a representative *sample* of the group. Surveys are conducted by telephone contact, mail, or personal interview. The sampling may be *random, systematic* (for example, every tenth or hundredth person in a telephone directory), or *stratified* (the exact proportion of the component members of the group; for example, 51 percent women and 49 percent men).

When evaluating a survey, ask: Was the sample truly representative? That is, did all members of the total population surveyed have an equal chance of being selected? Were the questions clear and unambiguous? Were they objectively phrased rather than slanted? In the case of a mailed survey, did a significant number fail to respond? If so, how might nonrespondents differ from respondents? Also, do other surveys corroborate the survey's findings?

FORMAL OBSERVATION

There are two kinds of formal observational studies. In *detached* observation the observer does not interact with the individuals being studied. A child psychologist, for example, might visit a school playground and watch how the children behave. In *participant* observation the researcher is involved in the activity being studied. An anthropologist who lived with a nomadic tribe for a period of months, sharing meals with them and taking part in their communal activities, would be a participant observer.

When evaluating formal observation, ask: Is it likely that the presence of the observer distorted the behavior being observed? Was the observation of sufficient duration to permit the conclusions that were drawn? Do the conclusions overgeneralize? (For example, the observations made of a single nomadic group might be generalized to all nomadic groups, ignoring the fact that other nomadic groups may differ in important ways.)

RESEARCH REVIEW

This kind of study is undertaken when a considerable body of research has already been done on a subject. The reviewer examines all the scholarly studies that have been done and then summarizes and compares their findings. Often dozens or even hundreds of studies are examined. A thorough review of research reveals areas of agreement and disagreement and provides a valuable overview of the current state of knowledge on the subject.

When evaluating a research review, ask: Do the reviewer's conclusions seem reasonable given the research covered in the review? Has the reviewer omitted any relevant research? (As a lay person, you may find the latter question impossible to answer yourself. You could, however, ask it of another expert in the field who is familiar with both the actual research and the review.)

One additional question is applicable to all kinds of evidence: Is this evidence *relevant* to the issue under consideration? If it is not relevant, it deserves no consideration, no matter how excellent it may be in other respects. Here is an actual example of an issue that has been badly confused by the use of irrelevant evidence. Many college administrators have rejected instructors' requests for a reduction in class size for courses such as writing, speaking, and critical thinking. The administrators cited scholarly studies demonstrating that teaching effectiveness is unrelated to class size—in other words, that teachers can be as effective with fifty students in the classroom as they are with fifteen. Yet the scholarly studies in question examined only courses that impart information, not those that develop skills. For the latter, the very courses in question, the evidence had no relevance.

Evaluating Evidence

We all like to think of ourselves as totally objective, equally open to either side of every issue. But that is rarely the case. Even if we have not yet taken a firm position on an issue at the outset of our evaluation, we will usually be "tilted" in one direction or the other by our overall philosophy of life, our political or social views, our opinions on related issues, or our attitude toward the people associated with the various views. This tilting, also known as *bias,* may be so slight that it has little or no effect on our judgment. On the other hand, it may be significant enough to short-circuit critical thinking. The more we tilt on an issue, the greater our thinking deficit is likely to be.

How can you tell when bias is hindering your evaluation of evidence? Look for one or more of these signs:

- You approach your evaluation *wanting* one side to be proven right.
- You begin your investigation assuming that familiar views will prove correct.
- You look for evidence that supports the side of the issue you favor and ignore evidence that opposes it.
- You rate sources by how favorable they are to your thinking rather than by their reliability and the quality of their research.
- You are nitpickingly critical of evidence for views you oppose and uncritical of evidence for views you favor.
- When you encounter evidence that opposes your bias, you begin arguing against it, often before you have completed examining it.

Although you may not be able to eliminate your biases, you can nevertheless identify and *control* them, and that is all that is necessary. The purpose of evaluating evidence is to discover the truth, regardless of whether it is pleasant or unpleasant, and the only way to do so is to evaluate *fairly*. Such an evaluation will sometimes require you to conclude that the view you leaned toward (or actually held) is mistaken. Never hesitate to do so. Changing your mind is not dishonorable, but maintaining a false view in order to save face is not only foolish but also intellectually dishonest.

What Constitutes "Sufficient" Evidence?

It is seldom easy to decide when your evidence, or that of the person whose opinion you are evaluating, is sufficient. In making your determination you will have to consider both the quantity and the quality of the evidence. No simple formula exists, but these general guidelines will help you decide particular cases:

1. *Evidence is sufficient when it permits a judgment to be made with certainty.* Wishing, assuming, or pretending that a judgment is correct does not constitute certainty. Certainty exists when there is no good reason for doubt, no basis for dispute. The standard for conviction in a criminal trial, for example, is "guilt beyond a reasonable doubt." Certainty is a very difficult standard to meet, especially in controversial issues, so generally you will be forced to settle for a more modest standard.

2. *If certainty is unattainable, evidence is sufficient if one view of the issue has been shown to have the force of* probability. This means that the view in question is demonstrably more reasonable than any competing view. In civil court cases this standard is expressed as "a preponderance of the evidence." *Demonstrating* reasonableness is, of course, very different from merely *asserting* it, and all possible views must be identified and evaluated before any one view can be established as most reasonable.

3. *In all other cases, the evidence must be considered insufficient.* In other words, if the evidence does not show one view to be more reasonable than competing views, the only prudent course of action is to withhold judgment until sufficient evidence is available. Such restraint can be difficult, especially when you favor a particular view, but restraint is an important characteristic of the critical thinker.

Applications

1. Many years ago an expert on thinking made this observation: "Probably the main characteristic of the trained thinker is that he does not jump to conclusions on insufficient evidence as the untrained man is inclined to do."[1] (Note: at that time, *he* and *man* were commonly used to denote both men and women.) Think of several recent occasions when you formed opinions with little or no evidence. In each case state the opinion and explain what kind of evidence would be necessary to support it adequately.

2. Some years ago, a well-known television actress was on a talk show, discussing a number of topics, including an episode of her show in which two lesbians kissed on camera. The actress volunteered this opinion: "This is a time in our society when homophobia is really huge and crimes against gays are at an all-time high." If the talk show host had been a critical thinker, what questions would he have asked at that point? What kind of evidence would be helpful in testing the reasonableness of her opinion?

3. In Chapter 5, application 10, you responded to each of the following questions with an opinion. Review those opinions and the evidence you offered in support of them. In each case classify the evidence as *personal experience, unpublished report, published report, eyewitness testimony, celebrity testimony, expert opinion, experiment, statistics, survey, formal observation,* or *research review*. Decide whether your evidence was sufficient. If you find it was not, explain what kind of evidence would be necessary to support the opinion adequately.

   a. In divorce cases what guidelines should the courts use in deciding which parent gets custody of the children?
   b. Until what age should children be spanked (if indeed they should be spanked at all)?
   c. Should the minimum drinking age be sixteen in all states?
   d. In what situation, if any, should the United States make the first strike with nuclear weapons?
   e. Do evil spirits exist? If so, can they influence people's actions?
   f. Does the end ever justify the means?

g. Does attending class regularly increase one's chances for academic success?

h. Were teachers more respected fifty years ago than they are today?

i. Does binge drinking on weekends constitute alcoholism?

j. Is antisocial behavior increasing, or are the media just doing a better job of reporting it?

4. In Chapter 1, application 8, you expressed an opinion about each of the statements listed below. Reexamine each of your responses, following the directions in application 3, above.

a. Health care workers should be required to be tested for HIV/AIDS.

b. Beauty contests and talent competitions for children should be banned.

c. Extremist groups like the Ku Klux Klan should be allowed to hold rallies on public property or be issued permits to hold parades in city streets.

d. Freshman composition should be a required course for all students.

e. Athletes should be tested for anabolic steroid use.

f. Creationism should be taught in high school biology classes.

g. Polygamy should be legalized.

h. The voting age should be lowered to sixteen.

i. The prison system should give greater emphasis to the punishment of inmates than to their rehabilitation.

j. Doctors and clinics should be required to notify parents of minors when they prescribe birth control devices for the minors.

k. A man's self-esteem is severely injured if his wife makes more money than he makes.

l. Women like being dependent on men.

What Is Argument?

The word *argument* has several meanings, so our first task is to clarify each and note how it differs from the others. One common meaning is "a quarrel," as in the sentence "They had a heated argument, a real screaming match." Because a quarrel consists less of thought than of emotion, a clash of egos that frequently degenerates into mindless babble, this definition of *argument* has little relevance to critical thinking. For our purposes, therefore, an argument is not a quarrel.

Another meaning of *argument* is "the exchange of opinions between two or more people," as occurs in a formal debate. In this sense of the term, an argument is ideally a cooperative endeavor in which people with different viewpoints work together to achieve a deeper, more accurate understanding of an issue. In such an endeavor egos are controlled and everyone, though wanting to be right, is willing to be proven wrong. Since everyone emerges from the process with greater insight, no one loses. Alas, egos are not easily suppressed. Besides, most of us have been conditioned to believe there must be a winner and a loser in every argument, just as in every athletic contest. Thus, we often focus more on "scoring points" against our "opponent" than in growing in knowledge and wisdom, so even our best efforts tend to fall short of the ideal.

Although *argument* as "the exchange of opinions between two or more people" is relevant to critical thinking, there is another meaning of the term that is even more relevant to the challenge of *becoming* a critical thinker. *Argument*, in this third sense, means "the line of reasoning that supports a judgment." When we say, "John's argument on the issue of capital punishment was more persuasive than Sally's," we are focuing on the quality of his *individual* contribution to the overall deliberation. Because our main concern in this chapter, as indeed throughout this book, is the evaluation of individual arguments, your own as well as other people's, this third definition is the one we will focus on.

It may be helpful to think of an argument as a kind of verbal equation without mathematical symbols. A numerical equation has the form 1 + 1 = 2, or 2 − 1 = 1. A verbal equation expresses similar relationships without using minus, plus, or equal signs. Here is an example:

> The law prohibits teachers from leading class prayers in public schools.
> Wynona leads students in prayer in her public school classroom.
> Therefore, Wynona is breaking the law.

Like numerical equations, arguments may be complex as well as simple. Just as the sum in a numerical equation may be composed of many numbers (342 + 186 + 232 + 111 + 871), so the conclusion of an argument may proceed from many premises (assertions). And just as having an incorrect number in a column of figures will result in a wrong total, so having an erroneous assertion will lead to a wrong conclusion.* In the class prayer argument, if we mistakenly think that the law permits teachers to lead students in prayer, our conclusion would be that Wynona is not breaking the law, and that would be erroneous.

Numerical equations and arguments are not, however, entirely similar. One important difference is that an argument is often more complex and difficult to test. Does vitamin C prevent the common cold or lessen its severity? Does television violence cause real violence? Was John F. Kennedy killed by a single assassin? Did JonBenet Ramsey's parents kill her? In these and many other matters, the evidence is not yet complete, so there is room for disagreement.

The Parts of an Argument

The field of knowledge most closely associated with the study of argument is logic, which, like other fields that deal with complex matters, has its own special terminology. Since this book is more practical than theoretical, we will limit our concern to the terms that signify the parts of an argument. Those are the *premises* and the *conclusion.* In the argument about Wynona mentioned above, the premises are "The law prohibits teachers from leading class prayers in public schools" and "Wynona leads students in prayer in her public school classroom." The conclusion is "Therefore, Wynona is breaking the law." (The word *therefore* and synonyms such as *so* and *consequently* are often used to identify conclusions. Where they are not used, you can usually identify the conclusion

---

*The only exception to this is pure coincidence. Consider this argument: "Fair-skinned people are more susceptible to skin cancer than dark-skinned people. Florida has more fair-skinned people than Michigan. Therefore, the skin cancer rate is higher in Florida than in Michigan." The argument is defective because the second premise lacks a basis in fact. Yet the conclusion happens, coincidentally, to be true.

by answering the question, Which assertion do the other assertions support or reinforce?)

The basic principles logicians use in evaluating arguments are as follows:

1. The premises are either *true* or *false* (correct or incorrect).
2. The reasoning that links the premises to the conclusion is either *valid* or *invalid*. (To be valid, the stated conclusion, and only that conclusion, must flow logically from the premises.)
3. Correct premises plus valid reasoning equal a *sound* argument.
4. Either an incorrect premise or invalid reasoning will render an argument *unsound*.

Mistakes are as common in thinking as in mathematics. This is true not only of other people's thinking but of our own as well. Just as we can have accurate numbers and do our best to add carefully yet come up with the wrong answer, so, too, we can proceed from accurate information to a wrong conclusion. Of course, when we *start* with inaccurate or incomplete information or reason *recklessly*, the chances of error are compounded.

Inappropriate attitudes toward ideas and the reasoning process can also lead to errors in argument. For example, if you regard your first impressions as infallible, you are likely to embrace them uncritically, seek out evidence that supports them and reject that which challenges them, and defend them rabidly. Such an approach leaves you vulnerable both to self-deception and to manipulation by others. In contrast, if you regard your first impressions tentatively—as interesting possibilities rather than certainties—and compare them to other ideas before making up your mind, you are less likely to fool yourself or be deceived by others.

Evaluating Arguments

The basic approach to evaluating arguments can be stated simply: *Decide whether the premises are true or false and whether the reasoning that leads from them to the conclusion is valid.* If both criteria are met, the argument is sound. When the argument is clearly and fully stated and you ask the right questions, this approach is relatively easy to follow. You may, of course, have to do some investigating to determine the truth or falsity of one or both premises. Here are some examples of clear, fully stated arguments:

The Argument	*The Questions*
All men are mortal.	Are all men mortal?
Socrates is a man.	Is Socrates a man?

Therefore, Socrates is mortal.	Does this conclusion logically follow from what is stated in the premises? Does any other conclusion follow equally well?

Comment: The premises are obviously true. Also, the conclusion offered, and only that conclusion, follows logically. Accordingly, the argument is sound.

The Argument	*The Questions*
Any activity that involves physical exertion is properly classified as a sport.	Are there any physical activities that are not sport yet are physically strenuous?
Bodybuilding involves physical exertion.	Does bodybuilding involve physical exertion?
Therefore, bodybuilding is properly classified as a sport.	Does this conclusion follow logically from what is stated in the premises? Would any other conclusion be as reasonable?

Comment: Even though the second premise is true and the conclusion follows logically from the premises, this argument is unsound because the first premise is false. Many physical activities are in no way related to sport yet are physically strenuous—moving pianos, for example. Note that showing this argument to be unsound does not prove that bodybuilding should not be classified as a sport. Perhaps some other argument could be advanced that would prove to be sound.

The Argument	*The Questions*
Guilty people usually fail lie detector tests.	Is this true?
Bruno failed his lie detector test.	Did he really?
Therefore, Bruno is guilty.	Does this conclusion follow logically from what is stated in the premises? Would any other conclusion be as reasonable?

Comment: Both the first and second premises are true. (The authorities could have lied about Bruno's score, but let's assume they didn't.) Still, the premises don't provide sufficient evidence to draw the conclusion that is given or, for that matter, any other conclusion. We need to know whether an *innocent* person can fail a lie detector test. If so, then Bruno could be innocent.

The Argument	*The Questions*
Success comes to those who work hard.	Does it always?
Jane is successful.	Is she?
Therefore, Jane worked hard.	Does this conclusion follow logically from what is stated in the premises? Would any other conclusion be as reasonable?

Comment: The first premise is not entirely true. Some people who work hard end up failing anyway because they lack the necessary aptitude or background experience to meet the challenge. Moreover, some people who do not work hard succeed anyway because they have wealth and/or influence. Even if we grant that the second premise is true, the argument must still be judged unsound because of the first premise.

Did you ever have the experience of hearing an argument on some issue, being impressed with it, and then hearing the opposing argument and being even more impressed with that? It happens often. For example, in the primary battles prior to the 2000 presidential election, a question arose as to whether candidate George W. Bush had used cocaine many years earlier. Some pundits argued that if he did, then he was a hypocrite because as governor of Texas he signed into law a bill containing tough penalties for cocaine users. The argument sounded good. But then other pundits argued that a person who had used drugs was in a better position to know their danger to individuals and society than one who had not. They reasoned that an alcoholic can speak more authoritatively than a teetotaler on the misuse of alcohol, a reformed criminal is more familiar with the evils of crime than a law-abiding citizen, and so on.

Remember that your evaluation of any argument is likely to be most effective when you are able to hear both sides or at least to consider the criticisms people on each side of the issue make of the other side's view.

More Difficult Arguments

Unfortunately, not all arguments are clearly and/or fully stated. Here are the main kinds of difficult situations you will encounter, along with guidelines for dealing with them:

When an argument is longer than a paragraph, summarize it before asking and answering your questions. The danger in summarizing, of course, is that you might misrepresent what the person was saying. If you are careful, however, you can avoid this problem.

When you are uncertain which statements are the premises and which is the conclusion, ask yourself exactly what idea the person is trying to get you to accept. (That is the conclusion.) Then ask what reasons are offered in support of that idea. (Those are the premises.)

When an argument contains more than two premises, ask and answer your questions about each. Don't be daunted if there are many premises—just take one at a time. After eliminating any irrelevant premises, decide whether the conclusion follows logically from the remaining premises and if it is the only conclusion that does. If more than one conclusion follows, decide whether the stated one is the most reasonable conclusion.

When you are evaluating opposing arguments, neither of which is persuasive (even if one is technically sound), look for a third alternative. Often the alternative will be one that draws a little from each. The ongoing debate over whether the Ten Commandments should be displayed in public school classrooms provides a good example. Here are some fairly typical opposing arguments that are offered in nonlegal discussions:*

The Affirmative Argument	*The Negative Argument*
Public schools (like other schools) should encourage moral values.	No cultural or religious group should be treated preferentially in public schools.
Displaying the Ten Commandments would encourage moral values.	Displaying the Ten Commandments in public schools would treat Christians and Jews preferentially.
Therefore, public schools should display the Ten Commandments.	Therefore, the Ten Commandments should not be displayed in public schools.

Comment: One alternative that draws upon each of these arguments but goes beyond them is to argue for the display of all versions of the Ten Commandments (and there are several), as well as any other religious or secular list of moral values. The reasoning would be that accommodating all perspectives is no more offensive than ignoring all and has the additional benefit of emphasizing the importance of moral values.

When an argument contains hidden premises, identify them before proceeding with your evaluation. Hidden premises are clearly implied ideas that are not recognized when the argument is conceived and expressed. When the hidden premise is accurate, no harm is done, but when it is inaccurate, it quietly corrupts the argument. Here are some examples of such arguments. Each is first presented as it might occur in informal

---

*In addition to these, of course, there are the legal arguments concerning constitutionality.

discussion. Then it is broken down into its component parts, including hidden assertions. The questions critical thinking would address are shown opposite each part.

1. *Argument:* They should never have married—they felt no strong physical attraction to each other during courtship.

The Component Parts	*The Questions*
Stated Premise: They felt no strong physical attraction to each other.	Did they feel no strong physical attraction to each other?
Hidden Premise: Strong physical attraction is the best, or perhaps the only, meaningful basis for marriage.	Is strong physical attraction the best, or the only meaningful basis for marriage?
Conclusion: They should never have married.	Do the premises lead to this conclusion and no other?

2. *Argument:* It's clear why Morton is an underachiever in school—he has very little self-esteem.

The Component Parts	*The Questions*
Stated Premise: Morton has very little self-esteem.	Does Morton have very little self-esteem?
Hidden Premise: Self-esteem is necessary in order to achieve.	Is self-esteem necessary in order to achieve?
Conclusion: It's clear why Morton is an underachiever in school. (The sense of this statement is*"This explains why . . ."*)	Do the premises lead to this conclusion and no other?

3. *Argument:* That book should be banned because it exposes children to violence.

The Component Parts	*The Questions*
Stated Premise: That book exposes children to violence.	Does the book expose children to violence?
First Hidden Premise: Exposure to violence is harmful.	Is exposure to violence always harmful? (Note that in the absence of limiting terms, such as *sometimes,* the general *always* is implied.)
Second Hidden Premise: Banning is the most appropriate reaction to such material.	Is banning the most appropriate reaction to such material?
Conclusion: That book should be banned.	Do the premises lead to this conclusion and no other?

4. *Argument:* Pure water is healthy to drink, and Pristine Mountain Water is pure, so I'm treating my body right by drinking it rather than tap water.

The Component Parts	The Questions
Stated Premise: Pure water is healthy to drink.	Is pure water healthy to drink?
Stated Premise: Pristine Mountain Water is pure.	Is Pristine Mountain Water pure?
Hidden Premise: The water from my tap is not pure.	Is water from this person's tap not pure?
Conclusion: I'm treating my body right by drinking Pristine Mountain Water rather than tap water.	Do the premises lead to this conclusion and no other?

It is tempting to think that the longer the passage, the less likely it will contain hidden premises, but this is not the case. It is possible to elaborate an argument with one or more hidden premises into a book-length treatment without detecting and expressing these premises. In fact, the longer the passage, the more difficult it is to identify such premises. Whatever the length of the passage you are evaluating (or composing), be alert for hidden premises.

Applications

1. Think of a TV talk show you've recently seen that examined a controversial issue and featured two or more guests who disagreed. (If you aren't familiar with such shows, find one in the TV guide and watch a segment of it.) Decide whether the exchange was a quarrel or an argument. Explain your answer.

2. Each of the following questions has sparked serious public debate in recent years. Select one of them and check the library database or the Internet for an article that presents a point of view (as opposed to a news article that merely reports the facts). Then evaluate the argument, applying what you learned in the chapter.

   a. Should youthful offenders be treated as adults?
   b. Should the states and/or the federal government provide vouchers to parents so they can send their children to the private or public schools of their choice?
   c. Should patients be able to sue their health maintenance organizations?
   d. Should a referendum be required before state and federal legislatures can raise taxes?
   e. Should marijuana be legalized for medical use?
   f. Should police be permitted to impound the cars of drunken driving suspects?
   g. Does home schooling provide as good an education as traditional classroom teaching?

3. When a serial murderer known as the "Railroad Killer" was being sought some years ago, the FBI interviewed people who had been in the areas of the crimes and may have seen the perpetrator. As a result of those reports, the FBI issued a "wanted" poster for a "Hispanic male" of a certain description. During one of the press briefings, a reporter asked the FBI agent in charge of the search whether specifying that the suspect was Hispanic constituted discrimination. How would you have answered if you had been that FBI agent? Present your answer in the form of an argument.

4. Evaluate the following arguments, applying what you learned in this chapter.

    a. The U.S. defense budget should be cut drastically, and perhaps eliminated entirely, because the former Soviet Union is no longer a threat to U.S. security.

    b. The present welfare system causes people to lose their self-respect and self-confidence and makes them dependent on the government. The entire system should be replaced by one that emphasizes responsibility and hard work.

    c. The schoolyard practice of "choosing up sides" is embarrassing, even humiliating, to children who are unskilled in sports. Therefore, it should be discouraged on the playground and abandoned in physical education classes.

    d. *Background note: College administrators are debating their campus policy after receiving complaints about professors dating students. They endorse the following argument:*
There is nothing wrong in two unmarried adults dating, so it is acceptable for professors to date students who are over eighteen years of age.

    e. Copying computer software violates the copyright law. Still, I paid full price for my software, and my friend not only needs it for his class but can't afford to purchase it himself. If I give him a copy of mine, he'll be helped and no one will be hurt. (The software company wouldn't have made a sale to him anyway because he's broke.) Therefore, I am justified in giving him the software.

    f. "All men are created equal," says the Declaration of Independence. Yet lots of Americans are victims of poverty and discrimination and lack of opportunity for education and careers. And the rich and social elites can buy a standard of justice unavailable to the average citizen. Equality is a myth.

    g. *Background note: The ancient religion known as Santeria is still practiced by a number of people in the United States. One of its beliefs is that the sacrifice of animals is pleasing to the god Olodumare. Thus, as part of their ritual, Santerian priests slit the throats of chickens, doves, turtles, and goats; drain the blood into clay pots; and prepare the animals' flesh for eating. Many other Americans complain to authorities about this practice, but its supporters argue:*
The United States Constitution guarantees the free exercise of religion. It does not exclude religions that displease the majority. However displeasing ritual animal sacrifice may be to other citizens, the law should uphold Santerians' constitutional rights.

    h. *Background note: In recent years many cities have experienced an increase in aggressive panhandling—the practice of approaching passersby and begging for money. Some panhandlers block people's paths and otherwise intimidate them. A number of cities have outlawed panhandling. The following argument has found expression in some court decisions:* Panhandling is a form of speech. Speech is protected by the Constitution. Therefore, panhandling is a right that cannot be abridged.

PART TWO

The Pitfalls

The first seven chapters explored the context in which thinking occurs. You now know, popular notions notwithstanding, that individuality doesn't come automatically but must be earned again and again, that critical thinking is as applicable to your own ideas as it is to other people's, that truth is discovered rather than created and genuine knowledge is elusive, that opinions are only as good as the evidence that supports them, and that argument is not a matter of "scoring points" or shouting down others but compiling accurate information and reasoning logically about it.

In this section we will examine the various errors that can impair thinking. We will also consider how you can best discover them in other people's writing and speaking and avoid them in your own. The most basic error, "mine-is-better" thinking, seems rooted in our human nature and paves the way for many of the other errors. The other errors are grouped according to when they occur. *Errors of perspective* are erroneous notions about reality that are present in our minds more or less continuously. *Errors of procedure* occur when we are dealing with specific issues; *errors of expression,* when we put our thoughts into words; and *errors of reaction,* when someone criticizes or challenges a statement or argument we have made. The final chapter in this section explores how these errors can occur in combination.

CHAPTER 8

The Basic Problem: "Mine Is Better"

> Our beliefs have been imbibed, how or why we hardly know. . . . But let a question be raised as to the soundness of our notions . . . and at once we find ourselves filled with an illicit passion for them; we defend them just as we would defend a punched shoulder. The problem, how reasonable they really are, does not trouble us. We refuse to learn truth from a foe.[1]

This observation was made by a scholar as he pondered the all too common tendency to justify beliefs rather than refine and improve them. This tendency is puzzling. People profess enthusiasm for personal growth and development, and spend billions of dollars on self-help books, tapes, and seminars; yet they act as if their minds have no need of improvement.

This tendency is attributable to a "mine-is-better" perspective, which we all have to a greater or lesser extent. It is natural enough to like our own possessions better than other people's.* Our possessions are extensions of ourselves. When first graders turn to their classmates and say, "My dad is bigger than yours" or "My shoes are newer" or "My crayons color better," they are not just speaking about their fathers or shoes or crayons. They are saying something about themselves: "Hey, look at me. I'm something special."

Several years later, those children will be saying, "My car is faster than yours" or "My football team will go all the way this year" or "My marks are higher than Olivia's." (That's one of the great blessings of students—though they may have to stoop to compare, they can always find someone with lower grades than theirs.)

Even later, when they've learned that it sounds boastful to *say* their possessions are better, they'll continue to *think* they are: "My house is more expensive, my club more exclusive, my spouse more attractive, my

---

*One exception to the rule occurs when we are *envying* others. But that is a special situation that doesn't contradict the point here.

children better behaved, my accomplishments more numerous, and my ideas, beliefs, and values more insightful and profound than other people's."

All of this, as we have noted, is natural, although not especially noble or virtuous or, in many cases, even factual. Simply natural. The tendency is probably as old as humanity. History records countless examples of it. Most wars, for example, can be traced to some form of "mine-is-better" thinking. Satirists have pointed their pens at it. Ambrose Bierce, for instance, in his *Devil's Dictionary*, includes the word *infidel*. Technically, the word means "one who is an unbeliever in some religion." But Bierce's definition points up the underlying attitude in those who use the word. He defines *infidel* this way: "In New York, one who does not believe in the Christian religion; in Constantinople, one who does."[2]

The results of a survey of a million high school seniors illustrate the influence of "mine-is-better" thinking. The survey addressed the question, of whether people considered themselves "above average." Fully 70 percent of the respondents believed they were above average in leadership ability, and only 2 percent believed they were below average. Furthermore, 100 percent thought themselves above average in ability to get along with others, 60 percent saw themselves in the top 10 percent, and 25 *percent considered themselves in the top 1 percent*.[3] (Perhaps this inflated view is partly responsible for the conviction of many students that if they receive a low grade, the teacher must be at fault.)

For many people, most of the time, the "mine-is-better" tendency is balanced by the awareness that other people feel the same way about their things, that it's an unavoidable part of being human to do so. In other words, many people realize that we all see ourselves in a special way, different from everything that is not ourselves, and that whatever we associate with ourselves becomes part of us in our minds. People who have this understanding and are reasonably secure and self-confident can control the tendency. The problem is, some people do not understand that each person has a special viewpoint. For them, "mine is better" is not an attitude that everyone has about his or her things. Rather, it is a special, higher truth about their particular situation. Psychologists classify such people as either egocentric or ethnocentric.

Egocentric People

Egocentric means centered or focused on oneself and interested only in one's own interests, needs, and views. Egocentric people tend to practice "egospeak," a term coined by Edmond Addeo and Robert Burger in their book of the same name. Egospeak, they explain, is "the art of boosting our own egos by speaking only about what we want to talk about, and not giving a hoot in hell about what the other person wants to talk about."[4] More important for our discussion is what precedes the outward expression of self-centeredness and energizes it: egocentric people's habit of mind. Following Addeo and Burger, we might characterize that habit as ego*think*.

Because the perspective of egothink is very limited, egocentric people have difficulty seeing issues from a variety of viewpoints. The world exists for them and is defined by their beliefs and values: What disturbs them should disturb everyone; what is of no consequence to them is unimportant. This attitude makes it difficult for egocentric people to observe, listen, and understand. Why should one bother paying attention to others, including teachers and textbook authors, if they have nothing valuable to offer? What incentive is there to learn when one already knows everything worth knowing? For that matter, why bother with the laborious task of investigating controversial issues, poring over expert testimony, and evaluating evidence when one's own opinion is the final, infallible arbiter? It is difficult, indeed, for an egocentric to become proficient in critical thinking.

Egocentrism makes the resolution of issues more difficult. Consider the problem of what to do about racially sensitive teaching materials such as Mark Twain's novel *Adventures of Huckleberry Finn.* Consider the following facts about the book: (a) it's considered a classic, (b) its theme is a positive one that in no way denigrates African Americans (or, for that matter, any other racial-ethnic group), (c) characters in the novel use the disparaging word "nigger" frequently, and (d) that word causes many African American students *understandable* discomfort and even pain. Fact d is arguably the central fact because it is the one that makes the teaching of the novel an issue. Nevertheless, the issue is not likely to be resolved unless *all* these facts are given appropriate consideration.

Egocentric individuals, however, tend to see only some of the facts. White egocentrics see only facts a and b and tend to think, "What's the big deal. We're only dealing with words here. African Americans are overreacting." (This reaction reminds me of a comment someone once made about a football coach: "He has a tremendous tolerance for *other people's* pain.") African American egocentrics, on the other hand, see only facts c and d and conclude that because the "*n*-word" offends them personally, the only acceptable solution is to ban the book for all students.

Ethnocentric People

Ethnocentric means excessively centered or focused on one's group. Note the inclusion of the word "excessively." We can feel a sense of identification with our racial-ethnic group, religion, or culture without being ethnocentric. We can also prefer the company of people who share our heritage and perspective over the company of others without being intolerant. The familiar is naturally more comfortable than the unfamiliar and to pretend otherwise is to delude ourselves. Accordingly, the fact that Korean Americans tend to associate almost exclusively with one another or that the local Polish American club does not issue invitations to Italians, Finns, or African Americans should not be regarded as a sign of ethnocentrism.

What distinguishes ethnocentric individuals from those who feel a normal sense of identification with their groups is that ethnocentrics believe (a) that their group is not merely different from other groups but fundamentally and completely superior to them and (b) that the motivations and intentions of other groups are suspect. These beliefs create a bias that blocks critical thinking. Ethnocentric people are eager to challenge the views of other groups but unwilling to question the views of their own group. As a result, they tend to respond to complex situations with oversimplifications. They acknowledge no middle ground to issues—things are all one way, *the way that accords with their group's perspective.* They also tend to form negative stereotypes of other groups, as psychologist Gordon Allport explained many years ago:

> By taking a negative view of great groups of mankind, we somehow make life simpler. For example, if I reject all foreigners as a category, I don't have to bother with them—except to keep them out of my country. If I can ticket, then, all Negroes as comprising an inferior and objectionable race, I conveniently dispose of a tenth of my fellow citizens. If I can put the Catholics into another category and reject them, my life is still further simplified. I then pare again and slice off the Jew . . . and so it goes.[5]

Ethnocentric people's prejudice has an additional function. It fills their need for an out-group to blame for real and imagined problems in society. Take any problem—street crime, drug trafficking, corruption in government, political assassinations, labor strikes, pornography, rising food prices—and there is a ready-made villain to blame it on: The "kikes" are responsible—or the "wops," "niggers," "spics," or "polacks." Ethnocentrics achieve instant diagnosis—it's as easy as matching column a to column b. And they get a large target at which they can point their anger and fear and inadequacy and frustration.

Controlling "Mine-Is-Better" Thinking

It's clear what the extreme "mine-is-better" attitude of egocentric and ethnocentric people does to their judgment. It twists and warps it, often beyond correction. The effect of the "mine-is-better" tendencies of the rest of us is less dramatic but no less real.

Our preference for our own thinking can prevent us from identifying flaws in our own ideas, as well as from seeing and building on other people's insights. Similarly, our pride in our own religion can lead us to dismiss too quickly the beliefs and practices of other religions and ignore mistakes in our religious history. Our preference for our own political party can make us support inferior candidates and programs. Our allegiance to our own opinions can shut us off from other perspectives, blind us to unfamiliar truths, and enslave us to yesterday's conclusions.

Furthermore, our readiness to accept uncritically those who appeal to our preconceived notions leaves us vulnerable to those who would manipulate us for their own purposes. Historians tell us that is precisely why Hitler succeeded in winning control of Germany and wreaking havoc on a good part of the world.

"Mine-is-better" thinking is the most basic problem for critical thinkers because, left unchecked, it can distort perception and corrupt judgment. The more mired we are in subjectivity, the less effective will be our critical thinking. Though perfect objectivity may be unattainable, by controlling our "mine-is-better" tendencies, we can achieve a significant degree of objectivity.

Does anything said so far in this chapter suggest that "mine is better" can never be an objective, accurate assessment of a situation? Decidedly not. To think that would be to fall into the fallacy of relativism discussed in Chapter 9. In the great majority of cases in which two or more ideas (beliefs, theories, conclusions) are in competition, one will be more reasonable, more in keeping with the evidence, than all the others. And if you are diligent in your effort to be a critical thinker, your idea will often prove to be the best one. But that determination is properly made *after* all the ideas have been evaluated. The problem with "mine-is-better" thinking is that it tempts us to forgo evaluation and take it for granted that our idea is best.

One way to gain control of "mine-is-better" thinking is to keep in mind that, like other people, we too are prone to it and that its influence will be strongest when the subject is one we really care about. As G. K. Chesterton observed,

> We are all exact and scientific on the subjects we do not care about. We all immediately detect exaggeration in . . . a patriotic speech from Paraguay. We all require sobriety on the subject of the sea serpent. But the moment we begin to believe in a thing ourselves, that moment we begin easily to overstate it; and the moment our souls become serious, our words become a little wild.[6]

Another way to control "mine-is-better" thinking is to be alert for signals of its presence. Those signals can be found both in our feelings and in our thoughts:

- *In feelings:* Very pleasant, favorable sensations, the desire to embrace a statement or argument immediately, without appraising it further. Or very unpleasant, negative sensations, the desire to attack and denounce a statement or argument without delay.

- *In thoughts:* Ideas such as "I'm glad that experts are taking such a position—I've thought it all along" and "No use wasting time analyzing this evidence—it must be conclusive." Or ideas such as "This view is outrageous because it challenges what I have always thought—I refuse to consider it."

Whenever you find yourself reacting in any of these ways, you can be reasonably sure you are being victimized by "mine-is-better" thinking. The appropriate response is to resist the reaction and force yourself to consider the matter fair-mindedly. Chances are this won't be easy to accomplish—your ego will offer a dozen reasons for indulging your "mine-is-better" impulse—but your progress as a critical thinker depends on your succeeding. The other errors in thinking covered in the next four chapters are at least aggravated by "mine-is-better" thinking.

Applications

1. Some people claim that contemporary American culture tends to increase rather than diminish egocentrism and ethnocentrism. If this is true, then the ability to think critically is being undermined. Study the media for evidence that supports or refutes this charge, and write a report on your findings. (Be sure to look for subtle, as well as obvious, clues—for example, the advice offered on talk shows and the appeals used in advertisements, as well as the formal statements of agencies promoting policy changes in government and elsewhere.)

2. Recall an occasion when you observed someone demonstrating one or more of the characteristics of ethnocentrism in his or her behavior. Describe the occasion, the way in which the characteristics were revealed, and the effect they had on the person's judgment.

3. Compose a summary of this chapter for the person whose ethnocentrism you described in application 2. Make it as persuasive as you can for that person. That is, focus on the particular occasion of his or her "mine-is-better" thinking and the effects of that thinking on his or her judgment.

4. Think of two illustrations of your own "mine-is-better" thinking. Describe that thinking and the way in which you first became aware of it. If you can, determine what caused you to develop that way of thinking.

5. Evaluate the following arguments as you did the arguments in Chapter 7, application 4. First identify the argument's component parts (including hidden premises) and ask relevant questions, as shown in that chapter. Then check the accuracy of each premise, stated or hidden, and decide whether the conclusion is the most reasonable one. Note that checking the accuracy of the premises may require obtaining sufficient evidence to permit a judgment. (Be alert to your own "mine-is-better" thinking. Don't allow it to influence your analysis.) If you find a

premise to be inaccurate or a conclusion to be less than completely reasonable, revise the argument accordingly.

a. *Background note: Many schools around the country are experiencing significant budget reductions. Forced to cut activities from their programs, they must decide where their priorities lie. Some follow the reasoning expressed in this argument.*

Argument: Interscholastic sports programs build character and prepare young athletes to meet the challenges of life. In addition, competition with other schools provides the student body with entertainment and an opportunity to express school spirit and loyalty. Therefore, in all budget considerations, interscholastic sports programs should be given as high a priority as academic programs.

b. *Background note: Concerned with the rise in teenage pregnancy, the Baltimore, Maryland, school system became the first in the nation to offer Norplant, a surgically implanted contraceptive, to teenagers. School officials' reasoning was probably, at least in part, as follows:*

Argument: Teenage pregnancy continues to rise despite efforts to educate students about the use of condoms. Norplant will effectively prevent pregnancy. Therefore, the school system should make Norplant available.

6. State and support your position on each of the following issues. Be sure to recognize and overcome your "mine-is-better" tendencies and base your response on critical thinking.

a. Carl F. Henry, a leading evangelical theologian, warns that the widespread attitude that there are no moral standards other than what the majority approves is a threat to our country. The survival of democratic society, he suggests, depends on recognizing definite moral standards, such as the biblical criteria of morality and justice.[7]

b. A Hasidic rabbi serving a three-year term (for bank fraud) in a federal prison petitioned a U.S. district court to order the prison to provide a kosher kitchen, utensils, and diet for him. He argued that his health was failing because the food served at the prison did not meet his kosher requirements. He could eat only lettuce, oranges, apples, carrots, and dry rice cereal.[8]

c. Both "heavy metal" and "gangsta rap" music have drawn pointed criticism from a number of social critics. They argue that such music at least aggravates (and perhaps causes) antisocial attitudes and thus can be blamed for the increase in violent crime.

d. Some people believe the penalty for driving while intoxicated should be stiffened. One provision they are urging be added to the law is mandatory jail sentences for repeat offenders.

7. Read the following dialogues carefully. Note any evidence of "mine-is-better" thinking. Then decide which view in each dialogue is more reasonable and why. (Be sure to guard against your own "mine-is-better" thinking.)

a. *Background note: On a trip to Spain in November 1982, Pope John Paul II acknowledged that the Spanish Inquisition, which began in 1480 and lasted for more than 300 years and resulted in many people's being imprisoned, tortured, and burned at the stake, was a mistake.[9]*

Ralph: It's about time the Catholic church officially condemned the Inquisition.

Bernice: The pope shouldn't have admitted that publicly.

Ralph: Why? Do you think five hundred years after the fact is too soon? Should he have waited for one thousand years to pass?

Bernice: Don't be sarcastic. I mean that his statement will undoubtedly weaken the faith of many Catholics. If you love someone or something—in this case, the church—you should do nothing to cause it shame or embarrassment. Of course the Inquisition was wrong, but it serves no good purpose to say so now and remind people of the church's error.

b. *Background note: When an unmarried high school biology teacher in a Long Island, New York, school became pregnant, a group of parents petitioned the school board to fire her. They reasoned that her pregnancy was proof of immorality and that allowing her to remain a teacher would set a poor example for students. The school board refused to fire her.*[10]

Arthur: Good for the school board. Their action must have taken courage. Pious hypocrites can generate a lot of pressure.

Guinevere: Why do you call them hypocrites? They had a right to express their view.

Arthur: Do you mean you agree with that nonsense about the pregnant teacher's being immoral and a poor example to students?

Guinevere: Yes, I suppose I do. Not that I think everybody deserves firing from his or her job in such circumstances. I think teachers are in a special category. More should be expected of them. They should have to measure up to a higher standard of conduct than people in other occupations because they are in charge of young people's education, and young people are impressionable.

8. *Group discussion exercise:* Reflect on the following statement. Does it make sense? Does anything you read in this chapter help to explain it? If so, what? Discuss your ideas with two or three classmates.

It doesn't matter if everyone in the world thinks you're wrong. If you think you're right, that's all that counts.

CHAPTER 9

Errors of Perspective

Imagine that you wear eyeglasses with serious distortions in the lenses but are unaware of the problem. You have every reason to believe that the people, places, and things you look at are as they appear, whereas in reality they are quite different. When you share your perceptions with others and they challenge them, you are surprised at first, puzzled at their inability to see the world as clearly as you do. Eventually you either stop communicating with others or become more assertive, hoping by the sheer force of your expression to solve what you are convinced is their problem.

Now imagine that, by some happy circumstance, you suddenly realize that the problem is not their faulty perception but your defective glasses. You rush to the nearest optician, purchase a new pair, see more accurately, grow in knowledge, and experience a new sense of confidence and contentment.

Errors of perspective are like seriously distorted lenses, except instead of being perched on our noses, they inhabit our minds. If you are prone to one or more of these errors, you can be sure that they will work their mischief more or less constantly. They will shape the attitudes and habits you bring to the evaluation of issues and create expectations that bias your thinking. Moreover, you may not even be aware of their existence unless you evaluate your patterns of thought. This chapter is designed to help you do that, and to root out whatever errors of perspective are obstructing your critical thinking. We will examine six specific errors: *unwarranted assumptions*, the *either/or outlook*, *mindless conformity*, *absolutisim*, *relativism*, and *bias for or against change*.

Unwarranted Assumptions

Assumptions are ideas that are merely taken for granted rather than produced by conscious thought. Making assumptions is natural enough, and many assumptions are not only harmless but helpful. When you get up in the morning and head out for class, you assume your watch is working, the car will start, and the professor will be there to teach. You may occasionally encounter a surprise—a broken watch, a dead car battery—but that won't invalidate the assumption or diminish the time it saves you. (You wouldn't get much accomplished if you had to ponder every move you made each day.)

When are assumptions *un*warranted? Whenever you take *too much* for granted—that is, more than is justified by your experience or the particular circumstance. Smokers who assume that because the habit hasn't caused them noticeable physical harm already, it never will, are making an unwarranted assumption. So are sunbathers who assume that their skin is impervious to solar radiation, and investors who assume a stock tip they found on an Internet bulletin board is reliable.

Many people, no doubt millions, assume that the current concept of childhood always existed. On the contrary, it is a relatively recent idea, dating back only a few centuries. Before that, children were not considered different from adults in their nature and needs. Examination of the historical accounts, paintings, and sculptures of earlier centuries reveals that children were regarded as little adults. They were expected to perform adult roles and meet adult standards of behavior. Moreover, they were included in adult society.[1] The concept of adolescence as an extended period of emotional upheaval and self-searching is a twentieth-century idea that the ancestors of contemporary Europeans and Americans, as well as people from very different cultures, would find strange and perhaps amusing. (Very likely much of the tension between young people and their parents could be eliminated by a clearer understanding of how dramatically attitudes toward children have changed.)

Many people assume that white slave owners in the United States assigned their slaves surnames. This belief is reinforced by the fact that today some African Americans adopt African names. However, the truth is that slave owners "actually forbade slaves to have surnames." In cases in which slaves had surnames, it was because they secretly took them in defiance of their masters,"to identify and dignify their forbidden family relationships."[2]

Many people who hold a "pro-choice" position on abortion assume that the right to an abortion is expressed in the U.S. Constitution, that the *Roe* v. *Wade* Supreme Court decision is logically unassailable, and that the "pro-life" position is based solely on religious faith. All three assumptions are unwarranted. Justice Byron White, in his *Roe* v. *Wade* dissent, rejected any constitutional basis for the majority decision, terming it an "exercise of raw judicial power." Columnist and author George Will makes these observations about the abortion issue:

The 1973 decision gave rise to the legal locution that a fetus is "potential life." The biological absurdity of that is today underscored by the development of fetal medicine. . . . [Furthermore] Roe rests on this doubly absurd proposition: No one knows when human life begins but the [Supreme] Court knows when "meaningful" life begins. . . . The Court declared a third-trimester fetus "viable" because it can lead a "meaningful" life outside the womb. The Court said states could ban third-trimester abortions—but not when a doctor determines that killing a "viable" fetus is "necessary to preserve the life or health of the mother." (Interesting noun, "mother.")[3]

As for the assumption that the pro-life position is based only on religion, that view has been the *legal* view in Germany since 1975. At that time the Constitutional Court of Germany concluded that "the life of each individual human being is self-evidently a central value of the legal order . . . [and] the constitutional duty to protect this life also includes its preliminary stages before birth." The German high court reaffirmed this position in 1993, holding that the state has "a duty to place itself protectively before unborn human life, shielding this life from unlawful attacks" and calling for prosecution of anyone who pressured pregnant women into having abortions.[4]

Remember that assumptions are usually implied rather than expressed directly, much like the hidden premises in arguments. To identify them, develop the habit of reading (and listening) between the lines for ideas that are unexpressed but nevertheless clearly implied. Once you have identified an assumption, evaluate it and decide whether it is warranted.

The Either/Or Outlook

The either/or outlook is the expectation that the only reasonable view of any issue is either total affirmation or total rejection. In other words, this outlook refuses to acknowledge or consider more moderate views. Ironically, the moderate view is often the most reasonable view. Take, for example, the troubling issue of welfare reform. One extreme position is to keep the present welfare system just as it is. The opposite extreme is to eliminate the system entirely. Might not one of those views be correct? Absolutely. But the only way to tell for sure is to consider *all* possibilities, including those that are less extreme. The best solution may be neither to keep nor to abandon the old system but to *change it for the better.*

Similarly, in the debate over school vouchers, the question is often posed, "Should we improve public schools or give parents vouchers to use in the schools of their choice?" Yet it is not necessary to accept one of these views and reject the other. It is possible to affirm *both*—in other words, to increase the funding of public schools *and* allow parents to use their children's share of the money to choose the particular school, public or private, they prefer.

Whenever you are examining an issue and find yourself considering only two alternatives, ask yourself whether additional alternatives exist, and if they do, give them a fair hearing.

Mindless Conformity

The term for behaving as others do is *conformity.* In some situations conformity is the wisest course of action. Children conform when they stay away from stoves and look both ways before crossing the street. We all conform when we enter and exit buildings through the designated doors, use the "up" escalator to go up, and go to the end rather than the front of the checkout line. Such conformity makes life easier and safer. (The person you cut in on may be bigger, stronger, and *armed!*) Another positive kind of conformity is imitation of good role models—people whose example is worth imitating. This kind of conformity helps us develop our capacities and become better individuals.

In contrast, mindless conformity is unreasonable and, in many cases, unreasoning. It consists of following others' example because we are too lazy or fearful to think for ourselves. In a well-known experiment, eight students entered a laboratory. Seven were in league with the professor; the eighth was the unknowing subject of the experiment. The students were shown four lines on an otherwise blank page and asked to decide which of the three lower lines (identified as A, B, and C) matched the top line in length. Line A was exactly the same length as the top line, ten inches. The other lines were clearly much shorter or longer. Each of the seven collaborators, in turn, gave the *wrong* answer, and the pressure mounted on the unknowing subject. When he or she was asked, the choice was clear: give the obviously *right answer and stand alone* or the *wrong answer and enjoy the support of the group.* Believe it or not, only one out of every five who participated in the experiment gave the correct answer.[5]

Many advertisers encourage mindless conformity. An excellent example is a Budweiser commercial that featured the line "Why ask why? Try Bud Dry." The various groups people belong to—from Friday night poker clubs to churches, political parties, fraternities, and unions—can also generate pressure to conform. Even groups pledged to fight conformity and promote free thinking can do so. "Hippie" communes in the 1960s were often as intolerant of dissenting ideas, values, and lifestyles as the "straight" society they rebelled against. Liberal colleagues praised author Nat Hentoff for his defense of freedom of expression as long as he agreed with them, but many were quick to denounce him when he took the position that a fetus is a human being and as such is entitled to the protection of the law.[6] Conservatives who favor gun control and black authors who oppose affirmative action have been similarly pressured to conform to the majority views of their groups.

The secret to avoiding mindless conformity is to resist whatever pleading, teasing, and prodding others exert to make you think and speak and act as they do. Instead of succumbing, ask yourself what is reasonable and right and follow that path, regardless of whether that places you in the majority or the minority.

Absolutism

Absolutism is the belief that there must be rules but no exceptions. Absolutists expect the truth about issues to be clear-cut, certain, and simple when, in reality, it is often ambiguous, less than certain, and complex. Because of their unreasonable expectations, absolutists tend to be impatient in their thinking and therefore susceptible to oversimplification and hasty conclusions. Moreover, once they have made up their minds, they tend to hold their views more dogmatically than critical thinkers—that is, they tend to be unwilling to entertain evidence that challenges them.

To say the vulnerability to errors and the reluctance to change one's mind characterize absolutists is not to suggest that other people do not possess the same weaknesses. (As noted in previous chapters, all human beings are susceptible to these and other cognitive shortcomings.) It is only to say that absolutists are more vulnerable than others—their aversion to exceptions makes them so. Note, too, that it is possible to believe in absolutes without being an absolutist. For example, you can believe that murder is always morally wrong but that in certain circumstances, such as self-defense, culpability for the act is diminished or eliminated.

The key to overcoming absolutism is this: When you begin to examine any issue, even one that you have thought about before, commit yourself to accepting the truth as you find it rather than demanding that it be neat and simple.

Relativism

Relativism is the polar opposite of absolutism. Whereas the absolutist does not acknowledge exceptions to rules, the relativist believes that the existence of exceptions proves there can be no rules. The central error of relativism is the belief that truth is created rather than discovered. If someone attempts to demonstrate that something is true, relativists tend to say,

"Whose truth are you talking about? Mine may be different from yours." They believe that whatever a person believes is true is, by that very fact, true for him or her. Relativism also holds that morality is subjective rather than objective—in other words, that moral rules are binding only on those who accept them. "If a person thinks any behavior is morally acceptable then it is acceptable for that person," is the relativist's credo.

Relativism opposes critical thinking, the study of ethics, and the processes of law. The point of critical thinking is to separate truth from falsity, reasonable from unreasonable; if nothing is false, bad, or unreasonable, critical thinking is pointless. Similarly, if everything that anyone wants to do is good, then nothing is bad and moral discourse has no purpose. And if choosing to do something is a justification for doing it, the laws against rape, child molesting, and murder are an infringement on the rights of the perpetrator.

The simple test of any perspective is whether it can be consistently applied in everyday life. Relativists can't challenge the correctness of other people's views without contradicting themselves. Nor can they protest genital mutilation in North Africa, genocide in Central Europe, slave labor in the Orient, or racism in North America without denying their own belief that morality is subjective. To overcome relativism, remind yourself from time to time that some ideas, and some standards of conduct, are better than others, and that the challenge of critical thinking is to discover the best ones.

Bias for or against Change

Are you for or against change? The only reasonable answer is "It depends on what the change is." Some changes improve matters; others make matters worse. Yet many people lack that balanced perspective. They have a bias for or against change. Bias for change is more common than it used to be, no doubt because we live in an age of unprecedented change, especially in technology; since many changes are beneficial, we may make the mistake of believing that all are.

Bias against change, however, is still more prevalent than bias for change. One reason is the force of familiarity. Most of us prefer ideas that we know and feel comfortable with.

When Galileo said, "The earth moves around the sun," people were upset, partly because thousands of sunrises and sunsets had told them the *sun* did the moving, but also partly because they simply had never before heard of the earth's moving. The new idea threatened their fixed belief that the earth was the center of the solar system. They had that idea neatly packaged in their minds. It was a basic part of their understanding of the universe; it was intertwined with their religion. And now this upstart Galileo was demanding no less than that they untie the package, or reopen the issue.

Shortly after the advent of bicycles, people said they would undermine "feminine modesty." Physicians said they would cause "nymphomania," "hysteria," "voluptuous sensations," "lubricious overexcitement," and "sensual madness."[7] Some people considered the movement to restrict child labor in sweatshops a communist plot. And when astronauts first landed on the moon, at least one elderly man expressed total disbelief. "It's a trick thought up by the TV people," he said. "It's impossible for a man to reach the moon."

Another reason that bias against change is so prevalent is our "mine-is-better" perspective. Our habits of thinking and acting seem to us the only right ways of thinking and acting. New ideas challenge our sense of security, so we tend to resist them. This explains why many people cling to outmoded traditions.* For example, the man in Robert Frost's poem "Mending Wall" kept repairing the wall between his land and his neighbor's, not because there was still any good purpose in doing so, but only because his father had done so before him. And consider this case of uncritical dependence on past ways: A girl was told by her mother, "Never put a hat on a table or a coat on a bed." She accepted the direction and followed it faithfully for years. One day, many years later, she repeated the direction to her own teenage daughter, and the daughter asked, "Why?" The woman realized that she had never been curious enough to ask her own mother. Her curiosity at long last aroused, she asked her mother (by then in her eighties). The mother replied, "Because when I was a little girl some neighbor children were infested with lice, and my mother explained I should never put a hat on a table or a coat on a bed." The woman had spent her entire adult life following a rule she had been taught without once wondering about its purpose or validity.[8]

Despite resistance to change, however, many new ideas do manage to take hold. We might think that when they do, those who fought so hard for them would remember the resistance they had to overcome. Ironically, however, they often forget very quickly. In fact, they sometimes display the same fear and insecurity they so deplored in others. An example occurred in psychiatry. Sigmund Freud and his followers were ostracized and bitterly attacked for suggesting that sexuality was an important factor in the development of personality. The hostility toward Freud was so strong, in fact, that his masterwork, *The Interpretation of Dreams,* was ignored when it was first published in 1900. It took eight years to sell six hundred copies of the book.[9]

---

*Don't make the mistake of thinking that the older the tradition, the less valuable it is. An ancient tradition may be more sensible than the latest vogue idea. The only way to be sure, of course, is to give it fair and impartial consideration.

Yet when Freud's ideas became accepted, he and his followers showed no greater tolerance; in fact, they ostracized and attacked those who challenged any part of his theory. Karen Horney, for example, challenged Freud's view of women as being driven by "penis envy." She believed, too, that neurosis is caused not only by frustrated sexual drives but also by various cultural conflicts, and that people's behavior is not only determined by instinctual drives but can in many instances be self-directed and modified. For these theories (today widely accepted), she was rewarded with rebuke and ostracism by the Freudian dogmatists.[10]

To overcome either variety of bias toward change, monitor your reaction to new ideas. Don't be surprised if you strongly favor or oppose an idea the first time you encounter it. Refuse to endorse your first impression uncritically. Instead, suspend judgment until you have examined the idea carefully. If the idea proves insightful and well substantiated, accept it regardless of its oldness or newness; if it is flawed, reject it.

Applications

1. Examine each of the following dialogues. Identify any assumptions made by the speakers. Be precise. If possible, decide whether the assumptions are warranted.

   a. *Olaf:* Did you hear the good news? School may not open on schedule this year.
   Olga: How come?
   Olaf: The teachers may be on strike.
   Olga: Strike? That's ridiculous. They're already making good money.

   b. *Janice:* What movie is playing at the theater tonight?
   Mike: I don't know the title. It's something about lesbians. Do you want to go?
   Janice: No thanks. I'll wait for a quality film.

   c. *Boris:* Boy, talk about unfair graders. Nelson's the worst.
   Bridget: Why? What did he do?
   Boris: What did he do? He gave me a D– on the midterm, that's all—after I spent twelve straight hours studying for it. I may just make an appointment to see the dean about him.

   d. *Mrs. Smith:* The Harrisons are having marital problems. I'll bet they'll be separating soon.
   Mr. Jones: How do you know?
   Mrs. Smith: I heard it at the supermarket. Helen told Gail and Gail told me.
   Mr. Jones: I knew it wouldn't work out. Jeb Harrison is such a blah person. I can't blame Ruth for wanting to leave him.

2. Apply your critical thinking to the following cases. Be sure to identify all your assumptions and decide whether they are warranted.

   a. A Cambridge, Massachusetts, man got tired of looking at his neighbor's uncut lawn and untrimmed shrubs, which reached above the second-story window, and took his grievance to court. The neighbor admitted to the judge that he hadn't cut the lawn in fourteen years, but he argued that he preferred a natural lawn to a manicured one and untrimmed to trimmed shrubs. The judge decided he was perfectly within his legal rights in leaving his lawn and shrubs uncut, regardless of what his neighbor felt.[11] Do you think the judge's decision was fair?

b. Some parents who believed their college-age sons or daughters were being brainwashed by religious cults have kidnapped their children and had them deprogrammed. Should they be allowed to do this?

c. Some parents keep their children out of school in the belief that they can educate them better at home. Should this be permitted?

d. Many motorcyclists object to the laws of some states that require them and their passengers to wear helmets. They believe they should be free to decide for themselves whether to wear helmets. Do you agree?

3. Examine each of the following statements and decide whether it contains an error. If you find an error, identify it and explain it in such a way that someone who did not read this chapter would understand.

a. The only alternative to affirmative action is acceptance of discrimination against minorities.

b. We have to choose between creationism and evolution. No middle ground is possible.

4. List several examples of desirable conformity and several of undesirable conformity. Explain why each is desirable or undesirable.

5. Advertising frequently is designed to appeal to the tendency to conform. Describe at least three print ads or commercials that are so designed, and explain the ways they appeal to conformity so that someone who did not read this chapter would understand.

6. In each of the following situations, the person is conforming. Study each situation and determine what effects the conformity will have on that person and on other people. On the basis of those effects, decide whether the conformity is desirable. If your decision depends on the degree of the conformity or the circumstances in which it occurred, explain in what situations you would approve and why.

a. Bert is thirteen. His friends are insensitive to other people and even look for opportunities to ridicule them. If a classmate is overweight or homely or unusually shy or not too intelligent, they will taunt the person about it. If the person shows signs of being bothered by the cruelty, they will see this as a sign of weakness and increase the abuse. Bert knows this behavior is wrong and he derives no pleasure from it, but he goes along with it and even indulges in it from time to time so as not to appear weak to his friends. He realizes that in their eyes, if he is not with them completely, he is against them.

b. Rose works in a dress factory. Shortly after she began work, she realized that the other workers' output was unrealistically low and that she could complete twice as much work as the others without straining. Then, in subtle ways, her co-workers let her know that if she worked at a reasonable pace, the employer would become aware of their deception and demand increased production from them. Knowing she would at the very least be ostracized if she did not conform to their work pace, she decided to do so.

c. Alex is a freshman representative in the state legislature. When an important issue is being debated, he is approached by a powerful lobbyist who informs him that his political career will stand a better chance of surviving if he votes a certain way. The lobbyist mentions the names of half a dozen other representatives and suggests that Alex ask them about the wisdom of voting that way. He contacts them and they say, in effect, "We're supporting the position of that lobbying group; if you value your career, you'll do the same." He takes their advice and conforms.

7. Do you tend more toward absolutism or relativism? In what specific areas are you most likely to commit this error of perspective? Politics? Religion? Social issues? Moral decisions? Be specific in answering. The more fully you understand your characteristic tendencies to error, the more successful you can be in overcoming them.

8. Do you tend to be more biased for change or against it? Do you tend to be for it in some areas of life but against it in others? Be as specific as you can in describing your tendency.

9. Each of the following statements recommends a change. Note whether your reaction is favorable, unfavorable, or somewhere between. Then evaluate each idea, taking care to put aside whatever bias you may have and judge the idea fairly.
a. The national sovereignty of all countries, including the United States, should be surrendered to the United Nations, so that there will no longer be artificial boundaries separating people.
b. Cockfighting, dogfighting, and bullfighting should be televised for the enjoyment of the minority who enjoy these "sports."
c. A federal law should be passed requiring women to retain their maiden names when they marry (that is, forbidding them from adopting their husbands' names).
d. Cemeteries should open their gates to leisure-time activities for the living. Appropriate activities would include cycling, jogging, fishing, nature hiking, and (space permitting) team sports.
e. Federal and state penitentiaries should allow inmates to leave prisons during daytime hours to hold jobs or attend college classes. (The only ones denied this privilege should be psychopaths.)
f. Colleges should not admit any student who has been out of high school less than three years.
g. To encourage a better turnout at the polls for elections, lotteries should be held. (Voters would send in a ballot stub as proof that they voted. Prizes would be donated by companies.)[12]
h. Retired people should be used as teachers' aides even if they lack college degrees.[13]
i. Everyone should be issued and required to carry a national identity card, identifying himself or herself as a U.S. citizen.[14]
j. Churches and synagogues should remove all restrictions on women's participation in liturgical and counseling services, thus permitting women to serve as priests, ministers, and rabbis.
k. Colleges should charge juniors and seniors higher tuition than that charged to freshmen and sophomores.

10. Bill Beausay, a sports psychologist, suggests that sports be rated much as films once were: X, R, or G, depending on the amount of danger and/or violence in them. He urges that children not be allowed to take part in any X-rated sport at an early age. Such sports include motorcycle and auto racing, hockey, football, boxing, and horse racing.[15] Decide whether his suggestion has merit. Be sure to avoid resistance to change.

11. Decide whether you accept or reject the following arguments. Be careful to avoid both "mine-is-better" thinking and the errors discussed in this chapter, and to judge the issues impartially. You may wish to research the issues further before judging.

    a. Beer and wine commercials should be banned from television because they glamorize drinking, leading people to associate it with love, friendship, and happiness. Such associations are every bit as misleading as those used to sell cigarettes. Alcohol commercials surely are a contributing factor in the current increase in alcohol abuse by adults and children.

    b. Beauty pageants today give somewhat more attention to talent than pageants did in the past. But the underlying message is the same— "Beauty in a woman is strictly a surface matter. Only those with ample bosoms, pretty faces, and trim figures need apply." These pageants make a mockery of the truth that inner beauty, character, is the real measure of a woman (or of a man).

    c. *Background note: One reason the court system is clogged with cases is that prisoners are filing what some regard as frivolous lawsuits against the state or federal government—for example, suits claiming their rights are being violated because the prison food doesn't meet their dietary preferences. Law books are available in the prison library for prisoners to use in preparing their lawsuits. Argument:* Frivolous lawsuits clog the court system. The availability of law books in prison libraries encourages prisoners to file such suits. Therefore, law books should be removed from prison libraries.

    d. The duties of the president of the United States are too numerous and complex for one individual to fulfill, so the office of the presidency should be changed from a one-person office to a three-member board.

CHAPTER 10

Errors of Procedure

In Chapter 9 we examined errors of perspective, flawed outlooks that create significant obstacles to critical thinking even before we address any issue. In this chapter we will examine the kinds of errors that occur in the process of addressing specific issues: *biased consideration of evidence, double standard, hasty conclusion, overgeneralization and stereotyping, oversimplification,* and *the post hoc fallacy.*

Biased Consideration of Evidence

We have noted that though you may find it pleasant to believe you approach issues with perfect impartiality, that is seldom the case. You will generally lean in one direction or another. There's nothing odd or shameful about this fact. It's a natural reaction, not just for you but for everyone else as well. Nevertheless, it is important to understand how that leaning can cause you to commit the error of biased consideration of evidence. One form of this error is seeking only evidence that confirms your bias. Another form occurs when evidence is presented to you that challenges your bias—in this case you choose an interpretation that favors your bias, even if other interpretations are more reasonable.

Here is an example of biased consideration of evidence: Let's say you receive the assignment of developing and presenting a position on the issue of whether the tenure system improves or hinders the quality of college instruction.* The responsible approach would be for you to examine the evidence offered by both those who support and those who oppose tenure. But if you are biased one way or the other, your desire to be right

---

*Tenure, which is usually granted after several years of teaching, provides job security. Once professors have tenure, it is difficult for the institution to fire them unless they commit a serious offense. Substandard teaching is seldom considered such an offense.

may lead you to consult only presentations that support your view. You may acquire an impressive quantity of evidence in this way and persuade yourself that nothing of merit can be said on the other side of the issue. In reality, of course, you will have no way of knowing that because *you did not examine* the case for the other side.

The worst aspect of this error is that it often occurs innocently, without one's awareness, and not just to students. Even professional scholars can commit it. (That is why you should test the views of authorities for impartiality.) To avoid biased selection of evidence, begin your investigation by seeking out individuals whose views oppose your bias and then go on to those that support it. Also, choose the most reasonable interpretation, regardless of whether it flatters your bias.

Double Standard

Double standard involves using one set of criteria for judging arguments we agree with and another standard for judging those we disagree with. A typical form of this error is ignoring significant flaws and omissions in data that favor our view while nitpicking data that challenge it. Another form is minimizing the seriousness of charges against our side while maximizing the seriousness of charges against the other side. Political discussion provides many examples of the double standard. For example, when Clarence Thomas, a conservative nominee for the U.S. Supreme Court, was accused of making sexually suggestive remarks to a female subordinate, some Democratic members of Congress argued that the accusation alone was sufficient cause to reject his appointment. Then several years later, when President Bill Clinton was accused of sexual harassment and even rape, the same members of Congress argued that the charges must have been politically motivated and therefore were unworthy of consideration. The error of the double standard is also common in issues of free speech: Many people who are outspoken proponents of free speech for ideas they agree with are eager to censor those they disagree with.

To avoid the error of the double standard, decide in advance what judgment criteria you will use and apply those criteria consistently, even if the data in question do not support your view.

Hasty Conclusion

Hasty conclusion is a premature judgment—that is, a judgment made without sufficient evidence. It takes mental discipline to resist jumping to conclusions, but many people lack such discipline. They are in the habit of accepting the first judgment that comes to mind, never bothering to inquire whether a different judgment might be as reasonable, perhaps more so. If they see a man getting into a taxicab with a woman other than his wife, they immediately conclude she is his mistress, when she could just as well be a relative, a business associate, or a client. If a friend passes without speaking to them, they conclude that they have been snubbed, when the person may have been preoccupied and failed to notice them.

Hasty conclusions can occur in scholarly pursuits as well as in everyday situations. One of the most ambitious tests of human intelligence ever conducted led to hasty conclusions; almost a century later it remains a vivid testimony to the harm they can do. During World War I, psychologists administered intelligence tests to almost two million army recruits. The resulting scores, expressed in terms of mental age, were as follows: immigrants from northern Europe, 13; immigrants from southern and central Europe, 11; U.S.-born Blacks, 10. The psychologists leaped to the conclusion that southern Europeans and Blacks are "morons." (The term was considered scientific at that time.) This conclusion was instrumental in the framing of the 1924 immigration law that discriminated against southern and central Europeans and reinforced negative stereotypes of African Americans.*

If these psychologists had asked the simple question, Is the conclusion that southern and central Europeans and U.S.-born Blacks are 'morons' the only possible conclusion? they would have wondered whether the design and administration of the test might be at fault. They also would have found that the test directions varied from site to site—some were told to finish each part before moving on, others were not—and that recruits at the back of the test room sometimes could not hear the instructions at all. In addition, they would have found that the same form of the test was given to recruits who could read and write English, those who spoke only a foreign language, and those who had never learned to read and write.

What could have explained why the different *groups* had very different scores? On average, the northern Europeans had been in the U.S. for twenty or more years and therefore were fluent in English and reasonably well educated. In contrast, the southern and central Europeans had arrived more recently and were neither fluent in English nor (since many were poor) well educated. Finally, many U.S.-born Blacks had been denied the opportunity for an education.

To avoid hasty conclusions, identify all possible conclusions before you select any one. Then decide whether you have sufficient evidence to support any of those conclusions and, if so, which conclusion that is.

*For a fuller discussion of this subject, see Stephen Jay Gould, *The Mismeasure of Man* (New York: Norton, 1981), Chapter 5. Incidentally, many of the psychologists who embraced this conclusion went on to popularize the use of the IQ test in education. One of them, Carl Brigham, later developed the Scholastic Aptitude Test, popularly known as the SAT.

Remember that there is no shame in suspending judgment until you obtain additional evidence.

Overgeneralization and Stereotyping

Generalizing is the mental activity by which we move our understanding beyond particular experiences. A child hears one dog bark and concludes that barking is characteristic of dogs. This generalization is true, "barkless" Basenjis notwithstanding. When Mommy says "Be careful of that pencil, it can poke your eye out," the child understands, again rightly, that all pencils have that capacity. As these modest examples suggest, generalizing is not only natural but indispensable to learning. We never see things in general—that is, all dogs, all pencils, all mountains, all rivers, all teachers, or all anything else. Rather, we see particular members of a general class—individually or in groups—and generalize from them.

As long as we exercise reasonable care, generalizing serves us well. Unfortunately, it is easy to *over*generalize—that is, to ascribe to all the members of a group what fits only some members. If you visit New York City and meet a few rude people, you would be correct in saying, "Some New Yorkers are rude," but not "Most New Yorkers are rude," let alone "New Yorkers are rude."* Yet such sweeping generalizations are heard every day, not only about New Yorkers but also about liberals, conservatives, "born-again" Christians, politicians, homosexuals, feminists, environmentalists, intellectuals, and many other groups.

A stereotype is an overgeneralization that is especially resistant to change. The most common types of stereotypes are ethnic and religious. There are stereotypes of Jews, Poles, African Americans, Hispanics, Italians, fundamentalists, Catholics, atheists—and "dead, white, European males," or DWEMs. As you might expect, any generalization that is fixed and unbending may be considered a stereotype. Although stereotypes may be either positive or negative, they are more often negative. Sadly, people who deplore the negative stereotyping of their own groups often do not hesitate to stereotype other groups.

Does every reference to group characteristics constitute a stereotype? No. Recurring patterns of thinking and acting are observable in groups, and references to those patterns are therefore legitimate. In ancient times the Chinese were more creative than most other peoples; in the late nineteenth and much of the twentieth centuries, German industrial technology led the world; in recent decades the Japanese have demonstrated

---

*Note that any generalization that does not include a specific qualification such as *most, many, some, several,* or *Agnes* is understood to mean all members of the group. Thus, saying "New Yorkers are rude" is the same as saying "All New Yorkers are rude."

remarkable inventiveness and concern for quality. Furthermore, not all cultural patterns are complimentary. For centuries the Spanish and Portuguese disdained manual labor, thinking it a sign of *dishonor*, and emigrants to Latin America carried that attitude with them. Today Sri Lankans have a similar attitude. The prevalence of this attitude in these societies can be acknowledged without suggesting that all Hispanics and Sri Lankans are lazy. (Incidentally, the pattern of thinking that manual labor is dishonorable reflects illogical reasoning rather than indolence.) As Thomas Sowell points out, the acknowledgment and examination of all cultural patterns, desirable and undesirable, advantageous and disadvantageous, is essential to understanding the success and failure of groups, nations, and entire civilizations.[1]

Both overgeneralizations and stereotypes hinder critical thinking because they prevent us from seeing the differences among people within groups. To avoid these errors, resist the urge to force individual people, places, or things into rigid categories. In forming generalizations, keep in mind that the more limited your experience, the more modest you should make your assertion. In the continuums presented below, the center terms (*one or some, occasionally,* and *possible*) require the least experience. Each division to the right or left of the center requires additional experience.

The Subject Continuum

←—————————————————————————————————→

all / most / many / one or some / few / almost none / none

The Frequency Continuum

←—————————————————————————————————→

always / usually / often / occasionally / seldom / hardly ever / never

The Certainty Continuum

←—————————————————————————————————→

certainly so / probable / possible / improbable / certainly not so

Oversimplification

Simplification is not only useful but essential, particularly at a time like the present, when knowledge is expanding so rapidly. People who know a great deal about a subject find it necessary to communicate with those who know little or nothing about it. Teachers must explain to students, experienced employees to novices, attorneys to clients, physicians to patients, and scientists to the general public. Simplification scales down complex ideas to a level that can be understood by less knowledgeable people.

*Over*simplification, on the other hand, goes beyond making complex ideas easier to grasp; it twists and distorts the ideas. Instead of informing people, oversimplification misleads them. Unfortunately, oversimplified statements can sound insightful; in such cases, the errors can be detected only by careful analysis. Here are two typical examples of oversimplification:

OVERSIMPLIFICATION	ANALYSIS
If the students haven't learned, the teacher hasn't taught.	Students' not learning is sometimes the teacher's fault and sometimes the students' own fault for not putting forth the required effort. This statement suggests that the fault *always* lies with the teacher; thus, it oversimplifies.
We know ourselves better than others know us.	It is true that we know some things about ourselves better than others do: for example, our hopes, dreams, and fantasies. Yet there are things about ourselves that we unconsciously block to preserve our self-image: for example, personal faults such as envy, pettiness, and hypocrisy. These are often perfectly clear to others. By ignoring this fact, the statement in question oversimplifies.

Oversimplification often occurs in matters about which people have strong feelings. When laws were passed requiring restaurants to serve any customer, regardless of race, religion, or national origin, some restaurant owners were angry. They reasoned that people who invest their hard-earned money in a business have the right to serve or not serve whomever they please. That side of the issue was so important to them that they regarded it as the only side. But there was another important side: the right of citizens to have access to public places.

Similarly, when the Federal Aviation Administration published regulations governing hang gliders and ultralight motorized aircraft, the U.S. Hang Gliders Association protested. It argued that the government "has no business regulating an outdoor recreational sport that consists largely of people running and gliding down remote hills and sand dunes." The association was seeing one side of the issue, the side that affected it. Now if that were the only side, this position would be reasonable. But there is another important side to the issue: keeping the airspace safe for all who use it, including commercial and private planes. (The FAA reports that hang gliders have been observed as high as 13,000 feet.)[2] By ignoring that side, the association oversimplified the issue.

The desire for ratings and financial success has pressured some journalists to abandon the traditional ideals of balanced, accurate reporting and to sensationalize their stories instead. That is why a considerable amount of contemporary news and commentary deals in speculation, gossip, and unfounded opinion, and why shouting matches between proponents of opposing views often substitute for reasoned debate. The unfortunate result of this sensationalizing is that issues are oversimplified. Be alert for oversimplification in what you read and hear, and avoid it in your own thinking and expression.

The Post Hoc Fallacy

Post hoc is an abbreviation of a Latin term, *post hoc, ergo propter hoc,* which means "after this, therefore because of this." It expresses the reasoning that when one thing occurs after another, it must be the result of the other. The error in this thinking is the failure to realize that mere closeness in time does not prove a cause-and-effect relationship. One event can follow another by coincidence and thus be entirely unrelated to it.

The post hoc fallacy is likely the basis of most superstitions. Misfortune befalls someone shortly after he walks under a ladder, or breaks a mirror, or has a black cat cross his path, and he judges that event to be responsible for the misfortune.

Sam is in the habit of arriving late to English class. Yesterday the professor told him that the next time he was tardy, he would be refused admission. Today Sam got a composition back with a grade of D. He reasons that the professor gave him a low grade out of anger over his lateness. Sam has committed the fallacy of false cause. Maybe the professor did lower the grade for that reason, and maybe not. The paper could have been graded earlier, or it may simply have been inferior. Without additional evidence, Sam should withhold judgment.

There is nothing wrong with inquiring into cause and effect relationships. In fact, critical thinkers ask, Why did this happen? more than other people. All you need do to avoid the post hoc error is to withhold judgment of a cause-and-effect relationship until you have ruled out other explanations, including coincidence.

Applications

1. Ebonics is an African American dialect that some educators wanted to make a legitimate second language in California schools. One critic of the proposal wrote the following: "In plain talk, 'Ebonics' is no more than African American gutter slang. . . . If Ebonics has any credibility at all, it is as the dialect of the street—the dialect of the pimp, the idiom of the gang-banger and the street thug, the jargon of the school dropout, a form of pidgin English that reeks of African American failure."[3] Does anything you read in this chapter apply to this quotation? Explain.

2. A newspaper columnist made this comment in his column: "I've never understood why Hispanic liberals, so sensitive to slights from the racist right, don't also take offense at the patronizing racists of the left who say that being Hispanic makes you an idiot."[4] Does anything you read in this chapter apply to this quotation? Explain.

3. Charles, an atheist, is writing a paper on the issue of prayer in public schools. He is well acquainted with the arguments advanced by those who oppose such prayer but unfamiliar with the other side of the issue. Charles reasons that because the paper he produces will be his own, it would be not only distasteful but foolish for him to read material that he knows he disagrees with and will ultimately argue against. So he confines his research to articles and books that oppose all prayer in the schools. Do you agree or disagree with his reasoning? Explain.

4. Describe one or more situations in which you or someone you know committed the error of the double standard. Explain the error in terms that someone who did not read this chapter would understand.

5. Describe one or more situations in which you or someone you know committed the post hoc fallacy. Explain the error in terms that someone who did not read this chapter would understand.

6. In late August, the Lees, a Chinese American family, moved into Louise's neighborhood, and Louise became acquainted with one of the children, Susan, a girl her own age. A week later, during school registration, Louise passed Susan in the hall, but Susan didn't even look at her. Which of the following conclusions was Louise justified in drawing? (You may select more than one or reject all of them.) Explain your answer with appropriate references to the chapter.
   a. Susan behaved rudely.
   b. Susan is a rude person.
   c. The Lees are a rude family.
   d. Chinese Americans are rude.
   e. The Chinese are rude.
   f. Asians are rude.

7. While reading her evening newspaper, Jean notices that her congressional representative has voted against a highway proposal that would bring revenue to the area. She recalls that a recent poll of the voters in the district revealed that 63 percent favor the proposal. Concluding that the representative has violated the people's trust, Jean composes an angry letter reminding the representative of his obligation to support the will of the majority. Is Jean guilty of an error in thinking? Explain your answer.

8. Ramona and Stuart are arguing over whether their ten-year-old son should have certain duties around the home, such as taking out the garbage and mowing the lawn. Ramona thinks he should. Stuart's response is as follows: "When I was a kid, a close friend of mine was so busy with household chores that he could never play with the rest of the guys. He always had a hurt look on his face then, and as he got older, he became increasingly bitter about it. I vowed a long time ago that I would never burden my son with duties and responsibilities. He'll have more than enough of them when he grows up." Evaluate Stuart's conclusion in light of the chapter.

9. Analyze the following ideas. Decide whether each is an oversimplification. Explain your reasoning carefully.

   a. "I need only consult with myself with regard to what I wish to do; what I feel to be right is right, what I feel to be wrong is wrong." (Jean-Jacques Rousseau)
   b. Elected officials should be held accountable to a higher ethical standard than is the average citizen.
   c. Guns don't kill people; people kill people.

10. Apply your critical thinking to the following cases. Be especially careful to avoid the errors explained in this and previous chapters.

    a. An Oklahoma man was sentenced to ninety-nine years in prison for indecent exposure. The prosecutor was able to ask for and get such a long sentence because the man had eleven prior convictions for burglary. The district attorney explained, "People are just tired of crime—they want the repeat offenders off the streets."[5] Do you support the sentence in this case?
    b. A Connecticut teenager who stabbed a neighbor to death argued that he had not been responsible for his actions because at the time he had been possessed by demons. Despite that defense he was found guilty.[6] Do you agree with the verdict in this case?
    c. A New York woman was having an argument with her neighbor over their children. In anger she used an anti-Semitic obscenity. Because it is a misdemeanor in New York to harass others with racial or ethnic slurs, the woman was sentenced to thirty-five hours of community service.[7] Do you think such a law makes sense?
    d. A high school anatomy class in Agoura, California, dissects human cadavers as well as cats and frogs. The teacher obtains the bodies from a university medical school.[8] Do you approve of this practice?
    e. Some people believe the college degree should be abolished as a job requirement. They reason that because it is possible to be qualified for many jobs without formal academic preparation (or, conversely, to be unprepared for many jobs even with a college degree), the only criterion employers should use for hiring and promoting is ability. Do you agree?

11. In application 1 above, you evaluated a quotation about Ebonics. The author of that quotation is Ken Hamblin, an African American author and radio talk show host. Does the fact that he is African American prompt you to change your assessment of the quotation? Should it? Why or why not?

12. In application 2 above, you evaluated a quotation about "liberal Hispanics." The author of that quotation is a Hispanic named Roger Hernandez. Does the fact that he is Hispanic prompt you to change your assessment of the quotation? Should it? Why or why not?

CHAPTER 11

Errors of Expression

We have already examined two categories of errors: those that create obstacles to critical thinking before we address any issue and those that occur in the process of addressing specific issues. In this chapter we will examine a third category: errors that occur in expressing our views to others, orally or in writing. These errors are *shifting the issue, contradiction, arguing in a circle, meaningless statement, mistaken authority, false analogy,* and *irrational appeal.*

At this point you may be wondering, Aren't the errors listed above *thinking* errors? If so, what's the point of calling them 'errors of *expression*'? Excellent questions, both. The errors in this chapter, like those we have considered and those we will consider in the next chapter, are without exception errors of thought because they originate in the mind, more or less consciously (sometimes dimly so). We would therefore be perfectly justified in treating all kinds of error under a single large heading—"Errors of Thought," for example, or "Logical Fallacies." In fact, many books on thinking treat them just that way.

The rationale for using four categories is that different errors tend to occur, or at least are most evident, at different stages in the overall process called thinking. Although errors of expression may begin to take shape in the mind at some earlier time, they are most easily recognized and corrected when we are speaking or writing. Treating them in a separate category, "Errors of Expression," helps us remember when to be alert for them.

Shifting the Issue

Shifting the issue consists of abruptly turning a discussion in a different direction. Not every shift constitutes an error. The new direction may be more promising. Or it may be a way to provide a timely but polite rebuke.

Suppose someone asks you a rude or inappropriately personal question, such as "What is your annual income?" or "Why don't you and your spouse have any children?" Having no obligation to reply, you might say something totally unrelated to the question, such as "I wonder which teams will make it to the Super Bowl" or "The northeast has had an unusually hot summer this year." This is a perfectly legitimate way of letting the person know the question was improper.

Shifting the issue is an error only when the original issue is appropriate and the shift is used deceptively. Sadly, this kind of shift is common in interviews of public figures. The interviewer asks a question, and the interviewee avoids that question and talks about something else. Clever individuals will manage to mention the subject of the question and thus create the impression that they are being forthright when in fact they are not. For example, a presidential candidate given the question What is your position on abortion? might answer something like this:

> The issue of abortion has divided our nation more than any other issue of the twentieth century. What disturbs me most is that the tone of discussion has become so harsh and the distrust of other people's integrity so intense that meaningful debate is all but impossible. We must have that debate, the issue cries out for it, and if I am elected, I pledge to do my part to create the conditions that will make it possible.

This is an eloquent, moving answer to *a question that wasn't asked!* Meanwhile, the question that *was* asked is left unanswered. In this case there is good reason to suspect that the candidate intended not to answer the question because any answer he could give would alienate some group of voters. In fact, he may have been warned by advisors before beginning his campaign, "Whenever you are asked about abortion, change the subject."

Politicians are not the only ones who shift issues to avoid addressing difficult questions or to escape potentially awkward situations. This tactic is used in all walks of life. In legal circles, for example, legend has it that an attorney's assistant once rushed into the courtroom and handed the attorney a note that read, "It appears we have no case. Abuse the plaintiff."

Intentionally shifting the issue is dishonest because it frustrates the purpose of discussion. To avoid this error, face difficult questions head-on. If you know the answer, state it. If the issue is too complex to permit a certain answer, state what you believe to be probable and explain your reasoning. If you lack sufficient knowledge to speak of probabilities, say so. No reasonable person will think less of you for candidly admitting ignorance.

Contradiction

One of the fundamental principles of logic is the principle of contradiction, which states that *no statement can be both true and false at the same time in the same way.* The best way to see its correctness is to try to construct a statement that disproves it. Here are just a few possibilities:

> *Argument:* O.J. Simpson murdered Nicole Brown Simpson. (*Comment:* The principle requires us to say he either did or he didn't. But what if he hired someone else to murder her? Wouldn't he then have murdered her yet not murdered her? Yes, but not "in the same way." He would have murdered her in the sense of being responsible for the act but not in the sense of having carried it out.)

> *Argument:* Buster weighs 198 pounds. (*Comment:* He either weighs 198 pounds or some other weight. It can't be both ways. But what if he was cramming a Twinkie in his mouth while you were uttering that statement and he gained a tenth of an ounce when he swallowed. Then we'd have to say that at one instant he weighed 198 and the next instant he weighed slightly more.)

> *Argument:* Franklin D. Roosevelt was an Olympic athlete who later became President of the United States. (*Comment:* This seems to challenge the principle of contradiction because the statement is only partly true—he was never an Olympic athlete. Yet if we examine the statement closely, we see that it is really two statements fused together, one of them false and the other true.)

Test the principle of contradiction with statements of your own, if you wish, but don't be disappointed when you fail to disprove it. Critical thinking in every subject from architecture to zoology depends on this principle.

When exactly does contradiction occur? When a person says one thing now and the opposite later. A suspect, for example, may today admit that he committed the crime he is accused of and tomorrow deny his guilt. Relativists argue that everyone creates his or her own truth and no view is more worthy than any other, and then contradict themselves by castigating people who disagree with them. A scholar who propounds the view that the material world is an illusion and only the immaterial or spiritual world is real may take his neighbor to court in a property dispute. More than a few television moguls make the rounds of talk shows arguing that the violent, sex-sodden shows they produce have no influence on people's behavior and then, almost in the next breath, praise public service announcements for AIDS prevention and responsible use of alcohol for making the world better.

To overcome contradiction, monitor what you say and write. The moment you detect any inconsistency, examine it carefully. Decide whether it is explainable or whether it constitutes a contradiction. If it proves to be a contradiction, reexamine the issue and take a view that is both consistent and reasonable.

Arguing in a Circle

With this fallacy a person attempts to prove a statement by repeating it in a different form. When the statement is brief, the circular argument may be quite obvious. For example, if someone says, "Divorce is on the rise today because more marriages are breaking up," few people would fail to see the circularity. But consider the same sentence in expanded form: "The rate of divorce is appreciably higher in the present generation than it was in previous generations. Before a reason can be adduced for this trend, a number of factors must be considered, including the difference in the average age at which a couple marries. However, most experts tend to believe that the cause is the increased number of failed marriages." Same circular argument but more difficult to detect. The point is not that writers deliberately construct circular arguments but that such arguments can develop without our being aware of them.

To detect circularity in your writing, it is not enough to read and nod in agreement with yourself. You must check to be sure the evidence you offer in support of your view is not merely a statement of the view in different words.

Meaningless Statement

The popular Dean Witter advertising slogan "We measure success one investor at a time" is delivered in a grave tone of voice. If sound were the measure of meaningfulness, this line would be truly profound. However, substance is the real measure, and this slogan fails the test. At best it means that each investor represents a single datum that, when added to others, equals their statistics of performance. Big deal. At other brokerage houses, that datum means the same thing. Another example of a meaningless statement is LensCrafters' slogan, "Helping people to see better, one hour at a time." This slogan conjures up an image of attentive optometrists constantly performing unspecified tasks that improve clients' vision, but in fact it is an oblique and rather silly reference to the company's promise to *make glasses* in an hour.

In the course of presenting ideas, people often find it useful or necessary to present the reasons that underlie their thoughts and actions. A meaningless explanation is one in which the reasons make no sense. A used-car dealer says in a commercial, "I'll cosign your loan even if you've had a bankruptcy. That's because we take the trouble to hand pick and inspect these cars before you even see them. . . . We guarantee financing because we only sell quality cars." The careful viewer wonders, how can care in selecting cars ensure that purchasers will meet their credit obligations? (Answer: It can't.) The following headline from a print advertisement for a furniture company offers another example of meaningless explanation: "Good news! Due to the unprecedented success of our giant furniture sale, we have extended it for ten days." If it was so successful, we might ask, how is it that they still have enough merchandise for a ten-day extension? (The more cynical among us might translate the headline as follows: "The sale was such a flop that we're left with a warehouse full of inferior merchandise and we're desperate to have people buy it.")

To detect meaningless statements in your writing, look at what you have said as critically as you do what other people say. Ask, Am I really making sense?

Mistaken Authority

This fallacy ascribes authority to someone who does not possess it. It has become more common since the cult of celebrity has grown in the media. The television interviewer committed the fallacy of wrong authority when he asked actress Cybill Shepherd, "Did your role in that television drama give you any insights into adoption fraud?" If acting in a drama about adoption fraud confers expertise, then shouldn't playing an auto mechanic give one the ability to fix a car and playing a plastic surgeon enable one to perform operations? A more subtle form of this error occurs when experts in one field present themselves as authorities in another. This happens more than you might imagine. A well-known astronomer used to stray into the field of ethics in his essays, and more than a few biologists and physicists have posed as experts in theology and biblical history.

To avoid the error of mistaken authority, check to be sure that all the sources you cite as authorities possess expertise in the particular subject you are writing about.

False Analogy

An analogy is an attempt to explain something relatively unfamiliar by referring to something *different but more familiar,* saying in effect, "This is like that." Analogies can be helpful in promoting understanding, particularly of complex ideas, but they have the potential to be misleading. An analogy is acceptable as long as the similarities claimed are real. Here is an example of an acceptable analogy. An author discussing the contemporary problems of some Black inner-city residents in America makes the point that not all these problems are effects of slavery. An analogy with cancer illuminates this point:

We can all understand, in principle, that even a great historic evil does not automatically explain all other subsequent evils. . . . Cancer can indeed be fatal, but it does not explain all fatalities, or even most fatalities.[1]

A false analogy, in contrast, claims similarities that do *not* withstand scrutiny. An infamous example is the analogy traditionally used by revolutionaries and terrorists around the world to justify killing people: "If you want to make an omelette, you've got to break some eggs." The critical thinker rightly responds, "But people are very unlike eggs!"

Always test your analogies to be sure the similarities they claim are real and reasonable, and that no important dissimilarities exist.

Irrational Appeal

An irrational appeal encourages people to accept ideas for some reason other than reasonableness. Such an appeal says, in effect, "There's no need to think critically about this idea or compare it with alternative ideas—just accept it." In reality, of course, it is always appropriate to think critically about ideas, because ideas that seem correct are sometimes incorrect and incorrect ideas can have harmful consequences.

The most common kinds of irrational appeals are to *emotion, tradition, moderation, authority, common belief,* and *tolerance.* However, it would be a mistake to conclude that every appeal to emotion, tradition, moderation, authority, common belief, or tolerance is *necessarily* irrational. Some appeals, as we will see, are legitimate; critical thinking demands we discern which are rational and which are not.

IRRATIONAL APPEAL TO EMOTION A *rational* appeal to emotion not only stimulates feelings but also demonstrates their appropriateness to the ideas being presented. For example, a public service commercial against drunk driving may use an accident scene to make us feel sadness and pity for the victims and thus take more seriously the verbal message "Don't mix drinking and driving." An ad for an international charity may show us the faces of hungry children as a narrator explains that the cost of feeding a child is only eighty cents a day. Such appeals are legitimate because they either explain the connection between the feelings and the ideas or at least invite us to think about that connection.

In contrast, an *irrational* appeal to emotion uses feelings as a *substitute* for thought. This kind of appeal stimulates feelings of fear, resentment, guilt, love of family or country, or pity without demonstrating their appropriateness. A politician may say that her opponent's budgetary proposal will take food out of the mouths of the nation's children or rob elderly people of their social security without offering any documentation for the charge. A lawyer may describe his client's love for his mother, kindness to animals, and overall feeling of benevolence toward the world in an effort to evoke sufficient sympathy to make the jury forget about the evidence against his client. The most audacious courtroom example of such an appeal (often used to define the Yiddish term *chutzpah*) is the case of the man who killed both his parents and then begged the court for mercy because he was an orphan!

IRRATIONAL APPEAL TO TRADITION To be *rational,* such an appeal must not only tell people how old and revered the tradition is but also show that it still deserves our endorsement. An *irrational* appeal urges maintaining the tradition merely because we've always done so. Irrational appeals of this kind have been used to obstruct advances in every field, including science, technology, and medicine. People initially argued against the toothbrush, the umbrella, the airplane, the telephone, the computer, and virtually every other invention because "our ancestors got along nicely without these newfangled gadgets." For many years, doctors refused to accept indisputable evidence that washing their hands between patients curtailed the spread of disease simply because filthy hands were traditional.

IRRATIONAL APPEAL TO MODERATION A *rational* appeal to moderation includes an explanation of why the more moderate idea or action is preferable to less moderate alternatives. An *irrational* appeal to moderation is offered on the erroneous presumption that moderation is always preferable. Consider the issue of slavery at the time of the Civil War. Some people regarded the keeping of slaves as a moral abomination that should be abolished, others as a legitimate form of ownership that should be preserved. The moderate view would have been to let each person decide for him- or herself whether to own slaves. (The slaves, of course, would not have a say in the decision.) Today no responsible person would endorse that view.

IRRATIONAL APPEAL TO AUTHORITY The authority cited may be a person, a book or document, or an agency (such as the Supreme Court). A *rational* appeal to authority says, "Here is what one or more authorities say," and proceeds to show why that view should be accepted. An *irrational* appeal to authority says, "Here is what one or more authorities say. Accept it unquestioningly." Since authorities enjoy no special protection from error, the idea that their pronouncements should never be questioned is foolish and therefore unacceptable.

IRRATIONAL APPEAL TO COMMON BELIEF A *rational* appeal to common belief says, "Most people believe this," and goes on to show the reasonableness of the belief. An *irrational* appeal to common belief says, "Believe this *because* most people believe it." Such irrational appeals are often accompanied by such phrases as "Everyone knows that," "No reasonable person would deny that," or "It's common sense." The problem is, many ideas that were at one time accepted as common sense—sacrificing virgins to ensure a good harvest and abandoning babies to die because they were thought to be cursed, for example—are now recognized as uncommon nonsense or worse. The fact that many or most people believe something is not a sufficient reason for us to believe it.

IRRATIONAL APPEAL TO TOLERANCE A *rational* appeal to tolerance explains why tolerance is appropriate in the particular situation in question. An *irrational* appeal says, "Because tolerance is good in general, it is the right response to every situation, including this one." This is sheer nonsense. Some acts—terrorism, rape, and child abuse, for example—cry out for condemnation. A society that tolerates these acts encourages them and commits a further offense against the victims.

The best way to distinguish between rational and irrational appeals is to ask whether the appeal is accompanied by an explanation of *why you should accept it*. If an explanation is offered and it proves reasonable, the appeal is rational. If no explanation is offered, or if the explanation that is offered is not credible, then the appeal is irrational.

Applications

1. Which of the errors presented in this chapter have you committed? In each case explain the error and describe the circumstances under which it occurred.

2. Read the following dialogue carefully. If you note any of the errors in thinking discussed in this chapter or in Chapters 9 and 10, identify them. Then decide which view of the issue is more reasonable and explain why you think so, taking care to avoid the errors discussed in this and previous chapters.

Background note: In past decades college officials debated whether to censor student newspapers that published stories containing four-letter words and explicit sexual references. The debate continues, but the issue has changed. Some student papers are publishing articles that ridicule African Americans, women, and homosexuals. And others are urging students to paint graffiti on campus buildings and take up shoplifting to combat conformity.[2]

> Ernest: Such articles may be childish and tasteless, but that's no reason to censor them.
> Georgina: Are you kidding? Minorities pay good money to go to college. And on most campuses, I'm sure, their student activity fee pays for the

student newspaper. Where's the fairness in charging them for articles that insult them or that encourage lawbreaking, which ultimately costs them as taxpayers?

Ernest: Why is everything a money issue with you? So a buck or so from every student's activity fee goes to the newspaper. Big deal. That doesn't give every student the right to play fascist and set editorial policy. The articles are written in a spirit of fun or for shock value. Censorship is not the answer. If a pesky fly buzzes around your head, you don't fire an elephant gun at it. Well, maybe you do, but no sensible person does.

3. Evaluate the following arguments, following the approach you learned in Chapter 7. Take care to avoid the errors in thinking discussed in this and previous chapters.

a. *Background note: From time to time people have challenged the recitation of the Pledge of Allegiance in public schools. Their objection is usually to the words "under God." Their reasoning is as follows:*
   Argument: A public school recitation that claims the United States is "under God" is an endorsement of religion and thus violates the constitutional requirement that church and state be kept separate. Therefore, the recitation of the Pledge of Allegiance should not be permitted.

b. *Background note: More and more communities are trying to do something about the growing problem of litter, which is not only unsightly but in many cases unsanitary and dangerous. Here is an argument addressing one aspect of the problem:*
   Argument: Things that have monetary value are less likely to be discarded (or at least more likely to be recovered) than things that don't have such value. For that reason a twenty-five-cent deposit on bottles and cans would virtually eliminate that part of the litter problem.

4. Examine each of the following issues. If you need more information to make an informed judgment, obtain it. Then determine what view of the issue is most reasonable. Be sure to avoid the errors in thinking discussed in this and previous chapters.

a. Many people believe that pornography exploits women by portraying them as objects rather than as persons and creating the false impression that they secretly yearn to be raped. Do you agree with this view?

b. Reports of human rights violations (such as imprisonment without formal charges or trial, torture, and even murder) continue to come from a number of countries that receive foreign aid from the United States. Many people believe the United States should demand that those countries end such violations as a condition of receiving foreign aid. Do you agree?

c. The Georgia Supreme Court ruled that a church founded by a woman who calls herself "a pagan and a witch" is entitled to a property tax exemption on the building her group uses for worship.[3] Do you endorse that court ruling?

d. There are many broken homes today, crimes of violence are reported in almost every edition of the news, and pornography is more available to young people than ever. Some people believe that teaching religion in the schools would go a long way toward solving these social problems. Would it?

e. Many people have spoken out in recent years for an increase in military spending. They argue that defense spending was dangerously reduced during the late 1990s. Are they correct?

f. It is often argued that the only reason conservative groups oppose pre-marital sex is prudishness. Is this true?

g. Six-year old Elián Gonzalez fled Cuba on a makeshift boat with his mother and a number of other people. The boat sank on the way to Florida, leaving only one survivor, Elián, who was found by fishermen and taken to his relatives in Miami. The legal battle that followed was in the news for months. The issue that divided the country, and indeed the world, was this: Should the boy have been allowed to stay in the United States, the country his mother was fleeing to, or should he have been returned to his father in Cuba? Which action was most reasonable under the circumstances?

CHAPTER 12

Errors of Reaction

Before you began studying critical thinking, you may not have imagined that so many pitfalls lie in wait for the unsuspecting. So far we have discussed six errors of perspective, six errors of procedure, and seven errors of expression—nineteen in all, and we're not quite done yet. The final category is errors of reaction, which occur *after* we have expressed our ideas and others have criticized or challenged them. What causes us to commit errors of reaction? Perhaps the best general answer to this question was offered many years ago by Rowland W. Jepson in a book he wrote on the subject of thinking.

> When we have once adopted an opinion, our pride makes us loth to admit that we are wrong. When objections are made to our views, we are more concerned with discovering how to combat them than how much truth or sound sense there may be in them; we are at pains rather to find fresh support for our own views, than to face frankly any new facts that appear to contradict them. We all know how easy it is to become annoyed at the suggestion that we have made a mistake; that our first feeling is that we would rather do anything than admit it, and our first thought is "How can I explain it away?"[1]

This determination to explain away whatever does not flatter us or our point of view reflects our urge to save face and preserve our self-image. Each of us has a self-image, and generally a favorable one. We like to think of ourselves as wise, responsible, intelligent, observant, courageous, generous, considerate, and so on. We also want others to think of us this way. Our errors and personal failings have the power to undermine our reputation, so we are tempted to escape responsibility for them. The child who loses his temper and punches his playmate, for example, may say, "It's not my fault; she made me do it by laughing at me." The student who does poorly in a course may say, "The *professor gave* me a D."

(Whenever she does well, of course, she will say, "*I earned* an A.") A business person who makes a mistake at work may claim, "It's not my fault. The directions were misleading."

Some people manage to resist the temptation to save face, but most of us fall victim to it from time to time. The trigger mechanism differs among individuals. Those who pride themselves on being good judges of people may be mature and balanced about many things, but when the candidate they voted for is found guilty of misusing his or her office, they may persist in denying the evidence, scream about the hypocrisy of the opposing party, and predict that in years to come the judgment will be reversed. They may do all of this merely to preserve the image of their perceptiveness in judging people.

Similarly, people who believe they possess unusual self-control may deny that they are slaves to smoking or drinking and strain good sense in defending their habit. ("No one has really *proved* that smoking is harmful; besides, it relieves tension," or "I don't drink because I have to but because I enjoy it; I can stop anytime I want to.") When people who think of themselves as totally self-sufficient are reminded that they owe someone money, they may find fault with that person for reminding them. Those who see themselves as sensitive to others and completely free of prejudice may denounce anyone who points, however innocently and constructively, to evidence that suggests otherwise. In each of these cases, the people may act to maintain their favorable self-image.

For many individuals the need to save face centers around a particular role in their lives. Sam thinks of himself as a very devoted father who sacrifices for his children and has a close relationship with them. One day during an argument, his son blurts out that for years Sam has been more concerned with his business and his own leisure pursuits than with his children; he has, in fact, ignored and rejected them. Sam turns to his wife and demands that she tell the boy his charge is untrue. His wife slowly and painfully replies that the charge is essentially *true.* Sam storms out of the house, angry and hurt, convinced that he has been grievously wronged.

For still others, it is neither the particular aspect of the image nor the role involved that triggers the face-saving reaction. It is the people who are observing. Are they friends or strangers? Parents or peers? Employers or co-workers? What some people think of us we may not care about at all; what others think of us we may care about beyond reasonableness.

To summarize, errors of reaction are face-saving devices we use to explain away criticism of our ideas. We will discuss four specific errors—*automatic rejection, shifting the burden of proof, "straw man,"* and *attacking the critic.*

Automatic Rejection

As critical thinkers we need a reasonable basis for accepting or rejecting any argument or claim, including challenges to our ideas. The only way to establish that basis is to evaluate the challenge and make an honest determination of its worth. Liking or disliking it, feeling pleased or displeased with it, is not enough. To reject criticism without giving it a fair hearing is to commit the error of automatic rejection.

Some years ago I was discussing a thought-provoking article on the effects of marijuana with a college instructor friend. The article, which appeared in the *Journal of the American Medical Association,* reported the results of a clinical study of marijuana use.[2] The authors concluded that "contrary to what is frequently reported, we have found the effect of marijuana to be not merely that of a mild intoxicant which causes a slight exaggeration of usual adolescent behavior, but a specific and separate clinical syndrome. . . ." The principal effects they noted were "disturbed awareness of the self, apathy, confusion and poor reality testing." They presented the details of thirteen actual cases to demonstrate these effects.

My friend confided that his own experiences with marijuana while in college showed all these signs and that the changes in his behavior closely paralleled those described in the thirteen cases. That is, he had become somewhat slovenly, irritable, and forgetful; had experienced difficulty concentrating on his studies and paying attention in class; and had suffered frequent headaches. Yet at that time, he explained, he not only dismissed the then-available medical research that challenged his view that pot smoking was harmless—he also denied *the testimony of his personal experience with the drug!* His automatic rejection of whatever challenged his view was so effective, he noted, that five years passed before he was able to consider the evidence fairly.

A college professor colleague of mine shared a similar experience of automatic rejection of unpleasant ideas. While reading a book that discussed effective teaching, she explained, she encountered a chapter that examined a particular classroom practice and showed how it was not only ineffective but actually harmful to learning. As soon as the approach was identified, she recognized it as one of her own favorite approaches. As she read further into the author's criticism of it (she recounted to me later), she began to feel defensive, and even angry. "No," she mumbled to herself, "the author is wrong. The approach is a good one. He just doesn't understand." The professor had nothing rational to base these reactions on—simply the impulse to save face. No one else was around. She was alone with the author's words. Yet defending the approach, and saving herself the embarrassment of admitting she didn't know as much as she thought she did, became more important than knowing the truth.

Eventually the professor realized what she was doing and forced herself to consider the author's arguments fairly, but doing so, she confided to me, took effort.

The temptation to automatically reject challenges to your ideas can be powerful. A good way to lessen that temptation is to put some emotional distance between your ideas and your ego. Think of them as possessions that you can keep or discard rather than as extensions of your self. This will make you less defensive about them.

Shifting the Burden of Proof

The error of shifting the burden of proof consists of demanding that others disprove our assertions. Let's say Bill asserts, "The greatest single cause of exploding health care costs in this country is unnecessary referral of patients for costly medical testing." Barbara then asks Bill to explain why he believes that to be the case. And he responds, "Can you cite any evidence to disprove it? If you can't, then say so." Bill is guilty of shifting the burden of proof. He made an assertion; he should be ready to support it if asked and not demand that others refute it. The rule is that whoever makes the assertion bears the burden of supporting it, and the more the assertion departs from what knowledgeable people believe, the greater the responsibility of the person making the assertion to support it.

You will be less likely to shift the burden of proof if you learn to expect your ideas to be questioned and criticized and prepare to support them before you express them.

"Straw Man"

This term was coined by logicians to denote an argument without substance. The term shares its meaning with the word *scarecrow,* a pile of straw stuffed in human clothing and placed in a garden or field to scare away birds. To commit the error of "straw man" is to put false words in someone else's mouth and then expose their falsity, conveniently forgetting that the other person never said them. Suppose that you are discussing with a friend whether the sale of assault weapons should be banned, and the conversation goes as follows:

> *You:*   I oppose any restriction on the sale of guns. It should make no difference whether we're talking about a pistol, a rifle, a shotgun, or an assault weapon. A gun is a gun. And a constitutional right is a constitutional right.
>
> *Your friend:*   You say it "should make no difference" what kind of gun is involved. I say it should make a difference because the guns you mentioned are very different from

> one another. Assault weapons are unlike other kinds of guns—they are not designed for hunting, or even for self-defense, but only for killing people, often indiscriminately. That's why they should be banned.

You [feeling defensive because you realize your friend's point will be difficult to answer]:

> So you believe you should decide what weapons are acceptable and what weapons aren't. It's exactly this kind of arrogance by self-appointed social reformers that everyone who values the Constitution should fear.

You have committed the error of "straw man." If your friend is alert, she will respond: "First you put irresponsible words in my mouth, and then you say I'm irresponsible. I'd prefer to hear your reaction to what I really said."

To avoid "straw man," be scrupulously accurate in quoting or paraphrasing other people's words.

Attacking the Critic

Attacking the critic is the attempt to discredit an idea or argument by disparaging the person who expressed it. People typically resort to this error of reaction after their ideas or behavior have been called into question. Instead of responding to the real issue, the actual ideas or behavior that have been questioned, they create a diversionary issue—the real or imagined failings, or the motivation, of the person who raised the issue. When Paula Jones accused President Bill Clinton of having made improper sexual advances toward her, one Clinton spokesman made the comment that almost anything could be accomplished "by dragging a hundred dollar bill through a trailer court," implying that Ms. Jones's character was suspect.

When other women came forward with charges that Clinton had harassed them, the president's advisors adopted what became known as the "nuts and sluts" strategy—that is, they insinuated that anyone who made such a charge must be mentally unstable or sexually promiscuous and therefore untrustworthy. Later, when Dick Morris, a former advisor to President Clinton, joined Fox News as a consultant and offered his analysis of President Clinton's behavior and the alleged cover-up strategies, some Clinton loyalists claimed that nothing Morris said was credible because he himself had committed sexual indiscretions and also was disgruntled over his loss of status in the White House.

Attacking the critic is an error because ideas and people are not synonymous. However interesting it may be to probe why people speak and act as they do, such exploration tells us nothing about the quality of the ideas and actions. Even people with questionable motives and outright liars sometimes tell the truth. This is not to say that honesty is unimportant or that we should unquestioningly accept the word of people whose integrity we have reason to suspect. It is only to say that it is unreasonable to substitute speculations or judgments about people themselves for judgments of their ideas. In short, judge the idea apart from the person.

Applications

1. Which, if any, of the following statements are consistent with the view detailed in this chapter? Explain your choices.
   a. The urge to save face and preserve our image is unavoidable.
   b. The urge to save face and preserve our image is a normal tendency.
   c. The urge to save face and preserve our image is dishonest.
   d. The urge to save face and preserve our image is harmful.
   e. The urge to save face and preserve our image is controllable.

2. Which of the errors presented in this chapter have you committed? Describe each error you have committed, and explain the circumstances under which it occurred.

3. We all know that it is difficult to forgive people who have offended us. But the ancient Roman philosopher Seneca argued that the reverse is also true— *it is difficult to forgive those whom we have offended.* Is this idea reasonable? If so, does anything you have learned in Chapters 9 through 12 provide insight into the idea? If not, why not?

4. The U.S. Supreme Court has ruled that state, city, and county governments may not hand over their decison-making power to churches. The Court's decision nullified a Massachusetts law giving churches a veto power over the (liquor) licensing of any bar or restaurant that would be established within five hundred feet of church buildings.[3] Was the Court's decision the most reasonable one? In deciding, take care to avoid the errors discussed in Chapters 9 through 12.

5. A woman wrote to "Dear Abby" complaining that her son was taking his financee's name when they married. Abby replied that the young man was an adult and free to make his own decision, so the mother should accept the situation gracefully. No doubt many people thought Abby's advice was sound, but others may have disagreed, reasoning that there's something bizarre and unmanly about a man giving up his family name. In this view the act insults his ancestors. Evaluate this issue, taking care to avoid the errors discussed in Chapters 9 through 12.

6. On some campuses, when damage occurs on a dormitory floor and the responsible person or persons are not identified, repair costs are charged to all those who live on the floor. Many students believe this is unfair. They claim that damage is sometimes done by strangers who are visiting the dormitory. And even when the perpetrators live on the floor, these students argue, this policy punishes innocent residents for other people's behavior over which they have no control. Are these objections to the policy reasonable, or is the policy the fairest solution to the problem? In making your decision, take care to avoid the errors discussed in Chapters 9 through 12.

7. Sherri is a sophomore in college. While she is home for spring vacation, she is very irritable with her parents. She seizes every opportunity to criticize them and their values and manages to take offense at their every comment to her. Just before she returns to college, she causes a row in which she accuses them of never having given her enough attention and love. Her parents are at a loss to understand her behavior. What they do not know is that for the past several months she has been living off-campus with her boyfriend and using the money her parents send her to help support him. Explain how this fact may have influenced her behavior toward her parents.

8. Evaluate the following arguments, following the approach you learned in Chapter 7. Take care to avoid the errors in thinking discussed in this chapter and previous ones.

   a. *Argument:* Taking animals from the wild and exhibiting them for human pleasure is a violation of their natural rights. Therefore, zoos should be outlawed.

   b. *Background note: In 1993 a gay organization took the Ancient Order of Hibernians (AOH), the organizers of New York's St. Patrick's Day Parade, to court. The charge was that the AOH illegally discriminated against the gay organization by excluding it from the parade. The reasoning of the AOH was as follows:*
   Argument: This parade honors one of the saints of our church. Our religion teaches that homosexuality is a sin. To require us to include gay organizations in the parade would be a violation of our rights.

   c. *Background note: In recent years an increasing number of people have complained about the level of violence and the amount of sexual material on television. Television industry spokespeople have generally dismissed the complaints, reasoning as follows:*
   Argument: Contemporary shows depict life more realistically than shows of twenty or thirty years ago. Our position is that such depiction does not cause or aggravate social problems, so until research proves otherwise, we will continue to produce programming that tells the truth about life, honestly and fearlessly.

   d. *Background note: In recent years a number of states have considered enacting "hate crime statutes," which assign harsher penalties for crimes in which the motivation was hatred of the victim's race, religion, or sexual orientation. In other words, the penalty for beating and robbing an African American (or Jewish) victim while shouting racial (or anti-Semitic) epithets would be greater than that for the same act perpetrated against a white (or gentile) victim minus the epithets.*
   Argument: The law is a good one because greater emotional harm is done to the victim when the crime is motivated by hatred.

   e. For years criminals have sold the rights to their life stories to publishers and movie producers. The more terrible their crimes, the more money publishers and producers have usually been willing to pay. This practice, in effect, rewards criminals for their crimes. This practice should be ended. The profits criminals receive in this manner should be placed in a fund to be distributed among the victims of their crimes.

   f. In 1983 the U.S. Supreme Court ruled that a driver's refusal to take a blood alcohol test could be used as evidence against him or her.[4] I believe the Court erred in making that decision. One reason for refusing to take a blood alcohol test is knowledge of one's drunken condition. But that is not the only possible reason. It's possible for a sober person to refuse the test because he sees it as an invasion of privacy. In such a case the "evidence" would probably be interpreted by the judge and the jury as a sign of guilt, and an innocent person would be convicted.

CHAPTER 13

The Errors in Combination

The previous five chapters examined the errors that occur at various stages of the thinking process. Those chapters had two aims: to help you to avoid the errors in your thinking and to recognize them when they occur in other people's thinking. Each error was treated in isolation—a hasty conclusion or oversimplification in one passage, an unwarranted assumption in another, an overgeneralization or stereotype in a third, and so on. Errors frequently occur just that way, singly. They can, however, occur in combination. For example, "mine-is-better" thinking may create a bias against change that leads us to biased selection of evidence and a hasty conclusion. Although the possible combinations that may occur are innumerable, they all have one thing in common: They pose a greater obstacle to critical thinking than any one error does by itself.

Before discussing combinations of errors further, let's summarize the individual errors and the strategies we discussed for avoiding them. You will recall that the most fundamental thinking error is "mine-is-better" thinking, in which we assume that our ideas must be superior to other people's simply because they are our ideas. In reality, of course, our ideas are as likely to be mistaken as anyone else's. To overcome "mine-is-better" thinking, we must be as critical of our own ideas as we are of other people's.

The other errors and antidotes are as follows:

Errors of Perspective

The Error	*How to Recognize and Deal with It*
Unwarranted assumptions	Assumptions are ideas that are taken for granted rather than consciously reasoned out. When what is taken for

granted is unjustified by one's experience or the situation, the assumption is unwarranted. Because assumptions are seldom expressed directly, the only way to identify them is to "read between the lines" for what is unstated but clearly implied.

Either/or outlook	The expectation that the only reasonable view of any issue will be total affirmation or total rejection. This error rules out the possibility that the most reasonable view might lie between the extremes. To avoid this error, consider all possible alternatives.
Mindless conformity	Mindless conformity is adopting others' views unthinkingly because we are too lazy or fearful to form our own. To overcome this error, develop the habit of resisting the internal and external pressures and making up your own mind.
Absolutism	The belief that rules do not admit of exceptions. This belief causes us to demand that the truth be neat and simple, when in reality it is often messy and complex. To avoid this error, accept the truth as you find it rather than requiring it to fit your preconceptions.
Relativism	The belief that no view is better than any other, that any idea you choose to embrace is automatically correct. Remind yourself that some ideas, and some standards of conduct, are better than others and that the challenge of critical thinking is to discover the best ones.
Bias for or against change	Bias *for* change assumes that change is always for the best; bias *against* change, that change is always for the worst. To avoid both errors, give any proposal for change a fair hearing and decide, apart from your predisposition, whether the change is really positive or negative.

Errors of Procedure

The Error	*How to Recognize and Deal with It*
Biased consideration of evidence	One form of this error is seeking evidence that confirms your bias and ignoring evidence that challenges it. Another is to interpret evidence in a way that favors your bias. To avoid this error, *begin* your investigation by seeking out individuals whose views oppose your bias, then go on to those that support it. Also, choose the most reasonable interpretation of the evidence.
Double standard	Double standard involves using one set of criteria for judging arguments we agree with and another standard for judging arguments we disagree with. To avoid this error, decide *in advance* what judgment criteria you will use and apply those criteria consistently, regardless of whether the data in question support your view.
Hasty conclusion	Hasty conclusion is a premature judgment—that is, a judgment made without sufficient evidence. To avoid drawing a hasty conclusion, identify all possible conclusions before you select any one. Then decide whether you have sufficient evidence to support any of those conclusions and, if so, which conclusion that is.
Overgeneralization and stereotyping	Overgeneralization is ascribing to all the members of a group what fits only some members. A stereotype is an overgeneralization that is rigidly maintained. To avoid these errors, resist the urge to force individual people, places, and things into hard categories. And keep in mind that the more limited your experience, the more modest you should make your assertions.

Oversimplification	Oversimplification goes beyond making complex ideas easier to grasp—it twists and distorts the ideas. Instead of informing people, oversimplification misleads them. To avoid this error, refuse to adopt superficial views and make a special effort to understand issues in their complexity.
Post hoc fallacy	This error is rooted in the idea that when one thing occurs after another, it must be the result of the other, when in reality the sequence may be coincidental. To avoid the post hoc fallacy, withhold judgment of a cause-and-effect relationship until you have ruled out other possible causes, including coincidence.

Errors of Expression

The Error	*How to Recognize and Deal with It*
Shifting the issue	Shifting the issue consists of abruptly and *deceptively* turning a discussion away from the issue under discussion. To avoid this error, face difficult questions head-on, rather than trying to avoid them.
Contradiction	To contradict yourself is to claim that a statement is both true and false at the same time in the same way. To avoid this error, monitor what you say and write. The moment you detect any inconsistency, examine it carefully. Decide whether it is explainable or whether it constitutes a contradiction. If it is a contradiction, revise your statement to make it consistent and reasonable.
Arguing in a circle	You commit this error whenever you attempt to prove a statement by repeating it in a different form. To avoid this error, check your arguments to be sure you are offering

The Error	*How to Recognize and Deal with It*
	genuine evidence and not merely repeating your claim.
Meaningless statement	A meaningless statement is one in which the reasoning presented makes no sense. To avoid this error, check to be sure that the reasons you offer to explain your thoughts and actions really do explain them.
Mistaken authority	This error consists in ascribing authority to someone who does not possess it. To avoid this error, check to be sure that all the sources you cite as authorities possess expertise in the *particular* subject you are writing or speaking about.
False analogy	An analogy is an attempt to explain something relatively unfamiliar by referring to something *different but more familiar,* saying in effect, "This is like that." A false analogy claims similarities that do *not* withstand scrutiny. To avoid this error, test your analogies to be sure that the similarities they claim are real and reasonable, and that no important dissimilarities exist.
Irrational appeal	Appeals to emotion, tradition, moderation, authority, common belief, and tolerance may be either rational or irrational. They are irrational, and therefore unacceptable, when they are unreasonable in the particular situation under discussion and/or when they discourage thought. To avoid this error, make sure your appeals complement thought rather than substitute for it.

Errors of Reaction

The Error	*How to Recognize and Deal with It*
Automatic rejection	Automatic rejection is the refusal to give criticism of your ideas (or

behavior) a fair hearing. To avoid this error, think of them as possessions that you can keep or discard rather than as extensions of your ego. This will make you less defensive about them.

Shifting the burden of proof	You commit this error whenever you demand that others *disprove* your assertions. To avoid this error, understand that the burden of supporting any assertion rests with the person who makes it rather than the one who questions it. Accept the responsibility of supporting your assertions.
"Straw man"	To commit the error of "straw man" is to put false words in someone else's mouth and then expose their falsity, conveniently forgetting that the other person never said them. To avoid this error, be scrupulously accurate in quoting or paraphrasing other people's words.
Attacking the critic	You commit this error whenever you attempt to discredit an idea or argument by disparaging the person who expressed it. To avoid attacking the critic, focus your critical thinking on ideas rather than the people who express them.

Sample Combinations of Errors

Now let's examine several combinations of errors and determine the specific ways they affect the thinking of the people involved.

EXAMPLE 1

Claude is an active worker for his political party. Because he feels a strong personal identification with the party and is therefore convinced that its platform and its candidates represent the salvation of the country, he is unusually zealous in his efforts. One day he is having lunch with Nell, a business acquaintance. The discussion predictably turns to politics. Claude delivers a few pronouncements on his candidate and the opposition. His candidate, he asserts, is a brilliant theorist and practitioner. Her opponent, in Claude's view, is a complete fool. Claude volunteers harsh judgments of the opponent's political record and of his family and associates and rattles on about how the country will be ruined if he is elected.

After listening for a while, Nell challenges Claude. She quietly presents facts that disprove many of Claude's ideas and points up the extravagance of Claude's assertions. Though there is nothing personal in Nell's challenge, and it is presented in a calm, objective way, Claude becomes angry. He accuses Nell of distorting his words, denies having said certain things that he did say, and stubbornly clings to others despite the facts Nell has presented.

Let's reconstruct what happened in terms of the problems we have been studying. Claude's initial problem was his "mine-is-better" attitude, which blinded him to the possibility that his candidate and platform were not perfect and that the opposition had some merit. In other words, it made him overvalue the things he identified with and undervalue those he did not. Accordingly, when he spoke about the candidates and the platforms, he was inclined to oversimplify. Then, when Nell called his errors to his attention (as someone sooner or later was bound to do), Claude was driven to relieve his embarrassment through face-saving devices. Because the more deeply one is committed to an idea, the less likely one is to admit error, Claude undoubtedly learned little from the incident.

EXAMPLE 2

When Sam was thirteen years old, he didn't really want to smoke, but his friends goaded him into doing so. He took to it well, though, feeling more like one of the guys with a cigarette dangling out of the corner of his mouth. As he progressed from an occasional cigarette to a pack-a-day habit, the cost became prohibitive, and he began to steal money from his parents to buy cigarettes. "Hey, it's either that or do without," he said, "and I'm not about to do without."

Now Sam is forty years old, married with a couple of children, and still smoking. He has developed a wheeze but attributes it to an allergy. Each new surgeon general's report on the dangers of smoking sends him into a tirade. "They haven't been able to *prove* smoking causes any disease," he argues, "so it's up to the individual to decide whether he'll be harmed by it."

More recently, when tobacco companies were accused of adding nicotine and suppressing unfavorable test results, Sam defended them. "Those executives are wealthy. They have no reason to harm millions of men, women, and children." What incenses him most of all is the nonsmoking zones at work, in airports, and in other public places. "I don't tell other people what to do and when and where to do it, so no one has any business telling me."

Sam's first error was being victimized by conformity. His rationale for stealing reveals either/or thinking. (There was an alternative to stealing—get a part-time job.) His attribution of the wheeze to an allergy showed face saving, and his tirades against the surgeon general's reports contained the unwarranted assumption that individual smokers are informed enough to decide whether they'll be harmed. His reasoning about executives assumed that wealthy people are not tempted to do wrong. But there are other temptations than financial gain, such as retaining prestige and being included in the inner circle of management. Finally, Sam oversimplified the issue of smoking in public places, notably by ignoring the problem of secondhand smoke.

EXAMPLE 3

Stephen enrolls as a freshman at Progress Technical College. He notices that he has an eight-o'clock English class three days a week. Because he's a late riser, this disturbs him. But when he attends the first class, he notices that the instructor's name is Stein. "Wow," he thinks to himself, "what better break could a Jewish kid who likes to sleep in the morning have than a Jewish instructor!" Over the next few weeks, he seizes any excuse to stay after class, talk with Mr. Stein, and win his favor. For his first two compositions, Stephen chooses subjects that will permit him to stress his Jewishness (and thereby impress Mr. Stein). Soon he decides that Mr. Stein "understands" him. He begins to cut class occasionally and hands in about one assignment out of four. When he sees Mr. Stein, Stephen plies him with pathetic tales of misfortune. His midterm grade is D, but he tells himself that Mr. Stein is just trying to scare him and will raise his grade in the end. Thus, he attends class even less frequently and does less work. Eventually, the semester ends, and he receives an F in English. His first reaction is disbelief. He rushes to see Mr. Stein, who says, "I made clear on the first day of class that students could expect to pass only if they attended class and did their homework faithfully. I'm sorry about the grade, but you deserve it." From that moment on, Stephen refuses to speak to Mr. Stein when he passes him on campus. And whenever the conversation in the snack bar or dorm turns to teachers, he loudly denounces Mr. Stein as a phony.

Stephen's first error was the unwarranted assumption that Mr. Stein is Jewish. (Many people named Stein are not Jewish.) Next he embraced the stereotype of Jews as quick to take care of their own. These errors led him to reject the most reasonable interpretation of his midterm grade and to believe instead that it was not cause for concern. When he finally failed the course, rather than acknowledge his dereliction and fallacious thinking, he resorted to the face-saving tactic of atttacking Mr. Stein's integrity.

A Sensible View of Terminology

From time to time you may experience difficulty calling an error by its proper name. For example, you may have trouble distinguishing among oversimplification, hasty conclusion, and unwarranted assumption. (This is a common source of confusion.) The following comparison should help eliminate, or at least minimize, that confusion.

Oversimplification . . .	*Hasty Conclusion . . .*	*Assumption . . .*
Is stated directly.	Is stated directly.	Is unstated but implied.

Occurs as a simple asserton or as the premise of an argument.	Occurs as the conclusion of an argument.	Often is a hidden premise in an argument.
Distorts reality by misstatement or omission.	Fails to account for one or more significant items of evidence.	May be either warranted (supported by the evidence) or unwarranted.

Knowing the right terminology is advantageous, but more important is recognizing where reasoning has gone awry and being able to explain the error in terms of the issue involved. In the vast majority of cases, plain language will do that job nicely.

Applications

1. In 1903 Mercedes automobile executives reasoned that the total world-wide demand for automobiles would never exceed a million vehicles because the number of people capable of being chauffeurs would never exceed that number.[1] Given the history of automobile sales in the twentieth century, that prediciton is laughable. But where exactly did the executives' thinking go wrong? What specific error or combination of errors did they commit?

2. Not many years ago prosecutors in some states stipulated that one or more of the following conditions must exist before they would file rape charges: (a) the force used by the rapist was sufficient to make the victim fear serious injury or death; (b) the victim earnestly resisted the assault; and (c) at least one other witness corroborated the victim's charge of rape. Are these conditions reasonable? What error(s) in thinking, if any, do they suggest? Explain your answer.

3. Three Southern California professors of medicine devised a hoax as an experiment. They paid a professional actor to lecture three groups of educators. Armed with a fake identity ("Dr. Myron L. Fox of the Albert Einstein University"), false but impressive credentials, and a scholarly sounding topic, ("Mathematical Game Theory as Applied to Physical Education"), the actor proceeded to present one meaningless, conflicting statement after another. His words were a combination of double-talk and academic jargon. During the question-and-answer period, he made even less sense. *Yet not one of the fifty-five educators in his audience realized they had been tricked.* Virtually all of them believed they had learned something. Some even praised the impostor in this manner: "Excellent presentation, enjoyed listening. Has warm manner . . . lively examples . . . extremely articulate."[2] Explain what combination of the problems discussed in Chapters 9–12 may have accounted for the audience's gullibility.

4. Analyze the following case as was done in the chapter with the cases of Claude, Sam, and Stephen:

> A middle-aged couple, Ann and Dan, learn that their twenty-two-year-old daughter, a senior in college, is a lesbian. They are appalled. They were raised to believe that lesbianism is willful moral degeneracy. Struggling to

cope with their new awareness, each begins to blame the other—Ann suggests that Dan has always been cold and aloof with the girl, and Dan claims that Ann has smothered her with affection. After many hours of arguing, they decide that there is a more direct cause of her deviance—the college. "You'd think educated people would be alert to the danger of degeneracy with all the girls crammed into dorms," Ann cries. Dan shouts, "Damn it, I'm going to send a letter to the chairman of that college's board of trustees. I want the dean of students fired."

5. Examine each of the following issues. If you need more information to make an informed judgment, obtain it. Then determine what view of the issue is most reasonable. Be sure to avoid the errors in thinking summarized in this chapter.
  a. When Alabama prisons and jails became seriously overcrowded, a U.S. district judge ordered that more than 300 convicts be granted early release. The group included murderers, rapists, and repeat offenders. The judge's argument was that serious overcrowding in prisons and jails is a violation of prisoners' rights against "cruel and unusual punishment."[3] Do you share the judge's view?
  b. U.S. law has accorded most charitable and educational groups tax-exempt status as long as they refrain from lobbying activities. However, veterans groups like the American Legion and the Veterans of Foreign Wars traditionally were regarded as exceptions; that is, they were permitted to lobby extensively on such issues as the ratification of the Panama Canal treaties, Alaskan national parks, national security, and Saturday mail delivery (as well as issues more directly involving veterans) without jeopardizing their tax-exempt status. Then in 1982 a federal appeals court eliminated special treatment for veterans groups, arguing that it violated the equal protection guarantees of the Constitution.[4] Do you agree with this court decision?

6. Evaluate the following arguments, following the approach you learned in Chapter 7. Take care to avoid the errors in thinking summarized in this chapter.
  a. Professor Wiley takes unfair advantage of his students by requiring them to buy a textbook *that he himself wrote and gets royalties from.*
  b. Frivolous lawsuits clog up the court systems and create a burden for people who have done no wrong. Therefore, people who lose such lawsuits should be compelled to pay both court costs and the attorney's fees of the person they wrongly charged.
  c. I never vote in national elections. I figure that my vote will be canceled by someone else's. Besides, all politicians are going to rob the public so it doesn't matter who gets elected.
  d. Dogfighting is a sport in which two specially trained dogs (often, but not always, pitbull terriers) do combat until one is killed or badly maimed. It is illegal in most states. But should it be? I say no. If I own a dog, it's my property and I should be able to do whatever I wish with it.
  e. Affirmative action originated as a system to overcome the effects of years of prejudice against minorities. But it has created discrimination against the majority. I favor eliminating affirmative action requirements and returning to the old system. For all its imperfections, it's far better than what we have now.

f. Whenever Americans buy automobiles, clothing, and electronic equipment from other countries, they undermine American business and hurt American workers. Patriotism demands that we refrain from buying from foreign competitors even when their prices are lower and their quality is higher.

g. It's absurd to believe in life after death because no one has ever returned from the grave.

h. Women in the military should be required to undergo the same physical training as are men. They should also not be exempted from frontline duty.

i. In 1982 New York State Social Services officials directed local adoption agencies not to reject applicants solely because they were homosexual or had a history of alcoholism or drug abuse, a criminal record, a dependency on welfare, or a severe emotional or physical handicap.[5] I think this is outrageous. People who fall into any of these categories are obviously not fit to be parents, and child welfare agencies have an obligation to protect children from them.

j. It's ironic that during the very time when baseball great Pete Rose was being castigated for his alleged gambling on sports events, newspapers were filled with stories about the Illinois and Pennsylvania lotteries and their respective $62.5 million and $115 million jackpots. Millions of people were placing bets on those lotteries, as well as dozens of other state lotteries, and that was regarded as perfectly legitimate. And yet a baseball legend was being threatened with disgrace and expulsion from the game he loved. The whole fiasco can be explained only in terms of monumental ignorance or hypocrisy.

k. For the past few decades, most Americans have swallowed the liberal line that everyone deserves a college education. As a result, college courses have been watered down, and the college degree has been rendered meaningless. It's high time we adopt a more realistic view. College should be reserved for those who not only have taken a demanding high school program but have excelled in it.

7. Read each of the following dialogues carefully. If you note any of the errors in thinking summarized in this chapter, identify them. Then decide which view of the issue is more reasonable and explain why you think so.

a. *Background note: A born-again Texas businessman and a television evangelist smashed $1 million worth of art objects and threw them into a lake after reading the following verse from Deuteronomy in the Bible: "The graven images of their gods shall ye burn with fire: thou shalt not desire the silver and gold that is on them, nor take it unto thee, lest thou be snared therein: for it is an abomination to the Lord thy God." The objects, which belonged to the businessman, were mostly gold, silver, jade, and ivory figures associated with Eastern religions.*
Cecil: That's a real measure of faith, the willingness to discard earthly treasures out of spiritual conviction.
Ellie: It's more like an act of lunacy. It's a terrible waste of wealth. If he'd wanted to express his religious conviction, he could have done something to help his fellow human beings.
Cecil: By doing what?
Ellie: He could have sold the objects, taken the million dollars, and given it to the needy of the world. Or he could have donated it to a religious organization or a hospital. Instead, he threw it away and helped no one.

Cecil: You don't understand. Selling the objects would have corrupted others. He's a religious man. The Bible told him what to do, and he had no choice but to obey.

b. *Background note: A former Florida policewoman filed a federal discrimination suit, alleging that she was fired because of a sex-change operation. The officer, now a man, charged that the firing violated his constitutional rights and asked for both monetary damages and reinstatement on the police force.*[6]
Christine: If the cause for the firing was as the officer describes it, then it was improper.
Renee: I disagree. A police officer is a public official and should not engage in behavior that disgraces that office.
Christine: What's disgraceful about having a sex-change operation?
Renee: It's sick, strange, and abnormal, and it makes the police department the laughingstock of the community.
Christine: Wrong. The only concern of the police department and of the general public should be the officer's performance of his or her duty. Whether he or she decides to have a sex-change operation is no more their business than if the officer decides to take up stamp collecting as a hobby.

c. *Teresa:* Abortion is always wrong. There is no such thing as a case in which it is justified.
Gail: I just read of a case in which I believe it is justified. I think even you'd agree.
Teresa: No way.
Gail: It happened in New York. The woman was a twenty-five-year-old ward of the state with the mental capacity of an *infant*. The doctor she was referred to said she was totally incapable of understanding who she was, let alone what it means to be pregnant. The experience of delivery would have been so traumatic and the consequences so tragic, in the doctor's view, that abortion was the only reasonable course of action.[7] Even though I'm against abortion, in a case like this, I'm convinced it's justified.
Teresa: The issue in that case is not whether the woman should be allowed to have an abortion but what should be done to the insensitive slob who took advantage of her retardation and got her pregnant. Capital punishment is too good for creeps like that.

d. *Quentin:* There'd be a lot less ignorance in the world today if parents didn't pass on their views to their children.
Lois: How can they avoid doing so?
Quentin: By letting children form their own views. There's no law that says Democrats have to make little Democrats of their children, or that Protestants have to pass on their Protestantism.
Lois: What should they do when their children ask them about politics or religion or democracy?
Quentin: Send them to the encyclopedia, or, if the parents are capable of objective explanation, explain to them the various views that are possible and encourage them to choose their own.
Lois: How can you ask a three-year-old to make a choice about religion or politics or philosophy?

Quentin: In the case of young children, the parents would simply explain as much as the children could understand and say that when they get older they can decide for themselves.

Lois: How would all this benefit children or society?

Quentin: It would make it possible for children to grow up without their parents' prejudices and would help control the number of ignoramuses in the world.

PART THREE

A Strategy

Part 1 of this book, "The Context," presented the fundamental "tools and rules" involved in critical thinking. In Part 2, "The Pitfalls," you learned the many ways in which thinking can go wrong and what you can do to avoid them. This third part of the book presents a step-by-step approach for you to use in addressing issues. Following this approach will enable you to integrate the habits and skills you have learned smoothly and effectively. Thinking, remember, is an active use of the mind, a *performance* activity, every bit as much as playing tennis or the piano, driving a car, or cooking Thanksgiving dinner. The quality lies in the doing.

The first chapter, "Knowing Yourself," draws together the insights you have been gaining about yourself since Chapter 1 and may even add a few new ones. (The more familiar you are with your strengths and weaknesses, the better you will be able to employ your skills.) The remaining chapters guide you through the process of critical thinking from *observation* to *judgment* and *expression* to others.

CHAPTER 14

Knowing Yourself

Western philosophy virtually began with Socrates' advice "Know thyself." Ever since, thoughtful men and women have realized that knowing oneself is the key to wisdom. As Sidney J. Harris observed: "Ninety percent of the world's woe comes from people not knowing themselves, their abilities, their frailties, and even their real virtues. Most of us go almost all the way through life as complete strangers to ourselves."

Some of what we have to learn about ourselves is pleasant, a certain amount is inevitably unpleasant, but all can make a valuable contribution to our self-improvement. The way to achieve such knowledge is by asking lots of probing questions. Here are some of the most fundamental ones:

Am I quiet or talkative? Generally optimistic or pessimistic? Hardworking or lazy? Fearful or brave? Serious or easygoing? Modest or proud? Competitive or noncompetitive? Am I nervous or at ease with strangers? Do I retain my poise and presence of mind in emergencies? Am I confident in everything I do? Do I resent certain types of people (the popular classmate, for example)? Would I be more accurately classified as a leader or a follower?

How trustworthy am I? Can I keep a secret or must I reveal it to at least one or two others? Am I loyal to my friends? Do I ever "use" people? How sensitive am I to the feelings of others? Do I ever purposely hurt others? Am I jealous of anyone? Do I enjoy causing trouble? Do I sow seeds of suspicion and dissension among people? Do I rush to spread the latest gossip? Do I talk behind friends' backs? Are my comments about others usually favorable or unfavorable? Do I criticize others' real or imagined faults as a means of boosting my own ego? Do I keep my promises? How tolerant am I of people's faults and mistakes?

Am I truthful with other people? With myself? How objective am I in assessing my skills and talents? How intelligent am I? How studious am I in school? How many different roles do I play with other people? Which of those roles are authentic? Which are masks designed to hide aspects of myself I would be ashamed or embarrassed to have others see? How reasonable are my plans for the future? Do I work well under pressure?

Critical Thinking Inventory

In addition to the foregoing questions, numerous questions are suggested by the previous thirteen chapters. The following questions will help you take inventory of the habits and attitudes that affect your thinking:

1. Exactly what influences have shaped my identity? How have they done so? How has my self-image been affected? In what situations am I less an individual because of these influences?

2. In what ways am I like the good thinker (as outlined in Chapter 2)? In what ways like the poor thinker? What kinds of situations seem to bring out my best and worst qualities?

3. To what extent has my perspective on truth been reasonable? (See Chapter 3 again if necessary.)

4. How careful am I about separating hearsay and rumor from fact? About distinguishing the known from assumptions or guesses? How difficult is it for me to say "I don't know"?

5. How consistent am I in taking the trouble to make my opinions informed?

6. To what extent do I think that "mine is better" (not only the personal "mine" but the ethnocentric "mine" as well)? In what ways has this kind of thinking affected my view of personal problems and public issues? To what extent does it affect my ability to listen to those who disagree with me? My ability to control my emotions? My willingness to change my mind and revise a judgment?

7. In what matters am I inclined to assume too much, take too much for granted?

8. To what degree do I tend to have the either/or outlook, expecting the right answer will always be extreme and never moderate?

9. To what or whom do I feel the strongest urge to conform? In what situations has this conformist tendency interfered with my judgment?

10. Do I tend to be an absolutist, demanding that truth be neat and simple, or a relativist, claiming that everyone creates his or her own truth? In what ways has my characteristic tendency hindered my development as a critical thinker?

11. In what matters am I most biased toward change? Am I overly accepting of change or overly resistant to it? What is the cause of this tendency and how can I best control it?

12. In what situations do I seek to confirm my biases rather than control them? In what situations do I interpret evidence in a way that flatters my bias?

13. How often do I approach issues with a double standard, overlooking flaws in arguments that agree with mine and nitpicking those that disagree?

14. To what extent do I tend to jump to conclusions? Do I tend to do so more in certain areas? If so, which? Do I draw my conclusions prematurely purely for the sake of convenience? Am I motivated by the desire to sound authoritative and impress people?

15. To what extent do I overgeneralize? What kinds of stereotypes do I most readily accept? Racial? Religious? Ethnic?

16. To what extent do I oversimplify complex matters? Am I just unwilling to take the trouble to learn the truth in its complexity? Or do I feel threatened by answers that are not neat and tidy? What has made me this way?

17. What errors of expression do I most often commit? Reasoning that if B follows A, A must be the cause of B? Shifting the issue to avoid difficult or embarrassing discussions? Contradicting myself? Arguing in a circle? Making meaningless statements? Confusing real with bogus authorities? Making false analogies? Using irrational appeals?

18. Which of the following errors are most characteristic of my responses to challenges and criticism of my ideas: Automatic rejection? Shifting the burden of proof? "Straw man"? Attacking the critic rather than discussing the issue?

Using Your Inventory

As important as the foregoing questions are, there is one question that is considerably more important: *How can you most effectively use your personal inventory to improve your critical thinking performance?* The answer is found by following these steps:

1. Answer all the questions in the critical thinking inventory honestly and thoroughly, acknowledging not only the pleasant facts about yourself but also the unpleasant ones. (If you ignore the latter, they will influence you no less; in fact, your refusal to face them may intensify the harm they do.)

2. Reflect on your answers, noting the areas in which you are especially vulnerable. Don't expect to be equally vulnerable in all circumstances; it is common for some to be more troublesome than others. Your goal here is to know your intellectual habits so well that you can predict exactly which thinking problem will arise for you in any particular situation.

3. Whenever you are addressing an issue, anticipate what problems are likely to undermine your thinking, and make a conscious effort to resist their influence.

Challenge and Reward

It is one thing to understand the steps to improving your thinking and quite another to use them effectively. The latter task is a formidable challenge. It will take continuing effort over a long period of time.

Is the challenge worth the effort? Let's consider what is known about the role of thinking in everyday life. The most respected educators stress the importance of going beyond mere memorization and reflecting on the significance and application of facts. Thinking skills are necessary to understand and profit from college courses. Business and professional leaders stress that proficiency in thinking is necessary to solve problems and make decisions on the job. (All the books written in recent years about excellence underline the value of thinking skills.)

In addition, more and more psychologists affirm that thinking skills play a crucial role in our personal lives. The leading form of psychotherapy in this country, in fact, is cognitive therapy. This therapy is based on the idea that most mental problems (neuroses) result from faulty thinking habits. Noted psychologist Albert Ellis, founder of the Institute of Rational-Emotive Therapy, claims, "Man can live the most self-fulfilling, creative, and emotionally satisfying life by intelligently organizing and disciplining his thinking."

Like other famous psychologists before him, Ellis notes that to organize our thinking, we must wrestle with our own negative tendencies. "As Freud and his daughter Anna accurately observed," he says, "and as Adler agreed, humans are prone to avoid focusing on and coping with their problems and instead often sweep them under the rug by resorting to rationalization, denial, compensation, identification, projection, avoidance, repression, and other defensive maneuvers."

In short, though the challenge of improving your thinking is great, no other kind of self-improvement can affect every area of your life so positively.

Applications

1. Examine yourself in light of the questions presented in the chapter. Don't settle for things you already know about yourself. Try to expand your self-awareness. And don't ignore your less favorable characteristics. Discuss the results of your self-examination.

2. Evaluate the following arguments, following the approach you learned in Chapter 7. Take care to avoid the errors in thinking summarized in Chapter 13.

 a. *Background note: The increase in juvenile crime around the nation has led many concerned people to consider more effective ways of addressing the problem.* *Argument:* Children's behavior is a direct reflection of the quality of their upbringing, so when a juvenile commits a crime, his or her parents should be held equally responsible. In other words, the parents should be co-defendants in any civil or criminal action brought against a juvenile.

 b. *Argument:* The environment—including rivers, lakes, oceans, forests, and beaches—is as entitled to an undisturbed existence as humans. Therefore, the government should enact laws acknowledging and protecting the rights of the environment.

3. Apply your critical thinking to each of the following cases. Make a conscious effort to apply your new self-knowledge, anticipate the problems in thinking to which you will be vulnerable, and resist their influence on your judgment.

 a. A California woman who owned two duplex apartments refused to lease to unmarried couples because she was a devout Presbyterian. The state charged her with illegal discrimination. She claimed that she had acted within her right to the free exercise of her religion. The court ruled against her, fined her $454, and ordered her to inform prospective tenants (a) that she had been in trouble with the state housing commission, (b) that her claim to the free exercise of religion was rejected by the court, and (c) that she now accepts the government's "equal housing opportunity" policy.[1] Was justice done in this case?

 b. Most people's consciousness has been raised about the evil of child abuse, some to the point of denouncing the practice of spanking children. But many others believe that spanking is not necessarily abusive and can be a positive means of developing children's sense of right and wrong and guiding them to responsibility and self-discipline. What is your view on this issue?

 c. A group of convicts brought legal action against the prison system, contending that their religious freedom was violated because they were not allowed to use an interfaith chapel to worship Satan.[2] Should prison officials have allowed them to use the chapel?

 d. Canadian government officials passed legislation to curtail cigarette company sponsorship of athletic and cultural events. Banned are logos on race cars and the displays of company names on signs at events sponsored by tobacco companies.[3] Should the United States follow Canada's example?

 e. A Stillwater, Oklahoma, police officer came home to find his daughter and her boyfriend copulating on the couch. The boy pulled up his pants and rushed past the officer. As he went by, the officer slapped him in the face with an open hand. Subsequently, the boy's mother called city officials and complained about the "assault." As a result, the officer was demoted and given a $700 pay cut. The city council later reversed the ruling but voted to fine the officer a week's pay.[4] Do you agree with the city's handling of this case?

 f. Some educators are urging that colleges become more selective than they have been in the past few decades. Specifically, these people propose that remedial courses be eliminated and entrance requirements tightened.

This would mean that students who are deficient in basic skills, had poor marks in high school, or did poorly on admissions tests would not be accepted into college. Do you agree with this view?

g. An outstanding senior English major (with a 3.7 grade point average out of a possible 4.0) at Princeton University submitted an analysis of a novel for her Spanish American literature course. Her professor determined that the paper was plagiarized—that is, that it was copied, virtually word for word, from a scholarly reference work without proper acknowledgments. The student subsequently claimed she had committed only a "technical error." The case was referred to a faculty–student committee on discipline, which, after a hearing, recommended withholding the student's degree for one year and notifying the law schools to which she had applied of the details of the decision. Believing the penalty was too harsh, the student took the matter to court.[5] Do you believe the committee's decision was too harsh?

h. A federal court has ruled that Christmas (like Hanukkah, Easter, and Passover) may be observed in the public schools as a cultural event but not as a religious holiday. Educational lawyers interpret that as meaning that songs like "Silent Night" may be sung in a class learning about religious customs or in a music appreciation class but not as a religious celebration.[6] Do you support the idea of banning all religious celebrations from the schools in this manner?

i. When Elizabeth Taylor learned that a TV movie based on her life was in preparation, she went to court to block its production, claiming that the so-called docudrama was "simply a fancy new name for old-fashioned invasion of privacy, defamation, and violation of an actor's rights." Some people would say her request should have been denied because it represents censorship. What do you think? (Would you think differently if the docudrama concerned the life of a deceased celebrity, like Kurt Cobain or Elvis Presley?)[7]

j. Shirley MacLaine, the well-known actress, is also a best-selling author. In her books she claims to have lived a number of former lives. For example, she says she once lived as a male teacher who committed suicide on the lost continent of Atlantis.[8] Do you find such claims believable?

CHAPTER 15

Being Observant

French chemist Louis Pasteur once said, "Chance favors the prepared mind." True enough. He might have added that it also favors the observant eye. Many obvious things wait to be seen, and yet we never notice them. What color eyes does your father have? Does your mother part her hair on the left or the right? What is the pattern of the wallpaper in your dining room? How many of the houses on your street have white roofs?

Being observant is not merely an interesting quality that livens our days. Clear and sound thinking often depends on subtleties that are revealed only by close observation. If there are gaps in our seeing and hearing, then the perceptions we base our judgments on are less likely to be complete and accurate. In addition, the keener our observation, the less likely we will be slaves to stereotypes, oversimplifications, and unwarranted assumptions.

Observing People

What people say and the way they say it (and sometimes what they *omit* saying) can be valuable clues to their unspoken views and attitudes. Noticing these things can help us decide which areas are sensitive to people, which their understanding seems weak in, and what approaches would be most fruitful in communicating with them.

When they are listening, people give certain signals to indicate approval or disapproval of what is being said. An occasional nodding of the head, an encouraging smile, even a low "uh-huh" of assent all signal "I'm in agreement with you." On the other hand, a slight shaking of the head, a raising of the eyebrows, a pursing of the lips as the eyes roll upward, a frown—all suggest at least partial disagreement. Similarly, people who are bored with a discussion will usually betray this feeling even if they are trying not to. The way they glance at their watches, sigh resignedly, turn their attention to someone or something outside the expected focus, nervously fidget with an article of their clothing, or frequently shift position communicates their wish to change the subject or their companions.

A great deal can be told from even a simple exchange of greetings by two people passing each other. Merely the tone in which the greeting is expressed can suggest whether the people like and respect each other and whether they consider each other equals. Few of these reactions, however subtle, are missed by observant people. And, as may be obvious, aside from the benefits to their thinking, careful attention is a great aid in making people more sensitive to and thoughtful of others.

A student in a writing class raises his hand and asks the teacher if he can borrow a pen. (The class is in its ninth week, and the in-class writing assignment was announced during the previous class.) The instructor gives him a searching look, slowly reaches into her pocket and extracts a pen, walks in a labored step to the student's desk, and hands it to him. No words have been spoken. No obvious gestures have signaled the instructor's displeasure. But if the student is observant, he will have seen the displeasure in the look and the resigned "what's the use" gait.

Good detectives are observant. They know that one small, easily overlooked clue can mean the difference between a solved and an unsolved case. Similarly, good trial lawyers are studious observers of people. The nervous glance of a witness when a certain aspect of the case is mentioned can suggest the most productive line of questioning. Likewise, we can conduct our critical thinking more effectively if we observe other people's behavior carefully.

Observation in Science and Medicine

We owe today's knowledge of the causes and treatments of heart attack in part to the careful observation of one doctor. Dr. James B. Herrick was the first physician to diagnose a heart attack in a living patient, without benefit of blood tests or electrocardiograms. In doing so, he opened the door to the modern era in heart care. Until that time, a heart attack was not recognized as a sign of heart disease. The symptoms that even lay persons have learned to recognize today were, until Herrick's discovery, regarded as "acute indigestion." Herrick established that most heart attacks are due to a clot in a coronary artery and that such an attack need not be fatal. (Interestingly, Herrick had earlier discovered the disease known as sickle-cell anemia.)[1]

Another well-known, fortuitous occasion when the power of observation paid handsome dividends for humanity took place in 1929. Sir Alexander Fleming accidentally contaminated a staphylococcus culture with a mold. He noticed that the staph colonies began to undergo dissolution. Recognizing the great value of whatever substance in the mold had caused the dissolution, he turned his attention to the mold. Eventually, he isolated the substance that has since saved countless millions of lives—penicillin. A few years earlier, in 1922, Fleming had made another dramatic discovery. Suffering from a cold and a runny nose, he was working with a glass plate on which bacteria were growing when a drop from his nose fell onto the plate. In a short time he noticed that the drop had destroyed some of the bacteria. Thus, he discovered a substance called lysozyme, a protein and enzyme also found in saliva and tears. Now some researchers believe that lysozyme may play a part in controlling cancer.[2]

The French Nobel Prize–winning molecular biologist Jacques Monod owes to his casual yet observant browsing through statistics his discovery that manic depression is genetically linked. He explains how it happened as follows:

> One day I was getting bored at one of the committee meetings we are always having to attend. I was leafing through some statistics from psychiatric hospitals, and I noted with amazement, under manic depressives, that women outnumbered men two to one. I said to myself, "That must have a genetic origin, and can mean only one thing; it is traceable to a dominant gene linked to sex."[3]

Note that, though Monod's insight initially occurred to him as a conviction (it "can mean only one thing"), he did not treat it as such. Rather, he made it a scientific hypothesis and set about to test it. That was wise because—his positive phrasing notwithstanding—the idea could have turned out to be a post hoc fallacy (see Chapter 10).

The Range of Application

Countless examples of the benefits of close observation could be cited in every field of study and work. Physicist Richard Feynman, for example, had extraordinary curiosity, or as he put it, a "puzzle drive." From early youth he was fascinated with all kinds of puzzles—from math problems to Mayan hieroglyphics—and when he ran out of prepared ones, he constructed his own. He observed paramecia through his microscope and learned things that contradicted the prevailing wisdom. He laid out food trails for ants and then studied their behavior.

Once, while sitting in the Cornell University cafeteria, Feynman noticed a student tossing a plate in the air; the plate wobbled, and the red Cornell medallion on it rotated. But one particular detail intrigued him—the medallion on the plate was rotating significantly faster than the plate was wobbling. Why the difference? he wondered. Fascinated, he wrestled with the problem; constructed an equation that expressed the relationship of angle, rotation, and wobble; and worked out "the motion of the mass particles." When he told an associate about his findings, the associate dismissed them as unimportant. But Feynman explored the wobble phenomenon more deeply, and what had begun as a playful exercise in curiosity eventually won him the Nobel Prize for physics![4]

Another example of the value of observation occurred in a small upstate New York town when a steam foreman named Eric Houck was degreasing valves. One of the valves accidentally fell into a vat of chemicals used to clean garbage cans. Houck grabbed a stick and fished the valve from the vat. As he did so, he noticed that the stick came out clean—the chemicals had stripped off the grime and paint. His curiosity aroused, Houck applied the chemicals to an old chair. It, too, came out clean to the bare wood. After that happy discovery, Houck built a thriving furniture-stripping business, with more than 200 franchises operating in thirty-five states. All this came from a chance happening that the average person would probably not even have noticed.

In the late 1950s, John T. Molloy was an instructor in a Connecticut prep school. He began to observe some connection between the kind of shoes a teacher wore and student performance. An instructor who wore laced shoes seemed to get consistently better results than one who wore penny loafers. Intrigued by this apparent connection, Malloy conducted a number of experiments. He concluded that the light-colored work clothing worn by the Boston Strangler (Albert DeSalvo, convicted of strangling several women in the 1960s) had apparently inspired trust in his victims. Molloy also found that secretaries more willingly follow the directions of people whose dress and manner suggest position and authority than they do those of people with a shabby appearance. These observations enabled Molloy to build a very successful "wardrobe engineering" consulting business (his services are sought by numerous executives) and to write the popular book *Dress for Success.*

For most of us, being observant may not have the dramatic results it did for Feynman, Houck, and Molloy. Nevertheless, it can help us relate more meaningfully to people and learn more about the things around us. Most important, it can aid our critical thinking.

Becoming More Observant

The way to be observant is to use all five of your senses to keep your mind from wandering aimlessly. All too often, people are unobservant because they are too absorbed in themselves—their own thoughts and feelings. When they speak, they are so busy forming their words and enjoying the sound of their voices that they forget their listeners. Observant people, on the other hand, have learned how to get outside themselves, to be constantly in touch with what is happening around them.

A good way to start becoming more observant is to practice receiving sense impressions more attentively. At the next meeting of an organization you belong to or any other gathering, try to notice things you would normally miss: objects in the room, the arrangement of the furniture, the positions of the people in relation to one another, the subtle reactions of people during the discussion. The next time you are walking to the store or the movies, try to see how many things you've been missing. Which houses are best cared for? How many people smile and nod or otherwise greet you? What activities are people you pass engaged in? Do they seem to be enjoying what they are doing? How many different sounds do you hear? Which sounds dominate? Are they pleasant or harsh? How many different styles of walking can you detect among the people you pass?

When you are reading a magazine or newspaper or watching TV, look for the significance of things. Consider the connections among ideas, even apparently unrelated ones. An article about an astronomer's location of a new galaxy may reveal something about concentration and mental discipline. A TV show about the effects of negligence and abuse on children may suggest a new perspective on marriage or divorce or the Hollywood image of romance.

Refecting on Your Observations

Observation will sometimes, by itself, bring valuable insights. But you can increase the number and quality of your insights by developing the habit of reflecting on your observations. The best way to do this is to set aside a special time every day—early in the morning, perhaps, or late in the evening (but not when you are exhausted). It needn't be long; ten or fifteen minutes may be enough. But be sure you are free of distractions. Review what you have seen and heard during the past twenty-four hours. Ask yourself what it means, how it relates to other important matters, and how you can use it to improve yourself or to spur achievement.

Let's say that you heard this proverb earlier today: "To be content with little is difficult; to be content with much, impossible." Reflecting on it might lead you to the conclusion that popular culture's emphasis on possessing things—new cars, stylish clothes, and so on—is a false value, that material wealth can never guarantee happiness.

Or you may have read about the Michigan court ruling that a fetus may be considered a person in a wrongful death lawsuit. After a man's wife and sixteen-week-old fetus were killed when she swerved her car to avoid hitting an unleashed dog, the man sued the dog's owners. (This decision departed from previous court rulings in Michigan that a fetus is not a person until it can survive outside the uterus.)[5] Here your reflection might lead you to consider the implications of this ruling for the issue of abortion.

Applications

1. Select a place where you can observe other people, as suggested in this chapter—the campus snack bar, for example, or a student lounge. Go there and stay at least half an hour. Try to notice more than the obvious. Look for subtleties, things you'd normally miss. Take notes on what you observe.

2. Ask your instructor in this course or one of your other courses for permission to visit another of his or her sections. Go to that class and observe carefully the reactions of individual students—for example, the subtle indications they give of attention or inattention. Take notes.

3. Make yourself look as sloppy and scruffy as you can. Put on old, wrinkled clothes. Mess up your hair. Rub dirt on your face and arms. Then go into a store and ask a clerk for assistance. Speak to other customers. Check the clerk's reaction and the reactions of other customers. A day or so later, return to the same store looking your very neatest and cleanest. Speak and act in the same manner. Note people's reactions. Compare them with those you got the first time.

4. Think about how mannerly the students, faculty, and staff at your college are. Observe their behavior in various campus situations, noting examples of courtesy and rudeness.

5. Many people have become so accustomed to advertisements that they no longer examine them carefully and critically. Pay close attention to the advertising you encounter in a typical day in newspapers and magazines, on television and radio, and elsewhere. Determine what appeals are used to elicit a favorable response from you and how much specific information about the products or services is presented in the advertisements. Record your observations.

6. Practice reflecting, as explained in this chapter, on the following quotations:

> If I am not for myself, who will be? But if I am only for myself, what am I?
> Rabbi Hillel

> Travel makes a wise man better but a fool worse.
> Thomas Fuller

> It is not easy to find happiness in ourselves, and it is not possible to find it elsewhere.
> Agnes Repplier

> You cannot really love God unless you love your neighbor.
> Anonymous

> The covetous man is ever in want.
> Horace

> The absent are always at fault.
> Spanish proverb

The girl who can't dance says the band can't play.
Yiddish proverb

7. Evaluate the following arguments, following the approach you learned in Chapter 7. Take care to avoid the errors in thinking summarized in Chapter 13.

a. *Background note: Concern over the possibly damaging effects of pornography on children has led many people to lobby for laws banning the sale of pornography to anyone under eighteen. Others object to this, sometimes offering the following argument:*
Argument: Young people today are more sophisticated than in any generation in this century. They are able to decide better than anyone else, including their parents, what books and magazines they should read. The ban on the sale of pornography to anyone under eighteen is a denial of young people's right to think for themselves and therefore should be opposed.

b. *Background note: The practice of infertile couples contracting with surrogate mothers to bear a child for them for a fee has given rise to thorny issues. For example, what should happen when the surrogate signs a contract, accepts a fee, is artificially inseminated, carries the baby to term, and then decides she will return the money and keep the child? Should she be held to the contract and be made to surrender the baby? Those who say no usually argue as follows:*
Argument: Although contracts should be honored in the vast majority of cases, this kind of case is an exception. The act of nurturing a new life within one's own body can establish the strongest of human bonds. No contract or legal ruling should ever be allowed to break that bond.

8. Apply your critical thinking to each of the following issues. Make a special effort to recall situations you have observed that are related to the issue, and ask yourself, "What conclusion do these observations point to?" (If your observations have been too limited, solicit the observations of other people.)

a. In recent years, books and articles have warned people of the dangers of "workaholism." During the same period there have been few, if any, warnings about chronic laziness. Which is more prevalent in this country today, workaholism or chronic laziness?

b. The view of winning attributed to Vince Lombardi is as follows: "Winning isn't everything—it's the *only* thing." Is this a healthy view to bring to athletic competition? To other forms of competition?

c. Many people believe parents should be held legally and financially responsible for children over the age of sixteen who live at home. Is this a reasonable stance?

CHAPTER 16

Selecting an Issue

The term *issue,* in the context of critical thinking, means any matter about which people tend to disagree; in other words, it is almost synonymous with the word *controversy.** The most prominent issues—the ones we see most often in the news—are moral, legal, and political: Is abortion murder? Should teenagers who commit serious crimes be tried as adults? Has "soft" money corrupted the financing of political campaigns? But controversies exist in other fields as well: Farmers are divided over the effects of pesticides on the environment. Investment analysts disagree over what percentage, if any, of the average person's portfolio should be in Internet stocks. Educators are at odds over the merits of tenure. Men and women in law enforcement differ about the issue of gun control.

Speaking and writing about issues is so common and so natural that it is often done too casually. (We noted earlier how the belief that everyone is "entitled" to his or her opinion has emboldened many people to express views for which they have no evidence.) Critical thinkers, however, understand that care in selecting issues is an important part of the thinking process.

The Basic Rule: Less Is More

This rule may sound strange, particularly if you are in the habit of choosing the broadest possible topics for your compositions. Fear of the blank page leads many students to this behavior. They reason as follows: "If I choose a limited subject, such as the Tampa Bay Buccaneers' chance of getting to the Super Bowl this year, the latest research on high blood pressure, or the Battle of Saratoga during the Revolutionary War, I may run out of things to say before I reach the required number of words. So I'll play it safe and pick a general topic such as sports, disease, or war."

*The expression "controversial issue," though commonly used, is redundant.

Any feeling of security this approach may generate is purely imaginary. Trying to do justice to a broad topic in a composition of 500 words, or for that matter in several thousand words, is as futile as trying to pour a gallon of water into a pint container. It just won't work, even in the case of a simple informative composition. And it has much less chance of working when you are analyzing issues, which are at least two-sided and often multi-sided. This means that many, perhaps most, of the people who will judge your analysis of an issue not only know its complexities but also have half a dozen reasons to disagree with you. A superficial, once-over-lightly treatment is sure to fail.

The only sensible solution to this dilemma is to limit the scope of your analysis. For example, if the issue has five or ten important aspects, examine only one or two. You will then have sufficient space to address complexities, make important distinctions, and deal with subtleties. This is the meaning of less is more—aiming for depth rather than breadth.

How to Limit an Issue

The following approach will help you identify the significant aspects of any issue and decide which one(s) you are most interested in and can explore within your time and space limitations:

1. *List as many aspects of the issue as you can.* In the case of an important, highly controversial issue, your list may include more than a dozen aspects.

2. *Decide exactly which aspects you will address.* Seldom will you be able to do an adequate job of treating all aspects. The one or ones you choose should not only meet your interest but also fit the occasion and purpose of your analysis and the amount of time and space you have available.

3. *Probe the aspects you are concerned with in one or more clear, carefully focused questions.* Doing this helps keep the subsequent inquiry focused and prevents your drifting from the issue. Write the questions out; then, if your thoughts move in a certain direction, you can quickly glance at the questions and decide whether that direction is likely to be productive.

Let's see how these three steps apply to some actual issues.

Sample Issue: Pornography

The word *pornography* is from a Greek word meaning "writing about prostitutes." Its modern definition, however, has no direct connection to prostitution. Pornography is any written, visual, or auditory material that is sexually explicit, although power and violence are frequently recurring subthemes. The opponents of pornography are diverse and include political conservatives, religious groups, and feminists. The controversy that has always surrounded pornography has intensified in recent years. Among the reasons are the increase in sex and violence in movies and television and the appearance of pornographic materials on the Internet. The central question in the current debate about pornography is the same as it has been in decades, indeed centuries, past: *Is pornography harmful?*

Aspect	Questions
The audience	Are the users of pornography male or female? Adults or children?
Themes	What categories of sex are included in books, magazines, films, and tapes? Premarital? Marital? Heterosexual? Homosexual? Voluntary? Forced? Adult–adult? Adult–child? Bestiality? What does the work say about the kinds of sex it treats? What messages does it convey?
Business arrangements	In pornographic films, are the actors paid? If so, does this constitute prostitution?
The actors	Is genuine acting talent required for pornographic films? Do many actors find a career in such films or only temporary employment? Do they look back on this employment, years later, with pride or shame?
Alleged harmful effects	What attitudes does pornography cultivate toward love, marriage, and commitment? Does it, as some claim, eroticize children, celebrate the brutalization of women, and glamorize rape? Does it make men see women as persons or as objects? Does it elevate or degrade those who read/view it?
Role of pornography in sexually transmitted disease	Does pornography play a positive or negative role in the effort to combat sexually transmitted diseases, including AIDS?
Free speech	Does the guarantee of free speech extend to pornography?

Sample Issue: Boxing

The *Ring Record Book* lists 337 professional boxers who have died from injuries sustained in prizefights since World War II. In the United States alone, 120 boxers have died from such injuries.[1] With the death of a Korean fighter, Duk Doo Kim, following a barrage of punches by Ray "Boom Boom" Mancini, an issue that had received the public's attention many times previously raged once again: *Should boxing be outlawed?* Like most other issues, this one has a number of aspects. Here is how the three-step approach to clarifying issues would apply to it:

Aspect	*Questions*
Boxer's right to earn a living	Would the outlawing of boxing be an unfair denial of the boxer's right to earn a living?
Boxing and mental health	Is the expression of violence that takes place in a boxing match an emotionally healthy experience for the fighters themselves? For the spectators?
The popularity of boxing	How valid is the argument that boxing should be allowed to continue because it has historically been, and continues to be, very popular?
The classification of boxing as a sport	Is boxing properly classified as a sport? That is, does the fact that the contestants aim to strike potentially harmful blows disqualify it from that classification?
Overcoming the dangers	Is it possible, perhaps by modifying the rules or the equipment, to eliminate or at least reduce the physical danger to fighters?
Effects of being punched	Exactly what effect does a punch have on the human body, particularly the brain? What is the cumulative effect of the punches received during ten or fifteen rounds of boxing? During a career?

Sample Issue: Juvenile Crime

For much of this century, juvenile criminals have been accorded special treatment in the courts. Because the emphasis was on rehabilitating rather than punishing them, the charges were different—"juvenile delinquency" rather than assault or murder, as were the proceedings and disposition of the case—"hearings" rather than trials, sealed records rather than publicity, and lectures rather than imprisonment. In recent years, however, the public has become dissatisfied with that system. Many people are demanding that juveniles who have committed criminal acts be treated as criminals, regardless of their age. The broad issue is usually expressed in these terms: *Should juvenile criminals be treated the same as adult criminals?* However, like the other issues we have examined in this chapter, this broad issue has a number of aspects, which you might address as follows:

Aspect	*Questions*
Causes of juvenile crime	Are juvenile delinquents alone responsible for their criminality? Are parents and others in society (makers of violent films, for example) also responsible? If others are responsible, should the law "get tough" with them? How?
The age of responsibility	Is it reasonable or fair to hold people responsible for their actions before they are old enough to understand their moral and legal quality? At what age does a person reach such understanding?
Similarities or differences between juveniles and adults	Is it reasonable to hold a fourteen-year-old (or a sixteen- or eighteen-year-old) as accountable as a twenty-one- or thirty-year-old?
Effects of publicity on juvenile crime	Will publicizing young people's crimes deter juvenile crime? Will it assist in the process of rehabilitation?
Effects of imprisonment on juveniles	What effects will imprisonment have on teenagers? On preteens?
Differences in crimes	Should all juvenile crimes be handled alike? That is, should the criminal's age be considered in certain crimes (vandalism and shoplifting, for example), but not in others (rape and murder, for example)?
Repeat offenders	Should chronic juvenile offenders be treated differently from first-time offenders? If so, in what way?
Prisons	If juvenile offenders are sent to prison (say, for crimes of violence), should they be housed in the same institutions as adult criminals?

If you follow the above approach and find that even the individual aspects are too broad to treat adequately in the time and space at your disposal, look for an aspect that can be divided and focus on one part of it. (Not all aspects lend themselves to such division, but in most cases you will find some that do.) Here are some examples from the issue of pornography discussed above.

Aspect	Questions	Way to Limit Focus
Themes	What categories of sex are included in books, magazines, films, and tapes? Premarital? Marital? Heterosexual? Homosexual? Voluntary? Forced? Adult–adult? Adult–child? Bestiality? What does the work say about the kind of sex it treats? What messages does it convey?	One way to limit your treatment would be to examine only forced adult-adult sex in a single medium, magazines. Or you could limit your treatment further by focusing on a single magazine.
Alleged harmful effects	What attitudes does pornography cultivate toward love, marriage, and commitment? Does it, as some claim, eroticize children, celebrate the brutalization of women, and glamorize rape? Does it make men see women as persons or as objects? Does it elevate or degrade those who read/view it?	You might focus on one of the four questions rather than all four. If you choose the first question regarding attitudes, you might focus on love, marriage, or commitment rather than all three. Similarly, if you choose the second question, you might select one of the three aspects rather than all three.

By limiting the scope of your treatment, you not only ensure a clearer focus and increase the chance of staying within your competency, you also make the task of analysis more manageable. The fewer matters that are competing for your attention, the less the danger of becoming distracted or confused. Even on those rare occasions when you are able to address more than a single subissue, careful identification of all of them will make your inquiry more orderly and purposeful. Finally, limiting your treatment will lessen the chance of your oversimplifying complex matters.

Applications

1. Apply the approach explained in this chapter to *two* of the following issues. Be sure to select issues that interest you, because applications in subsequent chapters will build on this one.
   a. Is the U.S. federal income tax system in need of reform?
   b. Is the teaching of sex education in elementary schools desirable?
   c. Should divorce laws be tightened so that obtaining a divorce is more difficult?
   d. Is it possible for a sane person to commit suicide?
   e. Are students' attention spans shrinking?
   f. Should prostitution be legalized?
   g. Should the lobbying of legislators by special interest groups be outlawed?
   h. Should all advertising be banned from children's TV (for example, from Saturday morning cartoon shows)?
   i. Is devil worship a threat to society?
   j. Is it reasonable to believe that some UFOs are extraterrestrial?
   k. Are male athletes superior to female athletes?
   l. Is "political correctness" a problem on your campus?

2. The following issues were included in the applications for earlier chapters. Apply the approach discussed in this chapter to *one* of them. (Disregard your earlier analysis of the issue.)
   a. Should all students be required to complete at least one composition course?
   b. Should creationism be taught in high school biology classes?
   c. Should polygamy be legalized?
   d. Should the voting age be lowered to sixteen?
   e. Should extremist groups like the Ku Klux Klan be allowed to hold rallies on public property?
   f. Should prisons give greater emphasis to punishment than to rehabilitation?
   g. Is the college degree a meaningful job requirement?
   h. When doctors and clinics prescribe birth control devices for minors, should they be required to notify the parents of the minors?

3. Select an issue that is currently in the international, national, or local news. State it in question form, and then apply the approach explained in the chapter.

CHAPTER 17

Conducting Inquiry

Inquiry is seeking answers to questions, investigating issues, and gathering information to help us draw conclusions. It enables us to get beyond our first impressions, feelings, preconceived notions, and personal preferences.

There are two basic kinds of inquiry: inquiry into facts and inquiry into opinions. Opinions, remember, can be informed or uninformed. Except in cases in which the purpose of our inquiry demands that both varieties of opinion be gathered, we should be more interested in *informed* opinion.

Often we will need to inquire into both facts and opinions. How much inquiry into each is needed will, of course, vary from situation to situation. If the specific issue were Which U.S. income group is most inequitably treated by the present federal tax laws? we would have to examine the tax laws to determine what they specify (*fact*) and consult the tax experts for their interpretations of the more complicated aspects of the laws (*informed opinion*). But to determine the degree of inequity, we would have to know the amount of income necessary to provide living essentials (food, shelter, and clothing). So we would also have to examine cost-of-living statistics (*fact*) and consult economists about more subtle factors affecting the various income groups (*informed opinion*).

Working with Inconclusive Results

Because the state of human knowledge is imperfect, not every question is answerable when it is asked. Some issues remain unsolved for years, even centuries. Before we traveled into outer space, no one knew exactly what the effects of weightlessness on the human body would be.

Many respected doctors argued that the rapid acceleration at blast-off would increase an astronaut's heartbeat to a fatal level. (There was strong medical evidence to support this view.) Others believed that weightlessness would cause vital organs to malfunction and atrophy.[1] Both dire predictions proved mistaken, but any inquiry into the issue undertaken before the first successful launch would necessarily have been incomplete.

Which mountain in the Sinai desert did Moses really climb? The Bible gives it a name (actually *two* names), but scholars differ on where it is located. Strong claims are advanced for three different mountains in three countries. No conclusive answer has been reached despite over three thousand years of inquiry.[2]

Some questions are even more resistant to inquiry—for example, the question, Are there intelligent life forms in our solar system or other systems? Our sun is one of billions of stars. The farthest ones we have discovered are believed to be between 12 and 13.5 billion light years away.[3] It's conceivable that any inquiry into this question made in the next million years will be inconclusive. Perhaps the answer will *never* be known.

However resistant to solution a question may be, though, inquiry is still useful. Even if it yields no more than the *untestable* opinions of experts, those opinions are more valuable than the casual speculations of the uninformed. So we shouldn't be intimidated by difficult issues. We should merely be realistic about how complete and final our answers are likely to be.

Where to Look for Information

Whenever possible, we should consult our own experience and observation. Even if what has happened to us or what we have seen happen to others pertains only indirectly to the issue or touches just one aspect of it, it should not be overlooked. Our observation of how people use stereotypes or face-saving maneuvers in everyday situations may help us evaluate a political candidate's speech or a party's platform. Our experience with conformity in ourselves and our friends can provide us with an insight into the effects of TV programming on the public. Being alert to the relevance of our experience to the issue we are investigating not only can give us valuable ideas but also can suggest important questions. Thus, it can provide our inquiry with better direction.

Of course, our own experience and observation will seldom be adequate by itself, especially on complex and controversial matters. We will need to consult other sources. What follows is a brief guide to what to look for and where to find it.

BACKGROUND ON THE ISSUE

Think of several general headings under which the issue might be classified. For example, if the issue concerns criminal investigation, the headings might be "crime," "criminology," "police," and one or more specific kinds of crime, such as "burglary." Then look up those headings in the *index volume* of a good general encyclopedia, such as *Encyclopedia Americana* or *Encyclopaedia Britannica*. (*Americana* has a separate index volume. *Britannica* is divided into two sets of books: the *macro*paedia set, which contains detailed articles on a limited number of subjects, and the *micro*paedia set, which contains brief articles and cross-references on a large number of subjects.) The articles you will find there have been written by authorities in the various fields. At the end of each article is a list of books and other articles you can consult for a fuller or more specialized treatment of the issue.

In addition to the general encyclopedias, there are numerous special ones: encyclopedias of art, business, history, literature, philosophy, music, science, education, social science, and many more. Most of these contain not only historical background but also titles of other books and articles you may find helpful.*

FACTS AND STATISTICS

Almanacs, published yearly, are treasuries of information on myriad subjects. *World Almanac* is available from the 1868 edition. *Information Please Almanac, The New York Times Encyclopedic Almanac,* and *Reader's Digest Almanac* are more recent publications. Because any almanac is arranged very compactly for efficient use, it is important to study the index before using it.

INFORMATION ABOUT PEOPLE

A number of biographical dictionaries and encyclopedias are available. Two of the most helpful ones are *Current Biography: Who's News and Why* and *Webster's Biographical Dictionary.*

INFORMATION ABOUT THE ENGLISH LANGUAGE

Many reference books are available, including the *Oxford English Dictionary (OED), Webster's New Dictionary of Synonyms,* and Eric Partridge's *Dictionary of Slang and Unconventional English.*

*Remember that background reading, though a helpful start toward analyzing an issue, is never an acceptable substitute for analysis. Your instructor will expect more from you than just background information.

ARTICLES IN NEWSPAPERS, MAGAZINES, AND JOURNALS

The most basic index to articles is the *Reader's Guide to Periodical Literature.* This guide lists articles from over one hundred magazines by subject and author. As with an encyclopedia, you should begin by thinking of the various headings under which the issue might be classified. Then select the volumes for the appropriate years (more current years are listed in unbound pamphlet form) and look up those headings. The entries will list the title and author of the article and the name and issue of the magazine it appeared in.

Many other indexes are available, even in moderate-sized libraries. The following is a partial list. (For a complete list, consult Eugene O. Sheehy's *Guide to Reference Books.*)

Social Science Index	*Applied Science and Technology Index*
Humanities Index	
New York Times Index	*Art Index*
Essay and General Literature Index	*Biography Index*
	Business Periodicals Index
General Science Index	*Biological and Agricultural Index*
Education Index	
United States Government Publications: Monthly Catalog	*Book Review Index*
	Business Periodicals Index
Index to Legal Periodicals	*Engineering Index*
MLA International Bibliography	*Music Index*
	Philosopher's Index
Magazine Index	*Religion Index One: Periodicals*

After you locate the article and read it, be sure to check the reader response in the letters-to-the-editor section of subsequent issues. Most newspapers and magazines have a "letters" section, and it will often provide reaction by informed readers supporting or challenging the ideas in the article. In weekly magazines, responses usually appear two issues after the article; in fortnightlies and monthlies, one issue later.

BOOKS

In addition to the lists of books provided in encyclopedias and those you find mentioned in the articles you read, you can consult your library's card or computer catalog, the key to the books available on its shelves.**

*Before 1965 these indexes were combined under the title *International Index.*

**One valuable source of information is college textbooks in fields related to the issue you are investigating.

Occasionally, if your library is small or if the issue you are investigating is obscure, the library holdings may be limited. In such cases, as in any situation in which you are having difficulty finding information or using the reference books, ask your librarian for help. (Remember that librarians are professionals trained to solve the kinds of research problems you may encounter.)

COMPUTER DATABASES AND ABSTRACTING SERVICES

Modern information retrieval technology has made it easier than ever to conduct a data search. The technology continues to evolve rapidly, but the cost of conversion from old systems to new can be considerable. Therefore, what is available in the marketplace will not necessarily be available on a particular campus. Today, as always, the most important factor in research is the campus librarian. She or he can tell you whether your campus library has the research tools mentioned here and, if not, what comparable tools are available.

The principal change that is taking place in library technology is the conversion of the print index to an *electronic index*. The kind of information traditionally found in the *Reader's Guide to Periodical Literature* is now accessible in, for example, *InfoTrak*, a system available in one of three forms: (a) as an electronic bibliographic guide without text, (b) as a bibliographic guide with some text available on CDs , and (c) as a complete on-line service. Where the first and second forms of this system are used, researchers still make extensive use of bound copies of periodicals and microfiche records. *InfoTrak* is generally available in public libraries and in small academic libraries.

A number of scholarly electronic indexes are in use, particularly in academic libraries. One popular one is the *General Academic Index*, which covers 960 scholarly titles in the arts and humanities, as well as the sciences and social sciences. This source indexes many of the same general periodicals as *InfoTrak*, but it also includes many scholarly journals not indexed there. *Lexis-Nexis* and *Westlaw* are the most widely used legal indexes. Other technical indexes include *PsycINFO, Health and Psychosocial Instruments (HAPI)*, and two specialized ones from *Medline: PubMed* and *Internet Grateful Med.* The World Wide Web offers many other sources of information.

Ask your librarian about the computer databases available to you, such as *PsycINFO* and *PsycLIT*. Also, check the abstracting services available in your library. Among the best known are *Psychological Abstracts, Sociological Abstracts, America: History and Life*, and *Dissertation Abstracts International*.

THE INTERNET

In the 1970s the Defense Department began coordinating research networks. Then in the 1980s the personal computer began to gain popularity, and the research network system evolved into the Internet, also called the World Wide Web (WWW or Web). Over the years it has become a major medium of communications and learning. All you need to access the Internet is a computer with a modem and an institutional or commerical Internet service provider (ISP).

Millions of Web sites are available, but you must know the address of a site before you can access it. Also—and this is especially important— you must enter the address exactly. (An added space or period or letter will prevent you from reaching the site.) Most Web addresses begin as follows: http://www. (If you see a Web address beginning with just www, understand that this is an abbreviation and you must add the first part of the address to access the site.) If you don't know what site is appropriate or have forgotten a Web address, you can consult one of the many available search engines such as www.askjeeves.com.

The ending of a Web address will tell you whether you are visiting a government site (.gov), an education site (.edu), or a commercial site (.com). Web sites reflect the biases and/or agendas of the people who created them. Generally speaking, government and education sites are designed to provide the public with useful information, whereas commercial sites are designed to sell products and services. Knowing whose site you are visiting will help you evaluate the reliability of the information you find there. Such evaluation is at least as necessary with the Internet as it is with books and other media, perhaps more so.

The following brief list of Web sites will provide a helpful starting point for your use of the Internet.

U.S. Census Bureau	http://www.census.gov/
General information searches	http://www.about.com, http://www.dogpile.com, http://www.lycos.com, http://www.go2net.com, http://www.infoplease.com, or http://www.loc.gov
Legal searches	http://www.lawguru.com
Health/medical searches	http://drkoop.com
News and commentary	http://newsmax.com, or http://www.nytimes.com

All of this may suggest long, monotonous, time- and energy-consuming research like that required for a doctoral dissertation. But that is a misconception. With a little practice, it is possible to use quickly and efficiently all the reference sources mentioned. Even books needn't be waded through page by page to find something useful. In a few seconds you can turn to the index (usually at the end) and look for the several headings your issue might be found under; then turn to the appropriate pages and read *only those pages.* If the book has no index, you can turn to the table of contents, read the chapter titles, decide which chapters seem most relevant, and then scan them.

Efficiency can be more difficult to achieve in Internet searches because distractions are often more frequent and tempting. Make a special effort to discipline your Internet searches, focusing your attention on relevant material only.

How Much Inquiry Is Enough?

It would seem that deciding when an inquiry is complete should be easy. More often than not, however, it is not easy at all. One insight can make a great difference. A single new fact can upset a mountain of evidence. For example, in the late 1960s and early 1970s, most social psychologists would probably have agreed that crowded living conditions are harmful to humans. Numerous experiments seemed to have settled the matter. Then anthropologist Patricia Draper studied a southwest African tribe of hunter-gatherers, the !Kung bushmen. Though their land offers ample space to spread out their settlements and huts, they crowd their dwellings together and often sit in tight groups, literally brushing against one another. Yet they have none of the medical conditions (such as high blood pressure) usually associated with crowding.[4] This one fact has caused reexamination of a scientific truism.

Since the aim of inquiry is to produce evidence, it will be helpful to recall the guidelines presented in Chapter 6 for determining when evidence is sufficient:

1. *Evidence is sufficient when it permits a judgment to be made with certainty.* Wishing, assuming, or pretending that a judgment is correct does not constitute certainty. Certainty exists when there is no good reason for doubt, no basis for dispute. The standard for conviction in a criminal trial, for example, is "guilt beyond a reasonable doubt." Certainty is a very difficult standard to meet, especially in controversial issues, so you will generally be forced to settle for a more modest standard.

2. *If certainty is unattainable, evidence is sufficient if one view of the issue has been shown to have the force of probability.* This means that the view in question is demonstrably more reasonable than any competing view.

In civil court cases, this standard is expressed as "a preponderance of the evidence." *Demonstrating* reasonableness is, of course, very different from merely *asserting it,* and all possible views must be identified and evaluated before any one view can be established as most reasonable.

3. *In all other cases, the evidence must be considered insufficient.* In other words, if the evidence does not show one view to be more reasonable than competing views, the only prudent course of action is to withhold judgment until sufficient evidence is available. Such restraint can be difficult, especially when you want a particular view to be proven superior, but restraint is an important characteristic of the critical thinker.

How much inquiry is enough? There is no easy answer. It depends entirely on the issue. In some cases, a brief inquiry will be more than adequate. In others, an exhaustive inquiry will be incomplete. However, though no absolute statement may be made about the amount of inquiry required, you can be reasonably sure your inquiries are complete when you have made a thorough and careful effort to learn the relevant facts and to consult informed opinion in all fields of study that have a direct bearing on the specific issue you are analyzing. The number of fields to be researched will, of course, vary with the nature of the issue. Here, for example, is a list of the fields that have a direct bearing on three specific issues we identified in Chapter 16:

Issue	*Questions*	*Fields with Direct Bearing*
Pornography's influence	What attitudes does pornography cultivate toward love, marriage, and commitment? Does it, as some claim, celebrate the brutalization of women and glamorize rape? Does it make men see women as persons or as objects? Does it elevate or degrade those who read/view it?	Sociology Psychology Literary criticism Ethics Religion
Effects of being punched	Exactly what effect does a punch have on the human body, particularly the brain? What is the cumulative effect of the punches received during ten or	Anatomy and physiology Medicine Psychology

Issue	Questions	Fields with Direct Bearing
	fifteen rounds of boxing? During a career?	
The age of responsibility	Is it reasonable or fair to hold people responsible for their actions before they are old enough to understand their moral and legal quality? At what age does a person reach such understanding?	Education Psychology Medicine Ethics Law

One of the greatest challenges to critical thinking is the temptation to stop inquiring when you find a knowledgeable person who supports your bias. The temptation will be especially strong when that person is the first one you encounter. You will want to say, "This is the definitive answer. Case closed!" If you follow this inclination, you will trivialize the issue and cheat yourself of genuine understanding. An issue is, by definition, a matter about which informed, careful thinkers may disagree. The following editorials illustrate this important point.

Background: Partial-birth abortion *is the common term for a procedure performed as late as the twenty-sixth week of pregnancy. It involves removing the fetus's legs and torso from the uterus, puncturing the skull, and crushing the skull or suctioning out the brain. Early in 1996 both the House and the Senate voted to ban the procedure, but on April 10 President Clinton vetoed the bill.*

EDITORIAL 1

NO ONE IS FOR ABORTION. And no woman who has ever undergone the rare and dreadful procedure Republicans now want to make into a campaign issue has done so without pain and sorrow.

President Clinton's veto Wednesday of a bill that would have banned a late-term abortion procedure is not about "infanticide" or "partial birth." Those are the inflammatory words presidential hopeful Bob Dole uses to describe what doctors call intact dilation and evacuation—a proce-

dure so rare that it is used in less than four hundredths of one percent of abortions. The medical procedure is done only as a last resort, generally to spare a woman's life or health after doctors have determined she is carrying a fetus that can't survive.

The issue here is not about "abortion on demand," as Dole says Clinton's veto signals. This is about women's health and those who would callously disregard it.

Clinton stood up for women this week by vetoing the extremist legislation. He also stood up for doctors, who could have faced up to two years in prison for doing what they deemed medically necessary and in their patient's best interest. Had Clinton signed the law, for the first time in twenty-three years doctors who treat women would have had to sacrifice their medical judgment to the political whims of Congress.

The families who bravely stood by the president as he vetoed the bill gave a personal face to this political issue. "I didn't make the decision for my child to die," said Vikki Stella, who underwent the proce-dure after doctors determined her baby had no brain.

Clinton would have signed the legislation, he said, had Republicans amended it to provide an exception to safeguard women's health. But women's health was never their concern. Their agenda is simply to make an ideological statement to create a campaign issue. The GOP would abolish a woman's right to decide her own reproduction, and return women to an era of dangerous and illegal abortions. They would have the country adopt the doctrine of a religious minority as national law. It is an agenda that may backfire.[5]

EDITORIAL 2

WEDNESDAY, THE DAY Bill Clinton vetoed the partial-birth abortion ban legislation passed by Congress, was a sad day indeed for Americans yearning for a return of moral sanity to our society.

In fact, Mr. Clinton has agreed to sign away the rights of our most helpless citizens because it's an election year, because he was afraid to alienate his natural constituency on the left; and because, as one of his advisers admitted to the Associated Press, backing down now might have looked like another flip-flop from the waffle king; but also because, all his protestations to the contrary notwithstanding, he is just as extreme on this issue as they come. To refresh memory as to what actually happens in a partial-birth abortion: late in pregnancy a baby is delivered almost totally, leaving only the head in the birth canal; a doctor then sticks a scissor into the base of the baby's skull, inserts a tube and sucks out the baby's brain. Doctors who perform such procedures make no bones about the fact that they are more often than not purely "elective," sometimes performed because of a birth defect as minor as a cleft palate or as unthreatening to life as Down's Syndrome. Witnesses to such procedures have described fully-formed hands and bodies and feet moving normally before the physician's assault on the brain stills them.

The issue of abortion has been a painful one since the Supreme Court created a constitutional right to it more than two decades ago. Americans now live with a national policy on the issue—and a policy they never even have a chance to vote on. They also live with the expansion of neonatal technology that makes fetuses viable—and abortion, thus, more worrisome—at ever earlier stages of development. It seems we'd all be a lot better off if the matter had been left where it belonged—in the hands of local legislatures—

so that citizens could exercise their democratic options by voting their conscience on abortion. But they can't.

So, for the past twenty years and more, men and women of good will have agonized instead—about abortion in cases of rape or incest; about abortion for pregnant children; about who makes the decision; about who pays for it; about how to define life and when it begins.

But partial-birth abortion has no place in that debate. Because the real, cruel truth about partial-birth abortion is that it kills living human babies, who if delivered but a few inches farther would be recognized as such and granted the full protection of the law. That's not abortion; it's infanticide. And it is one of those issues that must separate people of good will from those whose extremism in relation to abortion has led them to a dark place.[6]

These editorials address the very same issue, yet they take very different positions on it. By understanding these differences and subjecting each side to scrutiny, you increase your chances that your judgment of the issue will be insightful and wise.

A caution is in order here. To say that it is important to examine both sides of an issue does *not* mean that both sides are equal in merit. Often there will be enough merit on each side to make judgment difficult, but that never justifies the avoidance of judgment.

Managing Lengthy Material

Often your inquiry will take you beyond editorials and brief essays to full-length articles and books. These longer works are more difficult to evaluate because the core arguments are seldom presented neatly and compactly. The authors of these arguments do not intend to make analysis difficult—it is simply the nature of the writing process. Responsible authors of journal articles and books do not merely present lists of bald assertions; they support their views with evidence. They also add sufficient explanation to satisfy the demands of clarity and define the path their reasoning has taken. Sometimes the path has numerous turns, so secondary assertions must be added to complement and refine primary ones. As anecdotes multiply, as experimental and statistical data are reported and annotated, and as testimony is detailed, the essential argument can become almost as concealed as the hidden premises it sometimes contains—one premise may appear on page 2, another on page 5, and the conclusion on page 12. Before you can evaluate arguments in these cases, you need to consolidate the argument. Here is a strategy for doing so:

1. *After reading the article or book, go back and identify the key assertions.*
   Most paragraphs contain one or more assertions (topic sentences).
   Scan these and determine which are central to the argument.

Subheadings usually signal important assertions, as do capital letters, boldface, and italics. Look, too, for intensifying words such as *moreover, indeed, more (most) important,* and *more (most) significant.*

2. *Identify the author's conclusion.* The conclusion may appear anywhere, but commonly it appears as follows: in an article—right after the introduction, in the conclusion, or in both places; in a book—in the first or second chapter, in the last chapter, or in both places. Expressions like *for these reasons, thus, consequently, so,* and *therefore* signal conclusions.

3. *Notice any qualifying words used in the key assertions or the conclusion.* Is the writer speaking of *all* people, places, or things? Or is she speaking of *most, many, some, several, a few,* or *certain specified ones?* Is she saying *always, usually, sometimes, occasionally, seldom, never,* or *at certain specified times?* Often writers will make an assertion and then balance it in the next sentence. They often lead into the second sentence with words like *but, however, nevertheless, on the other hand, still,* or *yet.*

4. *Note the amount, kinds, and sources of evidence used to support the assertions.* Chapter 5 discussed eleven specific kinds of evidence. Review that chapter, if necessary.

5. *Notice the conditions the author includes.* Saying, for example, "Drug pushers should be given long jail terms if they are not themselves drug users and have been previously convicted of drug pushing" is very different from saying "Drug pushers should be given long jail terms." The "if" clause adds a special set of conditions. Similarly, saying "The United States should never fire a nuclear missile at another country unless first subjected to nuclear attack by that country" is quite different from saying, "The United States should never fire a nuclear missile at another country." Expressions like *if, unless, as long as, until,* and *before* can significantly alter the meaning of an assertion.

6. *Compose an accurate summary of the article or book from your analysis in steps 1–5.* This enables you to focus your attention and analyze the argument. The summary needn't be long; a paragraph or two is adequate in most cases. The summary should be a capsule version of the original work. (There is no room for carelessness in quoting or paraphrasing the original: If it says something *may be* a certain way, it is not saying that it *is* that way; similarly, *is* does not necessarily mean *should be.*) Here is a sample summary of an article recommending the abolition of grades. Although it extended to more than ten printed pages in the original, it is here condensed into a single paragraph without sacrificing accuracy.

> One of the biggest obstacles to learning—in grade school, high school, and college—is grades. The fear of bad grades hangs over the heads of young people from the time they are six to the time they are twenty or twenty-two. Their anxiety to do well, to succeed, to please

their parents so fills their minds that all the natural joy in learning evaporates. As a result, conscientious students are driven to view their schoolwork as oppressive drudgery, and marginal students are tempted to cheat and bluff their way to a degree. For these reasons I say grades should be abolished at all levels of education.

Applications

1. Traditionally, every state has been required to recognize marriages performed in all other states. In 1996, when it became known that Hawaii was about to legalize same-sex marriage, the Defense of Marriage Act was drafted to permit states to deny recognition of same-sex marriages performed in other states. On July 12, 1996, the House of Representatives passed the bill by a 342–67 vote. Passage of the bill generated much debate. Following are three editorials on the issue. Summarize each. Then extend your inquiry on the issue, using the approach explained in the chapter.

EDITORIAL 1

MORALS AND MORES ASIDE, overwhelming House approval of the "Defense of Marriage Act" was a sound vote for common sense.

The Senate should quickly follow suit.

The act defines marriage as a heterosexual union and limits marriage rights for gay men and lesbians.

Bipartisan support of the measure . . . is indicative of the fact that an estimated seven of ten Americans oppose marriage rights for homosexuals. Besides defining—for purposes of federal benefits—marriage as a union between a man and a woman, the act also allows states the prerogative of not recognizing same-sex marriages performed in another state.

The act allows each state the freedom to establish its own definition of marriage and pay corresponding benefits to gay partners, but it would not force the federal government or other states to recognize the legality of those marriages. That is welcome financial news to states already operating on stretched budgets.

Without the measure in place, it would take only one state's approval of same-sex marriages to create a scenario of people flocking to that state to be wed and returning home to demand full benefits for their union, under federal law.

Each state should have the right of self-determination in that regard. The Defense of Marriage Act ensures that right. . . .[7]

EDITORIAL 2

. . . WHILE THIS BILL will give anti-gay-union states legal ammo to resist recognizing such unions, opponents doubt it will survive U.S. Supreme Court scrutiny. At best,

the bill recognizes that seven of ten Americans are uncomfortable with the notion of identifying a same-sex union by the same name ascribed to heterosexual matrimony.

But the bill can also be seen more cynically as politicians making campaign hay by again pitting Americans against one another.

Gay men and lesbians seek an acknowledgement of the legitimacy of their lives. They want the right to inherit, to social security and pension benefits that accrue to life partners, the right to be appointed guardian or make health-care decisions for them. Their aim is not to destroy the institution of marriage, but to participate in it.

In the 1960s it was illegal for people of different races to marry in many states. In 1967, after a couple aptly named Loving were prosecuted in Virginia, the U.S. Supreme Court struck down antimiscegenation laws. The opinion called marriage one of the "basic civil rights of man," fundamental to our very existence and survival. It could not be restricted by invidious racial discriminations.

Americans face a rocky road reaching a live-and-let-live accommodation with formalized homosexual relationships. Politicians more intent on exploiting differences than finding a common ground don't help. . . .[8]

EDITORIAL 3

CONGRESS SHOULDN'T PASS bills that inflame prejudice.

Shame on the House for approving the so-called Defense of Marriage Act, an absurd title for a bill that would all but deny marriage rights to gays and lesbians.

. . . Allowing a minority group to enjoy the benefits of marriage would not hurt heterosexual marriages. . . .

Gays and lesbians contribute to society just as heterosexuals do.

They are workers, volunteers, friends and relatives. They deserve the same opportunities for spousal benefits as heterosexuals enjoy.

The underlying reason for outlawing same-sex marriages is homophobia. Some people in the heterosexual majority want to deny them rights simply because they have a different sexual preference. Call it by its real name: discrimination. . . .[9]

2. Choose one of the specific issues you clarified in application 1 or 2 of Chapter 16. Conduct your inquiry into this issue in the manner explained in this chapter. Take careful notes.

3. Choose one of the specific issues presented in Chapter 16 in the discussion of prostitution, boxing, and juvenile crime. Conduct your inquiry into this issue in the manner explained in this chapter. Take careful notes.

CHAPTER 18

Forming a Judgment

Judgments are conclusions arrived at through examination of evidence and careful reasoning. They are the products of thinking. Unlike feelings, judgments are not spontaneous and unconscious. They may, of course, contain elements of the spontaneous—such as intuition—but, like other data, these have first been weighed and evaluated.

The fact that judgments are products of evaluation and reasoning does not guarantee their worth. There are foolish as well as wise judgments, superficial as well as penetrating ones. A judgment can easily reflect misconceptions about truth, knowledge, and opinion. It can also involve one or more of the errors in thinking detailed in Chapters 8–13.

The strategy we have discussed for thinking critically about issues is designed to promote thoughtful judgments. By knowing ourselves and being observant, we improve our perception and guard against error. By systematically clarifying issues and conducting inquiry, we rescue our thinking from preconceived notions and first impressions. Next we must evaluate the evidence we have obtained, deciding what it means and how significant it is. One key aspect of this evaluation process concerns the resolution of apparent conflicts in evidence. As we have seen in previous chapters, experts do not always agree. Because people often view the same event quite differently, even the eyewitness reports of honest people can conflict.

It is a popular view that the more scientific the procedure, the less need exists for evaluation. But that view is mistaken. Scientific procedures generate or discover factual information that must be classified and interpreted to be meaningful. Consider, for example, this unusual case. An ancient tomb was unearthed in central China containing the body of a woman who died about 2100 years ago. Great care had been taken in burying her. She was placed in an airtight coffin filled with a special fluid. The coffin was encased in five larger boxes lined with five tons of charcoal. That larger unit was buried in a sixty-foot hole and surrounded by white clay.

Because of this extraordinary burial, when the woman's body was found, the flesh was still moist, the hair still rooted in the scalp, the joints still flexible, and most of the internal organs intact. Specialists conducted a careful autopsy. They performed chemical analyses of the woman's hair, stomach, muscles, bones, lungs, gallbladder, and intestines. They X-rayed her bones. To be useful, however, the mass of facts they obtained had to be *interpreted.* Only by studying the data, raising questions about it, and deciding what judgments were most reasonable did they conclude, for example, that she had borne children, had eaten a melon shortly before her death, and had probably died suddenly as the result of an obstructed coronary artery.[1]

Evaluation plays an important role not only in science but also in other fields. In fact, because in other areas the information may be less clear or more fragmentary and opinions may be more sharply in conflict, the quality of a judgment may depend even more heavily on evaluation.

Evaluating Evidence

Evaluating evidence consists of asking and answering appropriate questions. In Chapter 6 we discussed eleven kinds of evidence and the specific questions that should be asked in evaluating each. Here is a summary of that discussion.

The Kind of Evidence	*The Questions*
Personal experience (yours or other people's)	Are the experiences typical or atypical? Are they sufficient in number and kind to support the conclusion?
Unpublished report	Where did the story originate? How can I confirm that the version I heard is accurate?
Published report	Are the sources of important items of information cited? Does the author have a reputation for careful reporting? Does the publisher or broadcaster have a reputation for reliability? Which statements might a thoughtful person challenge? How well does the author answer the challenges?
Eyewitness testimony	What circumstances could have distorted the eyewitness' perception? What circumstances since the event could have affected his or her recollection?

Celebrity testimony	For advertisements or "infomercials," is the celebrity a paid spokesperson? For talk-show comments, does the celebrity offer any support for his or her views— for example, citing research conducted by more qualified people? Also, does the host ask for such support?
Expert opinion	Does the person have *specific* expertise in the particular issue under discussion? Does the expert support his or her view with references to current research? Do other authorities agree or disagree with the expert's view?
Experiment	For a laboratory experiment, has the it been replicated by other researchers? For a field experiment, have other researchers independently confirmed the findings?
Statistics Survey	Is the source of the statistics reliable? Was the sample truly representative—that is, did all members of the *total* population surveyed have an equal chance of being selected? Were the questions clear, unambiguous, and objectively phrased? For a mailed survey, did a significant number fail to respond? Also, do other surveys corroborate the survey's findings?
Formal observation	Could the observer's presence have distorted what occurred? Was the observation of sufficient duration to permit the conclusions that were drawn? Do the conclusions overgeneralize?
Research review:	Do the reviewer's conclusions seem reasonable given the research covered in the review? Has the reviewer omitted any relevant research?

One additional question is applicable to all kinds of evidence: Is this evidence *relevant* to the issue under consideration? If it is not relevant, it deserves no consideration, no matter how excellent it may be in other respects.

Evaluating Your Sources' Arguments*

In addition to evaluating the evidence we have obtained, we must examine the arguments others have advanced. Chapter 7 explained a helpful

*See Chapter 7, pages 71–74.

way to deal with arguments that are longer than a paragraph—condensing them to more manageable length by *composing a summary*. Chapter 17 offered detailed instructions for doing so effectively. Let us now see how to use a summary to *evaluate* an argument. The first summary we will examine is the one presented in Chapter 17.* For ease of reference, each sentence in the summary is numbered, and the questions that apply to it are numbered correspondingly.

THE SUMMARY

1. One of the biggest obstacles to learning—in grade school, high school, and college—is grades.

2. The fear of bad grades hangs over the heads of young people from the time they are six to the time they are twenty or twenty-two.

3. Their anxiety to do well, to succeed, to please their parents so fills their minds that all the natural joy in learning evaporates.

4. As a result, conscientious students are driven to view their schoolwork as oppressive drudgery, and marginal students are tempted to cheat and bluff their way to a degree.

5. For these reasons I say grades should be abolished at all levels of education.

THE QUESTIONS

1. Are grades an obstacle to learning? If so, are they at all three levels?

2. Do any young people between these ages fear bad grades? Do all of them? Is the fear a serious one (as "hangs over the head" implies)?

3. Is there any natural joy in learning to begin with? For all subjects? Do grades cause anxiety? If so, does the anxiety eliminate the joy? For all students?

4. Do any conscientious students view schoolwork as oppressive drudgery? Do all of them? Do many view it that way in certain circumstances but not in others? If they do view it as oppressive drudgery, is it grades that cause them to? Are any marginal students tempted to cheat and bluff? All of them? If some are, is it grades that tempt them to do so?

5. Would abolishing grades solve all these problems? Some of them? Would it create any additional problems? If so, would the resulting situation be more or less desirable? Would the effects differ at different levels of education?

Here is another example: the response of popular psychologist and author Joyce Brothers to a reader's question.[2] Because the response is brief, no summary is necessary. As in the previous example, numbers have been assigned to our paraphrase of Dr. Brothers's response and to our analysis.

*See Chapter 17, pages 168–170.

THE SUMMARY

The reader explained in her letter:

She works with a homosexual man and has formed a close platonic relationship with him. Her husband, however, disapproves of the man, calling him "sick," and becomes angry when she and the man converse on the telephone. (No other details of the situation were included in the published letter.)

Dr. Brothers said in her response:

1. In her view the woman's husband is afraid of homosexuality.

2. As is characteristic of all people who suffer from homophobia, the basis of the husband's fear is not concern that the man might proposition him but a perceived threat to his ego and apprehension about discovering that at some level he, too, has some "feminine" characteristics.

3. Homophobia can have harmful effects, including—in this woman's case—a possible weakening of her marriage.

4. The woman should discuss the situation fully with her husband and encourage him to examine his feelings rationally.

5. Such an approach could help the husband gain greater insight into the problem.

6. If for some reason this approach does not produce the effect the wife desires, she should consider seeking joint counseling, giving the husband an opportunity to change his viewpoint.

7. Regardless of the outcome of the counseling, whether the husband comes around to the wife's way of thinking or not, the wife should continue her relationship with her homosexual friend.

THE QUESTIONS

1. Could the husband's reaction be based on anger or revulsion or a firmly held belief or simple jealously that his wife shares much of her time with another man? Is it possible that his derogatory comments about her friend are masking jealousy (rather than expressing any deeply felt antagonism toward gays)? Nothing in the letter *requires* the conclusion that he is afraid.

2. Dr. Brothers's reference to homophobics in general moves the discussion beyond the individual case. It dismisses the possibility that a person might fear a homosexual advance. But what of people who were molested by homosexuals as children? Wouldn't it be normal for them to fear reliving that experience, just as people heterosexually molested would fear reliving their experience? It is possible that the husband's ego is threatened and that he is apprehensive about his own feminine qualities, but given the lack of details in the letter, it is *far from certain* that this is the case.

3. No reasonable person would dispute this idea.

4. What does it mean for the wife to discuss the matter with her husband: to have her mind made up in advance about his feelings and thoughts or to

ask him to explain them and listen to his answer with the expectation of learning something?

5. Shouldn't the wife be willing to explore her behavior as honestly as she expects her husband to explore his feelings? Shouldn't she, too, be attempting to achieve a new and deeper understanding of the situation than she presently has?

6. Is counseling likely to be more successful if one partner begins with the conviction that he or she is entirely right and the other person wrong?

7. Is maintaining a friendship necessarily more important than saving a marriage? Is more information than is provided in the reader's letter needed before concluding that the friendship in this case is worth more than the marriage? Wouldn't it be helpful to know how long the couple has been married; whether they have children and, if so, what ages; and whether their relationship was harmonious before this situation arose? (If the husband cherished her companionship, is it not possible that he is more motivated by feelings of neglect and loss than by homophobia?) Is it reasonable for Dr. Brothers to *assume* the woman is being fair to her husband and he is being unreasonable without knowing how often, at what times of the day, and for how long the woman talks on the phone to her gay friend? What if both husband and wife work and share responsibility for housework and parenting, but she now spends hours on the telephone every evening? Would not the best advice in that case be for *her* to get counseling and find out what's wrong with *her*?

As the examples demonstrate, taking the time to ask appropriate questions has several benefits. First, it gets us beyond judging on the basis of appearances. That is good because ideas that might seem appealing to us at first glance may not remain so when we examine them more closely. Second, it protects us from our own visceral reactions and permits us to get beyond a blanket, overall yes or no and consider the position in its various parts. Even the best thinkers, after all, are human and therefore fallible. So on a complex issue, any statement longer than a sentence or two could easily be neither perfectly reasonable nor perfectly unreasonable but partly each. And the longer the passage, the greater the likelihood that it is flawed and that we can therefore find both things to agree with and things to disagree with, both strengths and weaknesses. Finally, taking time to ask appropriate questions often suggests to us a structure around which to arrange our thoughts.

The answers we develop for the questions we raise comprise our response to the viewpoint. If we write out our response, we may either follow the organization suggested by the order of the questions or use a different organization. The decision depends on what order of presentation will make our ideas most coherent and provide the emphasis we intend.

Making Important Distinctions

Still another important consideration in evaluating evidence is making careful distinctions. The exact distinction needed, of course, depends on the situation. However, here are six kinds of distinctions that are frequently necessary to avoid faulty evaluations:

1. *Between the person and the idea.* It's easy to confuse the person with the idea. Just as we tend to overlook the faults of our friends and exaggerate those of our enemies, so we tend to look favorably on the ideas of people we like or admire and unfavorably on those we dislike or do not admire. Similarly, we tend to disregard the ideas of people who we feel *ought not to have* ideas on certain subjects—for example, white scholars on African American history or men on "women's issues." Such reactions are irrational because ideas are not synonymous with the people who hold them: Admirable people can be wrong, and despicable people can be right. Furthermore, a person's gender, color, nationality, or religion is not a proper basis for accepting or rejecting his or her ideas. It is possible for a man to be an authority on feminism (or for that matter to *be a feminist*), a white scholar to have insights about African American history (and vice versa), and a Chinese Buddhist to make a valuable contribution to the subject of American Protestantism. Therefore, we should make a conscious effort to keep our analyses of ideas separate from our feelings for the people who hold them.

2. *Between what is said and how it is said.* Style and substance are quite different matters. Unfortunately, the person with the clearest and most graceful expression does not always have the soundest idea. So, though it is natural for us to be impressed by eloquent writers or speakers, it's unwise to assume that their ideas are necessarily sound. As Saint Augustine once said, "Our concern with a man is not with what eloquence he teaches, but with what evidence."

3. *Between why people think as they do and whether what they think is correct.* It's common to judge people's *motives* for thinking and acting as they do. Though such judging is sometimes rash, at other times it is very helpful. Finding out that a senator has connections with the handgun manufacturing industry, for example, raises interesting questions about the senator's opposition to gun control laws. But it is important for us to remember that unworthy motivations do not necessarily contaminate the position. The soundness of an idea doesn't depend on the motivations of those who support it. It depends on how well the idea fits the realities of the situation.

4. *Between the individual and the group or class.* The individual person or thing may differ from the group or class in one or more significant respects. Therefore, the characteristics of the individual should not be carelessly attributed to the group, or vice versa.

5. *Between matters of preference and matters of judgment.* Matters of preference concern taste, which it is pointless to debate. However, matters of judgment concern interpretations of fact and theory, which are debatable. It is therefore appropriate to question matters of judgment.

6. *Between familiarity and correctness.* To respond less guardedly to the familiar than to the unfamiliar is natural. Yet familiar ideas are not necessarily correct. Accordingly, when judging correctness, we should disregard the familiarity or unfamiliarity of the idea. Then we will be open to insights from both sides of issues, not just from the side we favor.

Expressing Judgments

The act of expressing a judgment can alter it. Therefore, no matter how clear your judgment of an issue might be, it is best to consider it formless until you have expressed it accurately in words. The following guidelines will help you express all your judgments effectively:

1. Strive for a balanced view.
2. Deal with probability.
3. Make your subject appropriately specific.
4. Make your predicate exact.
5. Include all appropriate qualifications.
6. Avoid exaggeration.

Let's look more closely at each of these guidelines.

STRIVE FOR A BALANCED VIEW

A balanced view of an issue is one that reflects all the subtlety and complexity of the issue. The dominant view exerts considerable force on most people's thinking, particularly when the issue is controversial and emotion is running high. Without realizing it, people typically adopt fashionable perspectives and use fashionable arguments and even fashionable words. This happens even with people who are normally critical thinkers.

At such times, hordes of liberal thinkers sound alike, as do hordes of conservative thinkers. When someone finally exercises the mental discipline to break the pattern and take a balanced look at the issue, the result is a refreshingly original, and often insightful, view.

Consider the case of Salman Rushdie's book *The Satanic Verses*. Many Muslims, convinced that the book ridiculed their religion and the prophet Muhammad, reacted angrily. The Ayatollah Khomeini went so far as to put out a contract on the author's life and to threaten any individuals involved in publishing or distributing the book. The literary, journalistic, and intellectual communities' response to this extreme reaction was to hold rallies and publicly support Rushdie and his publisher. The theme of these rallies and statements was that freedom of expression is an absolute right.

There is no question that freedom of expression is a worthy principle and that the extreme reaction of Khomeini and his followers to Rushdie's novel was totally unjustifiable. And that is precisely why it was so tempting for sensitive people to support Rushdie and condemn Khomeini without qualification. (Adding to that temptation was the fact that Khomeini had previously earned the enmity of Westerners.) Yet achieving intellectual balance means making a conscious effort to moderate our reactions even in the face of strong temptation to overstatement.

At least a few writers displayed intellectual balance on this issue by reminding us that other principles are also important—notably, the principle of respect for the religious beliefs of others. Columnist John Leo spoke of "the fact that our [principle of tolerance] calls for a certain amount of deference and self-restraint in discussing other people's religious beliefs."[3] And Professor John Esposito observed that "the First Amendment right doesn't mean you should automatically say everything you want to."[4] *What made these views balanced is that they were made without denying the importance of freedom of speech and the outrageousness of Khomeini's threat.*

Consider another issue—the question of building self-esteem in people. For more than twenty years, writers of self-improvement books have emphasized the importance of self-esteem, particularly in young children. So great has been this emphasis that many people assume that success or failure in school and later life is largely a reflection of this factor. Almost any effort to make people feel good about themselves is applauded.

But Barbara Lerner, psychologist and attorney, was able to resist the powerful lure of the prevailing view and examine self-esteem critically. Her reward was the insight that self-esteem is not always good, that in some cases it can be an *obstacle* to achievement. There is a difference, she notes, between "earned" self-esteem and "feel-good-now" self-esteem. The former can lead to achievement and even excellence, whereas the latter promotes complacency and, ultimately, incompetence.[5]

To achieve a balanced view of the issues you address, you must be willing to look for the *neglected* side of the issue and, when there is good reason to do so, *challenge* the prevailing view.

DEAL WITH PROBABILITY

Despite our best efforts to investigate issues, sometimes we cannot accumulate sufficient evidence to arrive at a judgment with certainty. This is especially true with controversial issues. At such times, the irresponsible often raise their voices, choose more forceful words, and *pretend* certainty. That is a grave mistake, first because the pretense seldom fools good thinkers, but more importantly because it is intellectually dishonest.

As long as we have made a sincere effort to gain the evidence necessary to achieve certainty and are not deliberately choosing to ride the fence, there is no shame in admitting, "I cannot say for certain what the correct judgment is in this situation." On the contrary, there is virtue in doing so. Yet in such situations there is one further obligation we must meet as responsible thinkers. It is to explain, if possible, what judgment probability favors—that is, what judgment the evidence *suggests,* as opposed to *proves,* is correct.

The evidence, for example, may be insufficient to say with certainty that cigarette smoking *causes* lung cancer or that viewing television violence *definitely harms* people. Nevertheless, there is sufficient evidence on both issues to warrant your judgment about *probable* cause–effect relationships.

Whenever you cannot achieve certainty, focus on probability.

MAKE YOUR SUBJECT APPROPRIATELY SPECIFIC

The subject in a careful judgment is appropriately specific. Consider these sentences, in which the subject is italicized:

> *Today's college students* are less proficient in grammar and usage than their counterparts were ten years ago.

> *Today's U.S. college students* are less proficient in grammar and usage than their counterparts were ten years ago.

> *Today's U.S. two-year college students* are less proficient in grammar and usage than their counterparts were ten years ago.

> *Today's students at this college* are less proficient in grammar and usage than their counterparts were ten years ago.

If the evidence covers only students at a particular college, only the last judgment can be sound. The other three are too generalized. To avoid this kind of error in your writing and speaking, choose the subjects of your judgments with care.

MAKE YOUR PREDICATE EXACT

The predicate in a careful judgment asserts exactly what you want to assert. Compare these sentences, in which part of the predicate is italicized:

> Peace *has been* achieved.

> Peace *can be* achieved.

> Peace *must be* achieved.

Peace *should be* achieved.

Peace *could be* achieved.

Peace *will be* achieved.

Though these sentences are very similar in construction, their meanings are very different. Unless we deliberately embrace ambiguity (in which case we should expect to cause confusion), we should choose our predicates judiciously.

A good example of the kind of confusion that can result is shown in the sentence that triggered theological debate in the 1960s: "God is dead." It made a nice slogan, but exactly what did it mean? Taking it by itself, a person would have great difficulty answering. In addition to the obvious possibility, "There is no supreme being," there are at least seven others:

People no longer *want* to believe God exists.

People are no longer *able* to believe God exists.

People are no longer *certain* God exists.

People no longer *act* as if God exists.

People no longer *care* whether God exists.

People no longer *accept* some particular conception of God.

People are no longer *satisfied* with the limitation of traditional human expressions of belief in God's existence.

Unless the original writer or speaker made clear which of these meanings he or she had in mind, the audience would have been neither informed nor persuaded. To leave an audience guessing about your meaning is irresponsible and self-defeating.

INCLUDE ALL APPROPRIATE QUALIFICATIONS

Saying that something usually happens is different from saying that it frequently happens or that it happens every other Tuesday. The more care you take to include the qualifications necessary to express your thoughts precisely, the more defensible your judgment is likely to be. And that includes not only qualifications of time but those of place and condition as well. In the judgment "American men over forty who never attended college tend to be opposed to the idea of women's liberation advocated by the National Organization for Women" (which may or may not be true), almost every word is a qualification. It says (a) not all men but *American* men, (b) not members of all age groups and educational levels but those *over forty who never attended college,* and (c) not the idea of women's liberation in general but the idea *advocated by the National Organization for Women.*

AVOID EXAGGERATION

Most of us know one or more people for whom every occasion is "memorable," every problem is a "crisis," every enjoyable film is "worthy of an Academy Award nomination," and every attractive new car or fashion "incomparable." To such people nothing is merely good or bad—it is the best or worst. Their vocabulary is filled with superlatives. When someone is late for an appointment with them, they wait an "eternity." When they go to the dentist, the pain is "unbearable." Their debts are "titanic."

When such people report something to us, we have to translate it, scale it down to realistic proportions. If they say, "He was the biggest man I've ever seen, at least seven feet ten," we conclude that he was about six feet six. If they say, "You've got to hear Sidney Screech's new record—it's the most fantastic performance he's ever given," we conclude that it was a bit better than usual.

We may, however grudgingly, make allowances for the verbal excesses of friends, but we are seldom willing to extend that courtesy to strangers. Instead, we regard them as lacking in balance and proportion and dismiss their reports as unreliable. Others, of course, will regard us no differently. If you want your judgments to stand the test of scrutiny by others, avoid all exaggeration. When you cannot be certain your judgment is accurate, you should tend to err on the side of understatement rather than overstatement. In other words, you should take the more modest interpretation, the less extreme conclusion. That way, if you are wrong—as every human must sometimes be—you will at least have the saving grace of having demonstrated a sense of control and restraint.

If your evaluation and judgment meet the standards explained in this chapter, you have a right to be proud, for judgment carefully arrived at is the hallmark of humanity. It is the capstone to your capacity for thinking. As such, it separates you most dramatically from other creatures, enabling you to grow in knowledge and, considerably more important, in *wisdom,* and to improve your own life and the lives of others.

The critical thinking strategy presented in this chapter and the four preceding chapters may be summarized as follows.

1. Know yourself and remain mindful of the ways in which your habits of mind undermine your treatment of issues.
2. Be observant and reflect on what you see and hear.

3. When you identify an issue, clarify it by listing its aspects and raising probing questions about each.

4. Conduct a thorough inquiry, obtaining all relevant facts and informed opinions.

5. Evaluate your findings, and then form and express your judgment.

This summary makes a convenient checklist. Refer to it whenever you examine issues.

Applications

1. Analyze *two* of the following summaries in the manner demonstrated in the chapter. Be sure to get beyond your first impressions, and avoid the errors in thinking summarized in Chapter 13. Answer all the questions you raise, deciding exactly in what ways you agree with the idea and in what ways you disagree.

   a. Feeling and intuition are better guides to behavior than reasoning. We need immediate answers to many of our problems today, and feeling and intuition are almost instantaneous, while reasoning is painfully slow. Moreover, feeling and intuition are natural, uncorrupted by artificial values and codes imposed on us by society. Reasoning is a set of programmed responses—tight, mechanical, and unnatural. Thus, if we wish to achieve individuality, to express our real inner selves, the part of us that is unconditioned by others, we should follow our feelings and intuitions instead of our thoughts.

   b. It is commonly accepted that the best way to improve the world and relations among its people is for everyone to curb his or her own self-interest and think of others. This concern with others is the basic idea in the Golden Rule and in most religions. It is, of course, questionable whether that goal is realizable. But more important, it is mistaken. It is not selfishness but the pretense of altruism that sets person against person. If everyone looked out for him- or herself, and pursued his or her own interests, there would be not only less hypocrisy in the world but more understanding. Each person would be aware of where everyone else stood in relation to him or her. And no one would be dependent on others.

   c. The institution of marriage has outlived its usefulness. More and more people today, particularly young people, are realizing that it makes more sense to have informal relationships. A couple should live together only as long as both individuals want to. Whenever one wants to end the relationship, he or she should be able to do so, neatly, without legal complications. This could be done if marriage were abolished. Everyone would benefit. People would retain their individual freedom and be able to fulfill their own need to develop as a person, responding to their own changing values and interests.

   d. College instructors should not be permitted to set restrictive attendance policies; they should be made to treat students as responsible adults, leaving each student free to decide his or her attendance behavior. Students know their own strengths and weaknesses better than anyone else does and are mature enough to decide which classes they need to attend. Some courses will be new and challenging to them. Others will merely duplicate prior learning. Some instructors will add to the students' store of information and challenge their intellect. Others will merely read the textbook aloud. Left to exercise their own judgment, students can use their time wisely, attending the classes of the good, interesting, dedicated teachers and avoiding those of the dullards and deadbeats.

e. Every time parents tell their children how to look at an issue, they close the children's minds to other views. Every time parents present their political views or their philosophy of life (the principles they live by), they narrow their children's perspective. Every time parents take their children to church or make them sit in Sunday school, they shackle the children to one spiritual outlook. In each of these cases, parents rob the children of their freedom and independence and individuality. For these reasons, wise and loving parents, who wish their children to become free beings and not slaves to the thinking of others, will not teach them their principles and values but will leave them free to develop their own.

f. One of the reasons crime is so rampant in our society is that we put too much emphasis on determining why the criminal committed the crime and whether the police treated the criminal fairly. Those are important matters, but other, equally important ones seem to be neglected lately— like protecting law-abiding people from dangerous, irresponsible people and making punishments severe enough to deter crime. We cringe at primitive societies' handling of crime—for example, cutting off a thief's hands or a perjurer's tongue. But at least such punishments reflect a recognition that crime is an outrage against society that should not be tolerated. I am not suggesting that we return to such a standard of justice, only that we get tough with criminals. Two steps that would provide a good start would be setting determinate sentences for crimes instead of giving judges the wide latitude they now enjoy and refusing to let legal technicalities set aside a conviction when a person is clearly guilty.

g. Every year there is at least one major scandal involving a college athlete illegally accepting money from the coaching staff, alumni, or other supporters of the team. In recent years the number of scandals seems to be increasing. The best way to eliminate this problem is to discard the National Collegiate Athletic Association (NCAA) prohibition against playing for pay. Athletes get paid for their efforts at the professional level. There is no good reason to make them wait until graduation to be rewarded for their talents. The coaches are paid a salary, and the colleges often receive substantial sums of money for television rights to games. Only the athletes, the ones mainly responsible for generating the income, are deprived of financial gain. By continuing its archaic rule, the NCAA is being both unfair and hypocritical.

2. Apply what you learned in this chapter to the inquiry you completed for either application 2 or 3 in Chapter 17.

CHAPTER 19

Persuading Others

When you read the previous chapter, it may have seemed an appropriate place to conclude the book. That is an understandable impression. The thinking process could reasonably be considered complete when a judgment has been made and put into words. Why, then, has this chapter been included? The simple answer is, because thoughtful judgments deserve to be shared, and the way they are presented can strongly influence the way others react to them. By learning the principles of persuasion and applying them in your writing (and speaking), you will extend the benefits of your critical thinking beyond the confines of your own mind.

Persuasion means presenting your view so effectively that people who have no position on the issue will be inclined to agree with you, and those who disagree with you will be motivated to reconsider their own view. This task is more difficult than it may seem. Those who are neutral will be open to suggestion, but only if you demonstrate the reasonableness of your view. Those who disagree with you will be disposed to reject your view for the obvious reason that it disputes theirs. To accept yours entails discarding their own, which they may have formed after considerable thought and with which their egos are intertwined.

To appreciate how difficult it can be to persuade others, you need only reflect on your own resistance to ideas that oppose yours. If you still have trouble giving such ideas a fair hearing *even after a semester's study of critical thinking,* it is unreasonable to expect individuals who lack your training to respond more generously.

Guidelines for Persuasion

Here are eleven guidelines for persuasion. Each is designed to help you overcome a specific challenge. The more faithfully you follow these guidelines, the more effective you will be in demonstrating the merit of your ideas.

GUIDELINE 1: RESPECT YOUR AUDIENCE

This guideline may sound idealistic, but it is eminently practical. If you believe the people you are trying to persuade are doltish or intellectually dishonest, you are bound to betray that belief, if not directly then indirectly in your tone or choice of words. Moreover, they will generally sense your disparaging view of them and feel hurt or resentful, hardly the kind of reaction that will make them open to persuasion.

But aren't some people doltish or intellectually dishonest? Of course. The point is, you have no business thinking them so without clear and convincing evidence. If you have such evidence, don't write for that audience. If you lack such evidence, as is usually the case, you should give your audience the benefit of the doubt. Ask yourself what might account for their disagreement with you. Consider all the factors that can influence a person's perspective, including age, gender, race, ethnicity, family background, religion, income level, political affiliation, degree of education, and personal experience. If one or more of these could account for the difference in viewpoint, you will have good reason for regarding their disagreement as thoughtful and honest.

A caution is in order here. Don't feel you need to state your respect for your audience. Such statements have a way of sounding insincere. Work on feeling respect; if you can accomplish that, there will be no need to state it. It will show.

GUIDELINE 2: UNDERSTAND YOUR AUDIENCE'S VIEWPOINT

Many people make the mistake of thinking that knowing their own viewpoint is all that is necessary to be persuasive. "What my readers think about the issue is really irrelevant," they reason. "All that matters is what I'm going to get them to think." In addition to being pompous, this attitude ignores two crucial points. First, people's views matter very much to them, and when others refuse to acknowledge this fact, they feel offended. Second, we must know where people stand before we can hope to reach them.

How can you determine what your readers think about the issue you are writing about? The answer depends on the particular circumstances. Here are the most common situations:

Situation 1: You are writing for a single reader who has presented his or her ideas in an article, book, speech, or conversation. Review what your reader said, noting not only the person's position but also the reasoning that supports it. Determine both the strengths and the weaknesses of the person's position.

Situation 2: You are writing for a single reader who has not, to your knowledge, expressed a view on the issue in question. Suppose, for example, you are writing a letter to the president of a company objecting to the company's sponsorship of a controversial television series. You may not be sure the president disagrees with what you plan to say, but prudence suggests that you anticipate the "worst case scenario"—that he or she vigorously supports the sponsorship decision. Use your imagination to produce relevant questions: What might the president think about outsiders criticizing the company? That they have no right to criticize? That the company is answerable only to its stockholders? What might he or she think about the series in question—that is, about the characters, typical plot situations and themes? (The more closely you have studied the series, the more meaningful your answer will be.) Might the president view outside criticism as a form of censorship? Why or why not?

Situation 3: You are writing, not for a specific individual, but for all the people who hold an opposing view on the issue. This is the most commonly encountered situation in persuasive writing. Study what has been expressed by people who hold the opposing view. Look for frequently repeated arguments and themes. The more often a line of thought is expressed and the greater the number of people who express it, the more influential it is likely to have been in shaping people's views. The most influential errors in thinking represent the greatest challenge to persuasion.

GUIDELINE 3: BEGIN FROM A POSITION YOU HAVE IN COMMON WITH YOUR READERS

Beginning from a position of agreement with your reader is not an arbitrary requirement or a matter of courtesy or "good form." *It is a simple matter of psychology.* If you begin by saying—in effect, if not directly— "Look here, you are wrong, and I'm going to show you," you push your readers to defensive if not outright hostile reactions. They are likely to read the rest of your paper thinking not of what you are saying but of ways to refute it, concerned with measuring not the strengths of your arguments but only their weaknesses. And if they are unreasonable and unbalanced in their reading, the fault will be more yours than theirs.

In the persuasive composition, regardless of the issue or the words used, the beginning says in effect—though never directly—"You and I are both interested in this subject, and we both regard it as a serious and important one. Though our positions differ on many points, by communicating with each other we can further develop our positions and move a little closer toward the elusive truth that is our common goal." These statements reflect *the attitude* displayed in the beginning, indeed throughout, the composition. This attitude is not something that should be *stated* in the beginning, or in any other place in the composition. It is virtually impossible to state without the ring of insincerity or at least the effect of embarrassment for writer and reader alike. Yet this position of agreement must be present.

It is always difficult to find any points of agreement with someone whose views you strongly disagree with. This was the case with the student who wrote his composition supporting the view that students who fail out of his college should be allowed to apply for readmission. His readers were administrators who had expressed the view that they should not. He began as follows:

> I think students who fail out of this college should be allowed to apply for readmission because every student deserves a second chance. You have said that most readmits lack seriousness of purpose. But . . .

This student was probably quite sure that he and his readers could agree on nothing. So he began with a head-on collision that wrecked his chances to be persuasive. The readers' reaction, conscious or unconscious, undoubtedly was: "This student sees only his own biased position. He doesn't understand the complexity of the problem, doesn't consider the welfare of the total student body, apparently doesn't appreciate that a college education is not a right at all, but a privilege." Their reaction could be mistaken. The student may have been fully aware of all these considerations. But he failed to show his readers that he was. How much better an impression he would have made if he had begun like this:

> No one benefits—neither teachers nor other students—from the presence on campus of students for whom college means merely fun, or a rest, or a chance to make social contacts. Such students take up precious time and space, and usually serve only to distract more serious students. They fail in most cases to realize that a college education is a privilege that they must continue to earn, not an inviolable right. I agree that this college has its share of such students.

The "but" would still appear. The student would still argue his point, but only after he had impressed his readers with the scope of his understanding of the issue and with his desire to be reasonable.

GUIDELINE 4: TAKE A POSITIVE APPROACH

Whenever possible, build your case rather than tearing down the opposing case. To say you should never expose the weaknesses of the opposing side of the issue would be an oversimplification, and a foolish one at that. There are times when examining such weaknesses is the only responsible course of action. Keep in mind, however, that direct criticism of the opposing view will always *seem* harsher than it is to people who share that view, a brief criticism will *seem* protracted, and the mere *perception* that you are being negative will make your readers defensive. The solution is not to be so timid that you don't say anything meaningful but to be sensitive to your readers' reactions.

Consider, for example, this situation. Someone writes an article attacking gun control legislation. Two responses are printed in the following issue of the magazine. In summary the article and responses read as follows:

Article	*Response to Article*
Gun control legislation (a) penalizes the law-abiding more than the lawless, (b) denies citizens the most effective means of protecting self and property at a time when assaults on both are commonplace, (c) violates the U.S. Constitution.	1. Gun control legislation does not penalize the law-abiding more than the lawless. It does not deny citizens the most effective means of protection. It does not really violate the U.S. Constitution.
	2. Gun control legislation discourages crime by making the mere possession of a gun an offense of some gravity. It stresses the role of the police, rather than the individual, in law enforcement. It follows the spirit, if not the letter, of the U.S. Constitution.

Both responses disagree with the article on each of the three points it raised. But the first merely tears down the article's position; the second builds another position. In effect, the first says to the writer, "You are wrong, you are wrong, you are wrong"; the second says, "Here is another view." Whenever you can avoid direct refutation—that is, whenever you can effectively present and support your own views without direct reference to your reader's opposing views—do so.

GUIDELINE 5: UNDERSTATE YOUR ARGUMENT WHEREVER POSSIBLE

The sharpest points of disagreement between you and your readers should always be approached most carefully. These points represent the greatest obstacle to persuasion. If you overstate your position, you are bound to reinforce your readers' conviction about their position rather than dispose them to question their conviction. The student who wrote the following passage made this blunder:

> Most colleges have a "cut system"—that is, they permit a student a few unexcused absences from class without penalty. This college permits no

unexcused absences. Its system is harsh and uncompromising, and may well cause students to develop inferiority complexes.

The readers, who in this case support the college's "no-cut" system, are here not only reinforced in their position by the "inferiority complex" *overstatement* but are provided with an excellent opportunity for damaging rebuttal, such as this:

> That this college's "no-cut" system is demanding, I grant. But the suggestion that it causes students to "develop inferiority complexes" strains credibility. However, even if it were established that it does in fact cause such complexes, would we not be driven to the conclusion that students in such psychologically fragile condition need not fewer but more restrictions to prevent their breakdown?

The student who wrote the following passage made a similar mistake.

> If others treat us with respect and admiration we will become more respectable and admirable.

This student overstated the effect. The respect and admiration of others may encourage us to be respectable and admirable, but it will certainly not automatically make us so. The costliness of the mistake is measured by the fact that the readers, who would have tended to agree with understatement, are likely to reject the whole idea because of the writer's careless use of force.

Consider the following two passages, particularly the italicized words. The first is the forceful statement the writer was tempted to make. The second is the statement the writer actually made. It is an understatement. Note that it does not compromise the writer's position, but it does present the idea more effectively to readers who would be inclined to disagree.

1. If college students are not given *opportunities* to exercise responsibility and make their own choices while they are in college, they will have to adjust *all at once* when they leave college. And such adjustment will be *extremely difficult.*

2. If college students are not given *some opportunities* to exercise responsibility and make their own choices while they are in college, they will have to adjust *rather quickly* when they leave college. And such adjustment will *usually* be *more difficult.*

GUIDELINE 6: CONCEDE WHERE THE OPPOSING SIDE HAS A POINT

The natural tendency in all of us to value our own position too highly makes it difficult for us to admit that opposing views may also have merit. Overcoming this tendency can be accomplished only by remembering that in most controversial issues *no one side possesses the total truth.* If you can approach controversial issues with this thought, you are more likely to grasp the total truth, and to attract reasonable readers to your position.

Total commitment to the truth obliges us, moreover, to concede, not grudgingly but gladly and without hesitation. This does not mean placing a single short sentence at the beginning of the composition that says, "Everyone is right in some degree; I suppose you are too," and then launching into your own position. It means a specific and, if space permits, detailed explanation of where, how, and why the opposing viewpoint is correct.

Let's say, for example, that the issue is whether a comprehensive sex education program from kindergarten through twelfth grade should be initiated in your hometown. Your argument is that it should be. You reason that since a person's whole life is affected by the quality of his understanding of sex, it is too important a subject to be learned in the street; and that, since many parents neglect their responsibility to teach their children at home, the school must offer such a program. Your readers are opposed to the program because they believe classroom sex instruction does not meet two important requirements: individualized instruction at each child's level of understanding and a moral-religious context.

Any reasonable person would admit that the readers' points are well taken. Therefore, you should concede that it is difficult to identify those students whose level of maturity is significantly below the rest of the class, and that the presentation of material well beyond their grasp could be disturbing to them. Further, you should concede that, ideally, the home is the best place for the young to learn about sex, that the school cannot provide the moral-religious context that many parents consider essential. These concessions will not undermine your position. You will still be able to argue that the program is necessary, though you will probably have to qualify your endorsement, acknowledging that the details of the program must be worked out in light of your concessions and that teachers should be selected with care. The concessions will actually enhance your argument, for they demonstrate your grasp of the larger dimensions of the question.

Remember that the readers will give you as much as you give them, usually no less and no more. Only if you are open and honest in your concessions can you expect them to be in theirs.

GUIDELINE 7: DON'T IGNORE ANY RELEVANT FACTS

In studying an issue, we sometimes uncover facts that support the opposing position rather than our own. The temptation is strong to ignore them, especially if the other person has apparently not discovered them. Using them, it would seem, could only weaken our position.

However, the purpose of argument is not to defeat others but, through the exchange of views, to discover the truth in all its complexity. When that happens, everyone wins. When any part of the truth is hidden, no one wins, even though it may appear that someone does. By presenting all the facts, even those that force you to modify your position, you impress your readers with your objectivity and honesty and invite them to show theirs.

Consider the following situation. You believe that the present federally directed anti-poverty program is more beneficial to the poor than the proposed state-directed program would be. You are researching the subject further, preparing to write an article supporting your position for an audience of those who disagree with you. In researching the question you discover a not widely publicized report documenting serious inefficiency and waste in the present federal program. Moreover, it seems clear that these inefficiencies would be less likely to occur in the proposed program. You realize that your readers probably have not seen this report and that it would be damaging to your original position to mention it in your article. What should you do? If you have good reason to conclude that the report is not really relevant to the issue, it would be foolish to mention it. However, if you were convinced that it was relevant—in other words, if it caused you to modify your original position—honesty would require you to mention it and deal with the questions it raised.

GUIDELINE 8: DON'T OVERWHELM YOUR READERS WITH ARGUMENTS

The short paper (any paper of less than 3,000 words must in controversial matters be considered short) cannot be definitive. No serious writer would attempt to convey the impression that it is. Of necessity it contains *selected* evidence. On the surface it would seem that this would give more reason to fill the paper to overflowing with evidence for one's position, to make it as nearly definitive as possible. But on consideration it is clear that the readers' impression must also be considered. What is the impression of those who read a composition that they know cannot possibly be definitive but is devoted to arguing one side of an issue, piling detail on detail, example on example, without even implying that there is another side to the issue? There is no question that they will regard such a composition as *one-sided* and *unbalanced!* The way to avoid such an unfavorable reader reaction is to present only those arguments and that evidence which you feel are most relevant, most persuasive to them.

There is one other related point. Even when you succeed in avoiding an unbalanced argument, you may get so taken up with your presentation that you push the reader, possibly concluding your paper like this:

I think *I have proven* in this paper that there is no alternative to the one suggested by Professor Jones.

or

The evidence I have presented *seems irrefutable.* There can be no *question* that the proposal is harmful.

or

The *reasonable person* will not hesitate to endorse this view.

You cannot "prove" anything in a short paper. Although evidence may "seem irrefutable" to you and you may see "no question," remember it is wiser to permit readers to make their own judgment. And no reader enjoys feeling that agreement with the writer is required to be considered a "reasonable person."

GUIDELINE 9: FOCUS ON THE ARGUMENT BEST CALCULATED TO PERSUADE YOUR AUDIENCE

Different arguments appeal to different readers. Just as it is important to understand your readers' viewpoints on the issue, it is important to use arguments that will appeal to them. To ignore their frames of reference and choose arguments that you yourself find persuasive is a mistake.

Consider, for example, the issue of whether the United States should become involved in conflicts in other parts of the world. The following chart shows the various frames of reference and the arguments that are often made under each:

Frame of Reference	*Arguments for* *U.S. Involvement*	*Arguments Against* *U.S. Involvement*
Moral and/or religious	1. It is the moral obligation of the strong to protect the weak.	1. The Judeo-Christian tradition says to return good for evil, love for hate.
	2. To stand by and do nothing while atrocities are committed is unethical.	2. Modern warfare punishes the victims as well as the perpetrators.

Political and/or practical	1. Because technology has shrunk our planet, no part of the world is outside our country's interest.	1. Precisely because the world has grown smaller, we need to resist the urge to join other nations' battles.
	2. To refuse to stop tyranny is the same as encouraging it.	2. When we deplete our resources in foreign wars, we increase our own vulnerability.
Philosophic	1. A free nation has an obligation to stand up for freedom everywhere.	1. War corrupts all who engage in it.

Let's say you were writing a persuasive paper on this issue and you personally believed that the most telling arguments were moral and/or religious, but that you knew your readers would be more impressed with the political and/or practical or the philosophic arguments. Generally speaking, it would be foolish to follow your personal preference because doing so could defeat your purpose in writing.

GUIDELINE 10: NEVER USE AN ARGUMENT YOU DO NOT BELIEVE IS SOUND OR RELEVANT

This guideline should be understood as a qualification of the previous one. Sincerity and regard for the truth are among the most important characteristics of a writer. Without these there is no real persuasion, only clever presentation. Therefore, if you truly believe that only one argument is worthy of consideration, then by all means use only that argument. This dilemma, however, is not likely to arise very often. In most cases, you will be able to choose among a variety of arguments without compromising your integrity.

GUIDELINE 11: ALLOW TIME FOR YOUR VIEW TO GAIN ACCEPTANCE

It may be tempting to believe that when you present your view, your readers will immediately abandon their own and embrace yours. That expectation is unrealistic. Except in rare cases, the best you should hope for is that they will be moved to reconsider the issue in light of what you said and that your insights will *eventually* cause them to modify their view. The fact that "eventually" may turn out to be next week or next year rather than five minutes from now is not necessarily a comment on your skill in persuading others. It may merely reflect the reality that the bonds people form with their opinions are not easily broken.

Use the following summary of the guidelines for persuasion as a checklist whenever you wish to present your ideas persuasively:

1. Respect your audience.
2. Understand your audience's viewpoint.
3. Begin from a position you have in common with your readers.
4. Take a positive approach.
5. Understate your argument whenever possible.
6. Concede where the opposing side has a point.
7. Don't ignore any relevant facts.
8. Don't overwhelm your readers with arguments.
9. Focus on the argument best calculated to persuade your audience.
10. Never use an argument you do not believe is sound or relevant.
11. Allow time for your view to gain acceptance.

Now let's compare a persuasive composition with an unpersuasive one to see how these guidelines apply.

An Unpersuasive Presentation

A student chose to write a letter pointing out his complaints about the quality of the campus dining hall food and service. His reader was the dining hall manager, his task to impress the reader with his reasonableness and dispose her to reevaluate the performance of her staff.

Violates Guideline No. 3 *Doesn't begin on common ground*	There is continuous discussion taking place on this campus about the dining hall. The students are disgusted with the poor quality of the food and service, and the dirty dishes and silverware. As a student, I would like to point out the reasons for complaining.
Violates Guideline No. 5 *Sarcasm offends reader*	First, let us consider the quality of the food. The meat is either undercooked or overcooked. It is of such low quality that one wonders how it ever got on the market to be sold. The vegetables are completely tasteless, but this is all right because few students bother to eat them. Some students receive bonuses in their meals—such as hair in their soup or dead flies in their potatoes. These are only a few examples of how poor the food is.
No examples offered to support charge	Another complaint of students is the inefficient service. Because of the slow service, students often sit down to a cold meal. Many students have to skip their meals because

they don't have time to wait. Some are driven to eat in local restaurants at extra expense.

Violates Guideline No. 1

Perhaps the most common complaint is the dirty dishes and silverware the students are forced to use. I suppose everything goes through a dishwasher, but by some strange coincidence few things come out clean. However, the work staff don't worry about it—they just close their eyes to the dirt and pass the dishes and silverware on to the servers. Egg caked to the forks and pieces of meat stuck to the plate—it certainly raises a student's spirits when he's eating two meals for the price of one!

Actually suggests bad intention. (How can writer presume to know the intentions of staff when even the facts are in question?) Sarcasm offends reader.

Creates unfavorable impression upon reader (judges administrators rashly). Shows disrespect toward reader. Also implies that students are right, reader (and others) are wrong. No admission that students occasionally do embellish facts.)

The question is, what can be done to correct these problems? Students have already issued their complaints to administrative officials, but this has done no good. These people appear to have turned their heads from the problem. It is clear that something must be done. A lot of revising is needed. But will there be any? You know as well as I do. NO!

How should the student have approached his subject and reader? First, he should have realized that the dining hall manager must either be a dishonest person, caring little whether she runs the dining hall well or poorly, or a conscientious person, anxious to make the operation efficient and excellent. If the student were convinced that the manager is dishonest, he would have been wise *not to write the composition for that reader at all* but perhaps for the administrator to whom the manager reported.

If, on the other hand, he were sure the manager is conscientious and experienced he would have had to acknowledge that (1) she is familiar with the frequency and exaggeration of student complaints that are almost a tradition on college campuses, and that (2) despite her efforts to find all the flaws in her operations, she is apparently unaware of several. If the student had examined carefully the complaints he thought were justified—the poor quality of the food, the dirt in the food, the slow service, and the dirty dishes and silverware—he would have realized that they embrace the entire operation. Mentioning all of them was saying that nothing about the dining hall is acceptable—and such a comprehensive statement would surely have disposed the reader to reject the entire statement. Her natural (human) reluctance to see the faults in her operation would not have been overcome but reinforced. She would think, "It's not possible that I've failed to see all these problems. This student must be just a complainer."

A Persuasive Presentation

A student skilled in persuasive writing would have anticipated all these reactions from his reader and written his letter in this manner:

> What type of student constantly complains about the quality of food in the dining hall? Usually the one who's been catered to by his mother and finds it difficult to adjust to anything but dotingly personal service. During the first term in college my roommate was just such a person. He moaned for an hour after every meal he ate here (and he went without more than a few meals). Hamburger steak was "unfit for human consumption" in his view. Chicken à la king was "slop." And so on—there was an appropriately derogatory comment for every meal he forced himself to eat.
>
> John stayed here for about a month. He enjoyed his courses and did well in them. He made quite a few friends. But he came to speak constantly of his mother's cooking—two-inch steaks three times a week, lasagna, spaghetti with pork chops and meatballs and hot Italian sausage. So he left college to return to Utopia. Few students go as far as John did, of course, but judging by the frequency of the complaints I hear students make about the dining hall, he was not the only student hopelessly spoiled by his mother's cooking.
>
> The service and quality of the food in our dining hall are usually good. Sure, the meat is occasionally overcooked and the vegetables sometimes soggy, but that happened at home too (and my mother only cooked for five, not fifteen hundred). There are, in fact, only two things that I think might be improved.
>
> The first is waiting in line. I usually have to wait at least fifteen minutes to be served in our dining hall, and I arrive quite early. I know from friends in other colleges that a fast-moving line is the exception rather than the rule, so perhaps nothing can be done about it. But if the management found some way to "stagger" the serving or speed up the line, at least one student would appreciate it. The second is dirty dishes and silverware. At most meals I find that I have to wipe dirt from at least one plate or piece of silverware. It may be that in the interests of efficiency the dishwashers are reluctant to wash dirty pieces a second time. Or they may be too busy to notice. But spotless dishes and silverware do help to make the food more appetizing.
>
> Neither improvement would satisfy students who, like John, are spoiled or who enjoy complaining. But they would help to make our dining hall an even better place to eat.

The difference between these two presentations should be obvious. The most conscientious, eager-to-please dining hall manager could not help discounting the first as an exaggerated "blast" written by a chronic complainer or as a release of hostilities by a student angry not only with the dining hall staff but also with his girlfriend, his professors, his parents, and the world. But any reasonably conscientious dining hall manager could not help but regard the second letter as the work of a reasonable, understanding, mature student. It would make her want to improve the service. In other words, it would be *persuasive*.

Applications

This application section is somewhat different from earlier ones. It presents an extended list of contemporary issues. Each has been the subject of considerable public debate. Some have had long, complex histories. For most, a sizable amount of written interpretation and argument is available.

Examine the list carefully to find an issue that interests you. Then analyze it, applying what you have learned from this book, particularly the lessons of Part Three, "A Strategy," which begins with Chapter 14. Keep in mind that the issues are identified here in a very general way. It is up to you not only to find and study the available information but also to select the particular aspects you will focus on. As you have seen, it is better to treat one or two aspects in depth than a larger number superficially.

Finally, write a persuasive composition. (On a separate sheet, specify your audience and explain the audience analysis that guided your composition.)

1. In February 1997 a landmark scientific achievement was announced. For the first time in history, a mammal had been cloned. Scientists had used the DNA from one sheep to produce another sheep, genetically identical to the first. Some scientists had predicted the feat would never be accomplished. Now most agreed that no real barriers exist to cloning human beings, though scientific difficulties would have to be worked out.[1] The procedure would offer possibilities previously dreamt of only by science fiction writers. Here are just a few: (a) A couple who lost a beloved child in an accident could have another just like him or her; (b) fans could buy celebrities' DNA and enjoy the ultimate in memorabilia; (c) dictators could ensure that their rule was passed on, not just through their children but, in a sense, through *themselves*; (d) wealthy people could produce clones to be used for *spare parts* should they contract a disease. As these examples suggest, human cloning poses difficult legal and ethical questions, all of them arising from a single awesome fact—the process would produce not robots but human beings! What is the wisest position for society to take on the issue of human cloning?

2. A survey reveals that U.S. children are more likely to die of homicide, suicide, or accidental shooting than young people in any of twenty-five other industrialized countries.[2] Public response to such statistics varies dramatically. Handgun sales continue to rise, indicating that many people believe having a weapon will ensure their safety. But many others argue that the easy availability of handguns is a major *cause* of violence. They argue that the United States should follow the example of other countries and ban handguns. Which viewpoint is more reasonable?

3. Typically, college teachers are hired on a year-to-year (or several-year) basis and, after a specified period of time, are considered for tenure—that is, permanent appointment. Once teachers receive tenure, they can only be fired for serious cause. Tenure was originally designed to ensure that teachers would enjoy the right to teach their subject without fear of punishment for having unpopular views or taking an unorthodox approach to their subject. This right is known as

"academic freedom." Over the past couple of decades, administrators, facing budgetary restrictions, have sought to save money on teachers' salaries. Unable to fire the higher-paid tenured teachers, they classified many teaching positions "non-tenure-track" and filled them with temporary or "adjunct" faculty, whom they paid considerably lower salaries. In many institutions a majority of the faculty are in this category. As a result of this development, the entire tenure process is now being questioned. Many people favor its abolition, while others argue that the need for a guarantee of academic freedom is as great as ever. Should tenure be abolished?

4. Some people argue that we would have better government if members of Congress were limited to a certain number of terms, say two or three. Disagreement over this issue continues to be sharp and spirited. Do the advantages of "term limits" outweigh the disadvantages?

5. Reportedly, 40 percent of American single women have more than one sexual partner. Moreover, many of them pay no attention to the dangers of unprotected sex.[3] How can this casual attitude toward disease be explained in light of the spread of AIDS and other sexually transmitted diseases? What is the best approach for public health officials and educators to take in solving this problem?

6. From the 1960s to the mid-1970s, the time allotted for serious television news coverage dropped dramatically. A typical analysis segment ran twenty-five minutes in 1960 but only seven minutes in 1976,[4] and it has shrunk still further since then. What caused the shrinking of analysis time? Was the time allotted for analysis in the 1960s too long? Is the time now allotted too short? What, if anything, should be done about this situation, and who should do it?

7. The TV rating system was designed to help parents distinguish shows that are appropriate for their children from those that are not. Yet many parents say that the system does not provide enough information about program *content* for them to make an informed judgment. Are these parents mistaken, or is a change in the rating system necessary? If a change is needed, what should it consist of?

8. In 1982, in a 5–4 decision, the U.S. Supreme Court ruled that current and former presidents enjoy "absolute immunity" from lawsuits seeking monetary damages for misconduct in office. Justice Byron White, one of the four justices who opposed the decision, wrote this dissenting opinion: "[As a result of this decision] a president acting within the outer boundaries of what presidents normally do may, without liability, deliberately cause injury to any number of citizens even though he knows his conduct violates a statute or tramples on the constitutional rights of those who are injured."[5] Do you share Justice White's opposition to the decision?

9. National Basketball Association rules *forbid* players from wagering on basketball games and *discourage* their wagering on other sports. Is this rule fair, or should it be revised? If you believe it should be revised, how should it be?

10. Several television information programs have sent undercover reporters to apply for jobs or purchase automobiles and other products to determine whether women applicants/consumers are treated differently from men. The general conclusion has been that many employers and salespeople harbor negative stereotypes of women—for example, that they are less intelligent than men, less able to understand complex matters, less interested in matters of substance, and less qualified to perform work assignments that are more demanding than

answering a telephone or carrying out simple tasks. Is the behavior depicted in such reports typical of society's treatment of women, or is it a dramatic *exception* to the rule?

11. In recent years debate has continued, sometimes heatedly, over "family values." The principal issues have been whether America has lost them, who has been responsible for the loss (if, indeed, there has been one), and who can best restore them. Many debaters seem to have taken for granted that the term itself has one meaning that everyone understands. Is their assumption warranted? Investigate and determine the meaning (meanings?) of "family values." If you find significant differences in people's definitions, build a reasonable composite, explain it thoroughly, and answer the objections critics might raise about it.

12. Many of today's talk shows are sensational. Friends and relatives typically confront one another, talk escalates to screaming obscenities and, not infrequently, physical combat. Critics of these shows claim that their display of antisocial behavior has the effect of glamorizing it and encouraging imitation. Is there any validity to this charge?

13. "What people view on television or in films can't affect their thinking and actions," argue many in the artistic community. Those who disagree point out that the same artistic community creates public service messages aimed at changing people's minds about drinking and driving, having sex without condoms, and abusing the environment. These critics reason that if a medium has the power to help, it also has the power to harm, and they urge artists and programmers to take an honest look at the messages they put on the screen. Which point of view is more insightful?

14. In recent years the contract negotiations of professional athletes have been given considerable attention by the media. Better-known players frequently demand and receive salaries that were unheard of ten or fifteen years ago. Numerous questions have been raised about players' salaries. Among them are the following: How much higher than the average are the superstars' salaries? Is there anything wrong with players earning more than senators and presidents? What effect is the present trend of athletes demanding more and more money likely to have on sports? On the economy? What do you think the consequences of this trend will be?

15. In Asian cultures marriages have traditionally been arranged for young people. In our culture young people are free to choose their own spouses. Might it be a good idea, with our divorce rate soaring and so many families in disarray, for our culture to follow the Asian custom?

16. Since television became a major entertainment medium in the late 1940s and early 1950s, the TV commercial has become as familiar as the newspaper. Yet few people know very much about commercials. How much do they cost? Who really pays for them? What effects do they have on our lives? Would pay TV be more desirable?

17. Animal intelligence has been a matter of scientific interest since at least the time of Darwin. Can animals "think" in any meaningful sense of the term? Can they form categories (friend, master, my species, and so on)? Are they aware of themselves and their activities? Do they have a sense of past and future, or do they perceive only the present moment?[6] What is the most reasonable view of such issues?

18. Interscholastic and intercollegiate sports competition is as American as apple pie. To many people the mere suggestion that these programs should be abolished is the ultimate heresy. But should they be so sacred? Where did the idea of varsity sports originate? Is it older than intramural competition? What are its good and bad points?

19. Proponents of a guaranteed annual wage argue that by giving every adult person an assured amount of money, we would not only eliminate poverty and its terrible effects, we would also eliminate an entire bureaucracy—the giant welfare system—and perhaps even save money. Opponents see more harmful effects. What are some of those effects? Might they outweigh the benefits?

20. Laugh tracks and applause tracks are so much a part of television comedy shows that most people undoubtedly give them little thought. But some people object strongly to them, regarding them as manipulative and insulting. They propose banning them. Would you support such a proposal?

21. Historically in this country, high school and college athletic budgets have been divided unevenly, with men's teams getting a larger share than women's. Many object to this unequal treatment; others believe it is justified because men's teams have traditionally demonstrated a higher level of skill. Which view is more reasonable? What changes, if any, should be made in the distribution of funds?

22. Compulsory education is so common today that we tend to forget it is a fairly recent historical development. However, some social critics are not only aware of its recency, they are convinced it is no longer a sound idea. In their view children, even as young as six or eight, should be permitted a free choice of whether they will study or not and, if they decide to do so, of what and where they will study. Among the important questions to be considered are these: Why was compulsory education begun? Was it a good idea then? Have the social conditions changed significantly since that time?

23. In some states the testimony of a woman who has been raped is not considered sufficient to bring charges against her assailant. There must be corroborating testimony. Many women and men feel that the reasoning that underlies such a law is specious. In their view any such law is discriminatory and should be abolished. Others maintain that without such laws innocent men could be easily victimized. Which view appears to be the more reasoned? Are there other alternatives?

24. Yale University's Dr. José Delgado dramatized the effectiveness of electrical stimulation of the brain (ESB) as a means of controlling behavior. He demonstrated that by "wiring" the brain of a fighting bull and merely pushing a button that transmits an electrical charge to the animal's brain, he can stop it in the middle of an enraged charge. He also established that repeated electrical stimulation diminishes a bull's natural aggressiveness. Similar experiments have shown that chemical stimulation of the brain (CSB) by the strategic placement of tiny tubes of time-released substances is similarly effective. Some people believe it would be desirable to use these techniques on criminals or mental patients or students with certain impediments to learning. Others see any such use as an Orwellian nightmare. What might be the dangers of the use of such techniques on humans? Might their use be regulated to minimize abuses?

25. Some argue that the parents of students who attend private and parochial schools should be allowed to deduct tuition expenses on their federal income tax

forms. For several decades advocates of the idea have argued that fairness demands it because such parents already support the public schools through taxes and must at present bear an additional financial burden for exercising free choice over their children's education. Opponents argue that the proposal violates the principle of separation of church and state (at least in the case of parochial schools) and would harm the public school system. Which viewpoint is more reasonable?

26. The 1990s witnessed the beginning of a new phenomenon—children *divorcing* their parents. What possible effects could this phenomenon have on the relationships between children and parents? Between government and families? Which of these effects are most *likely* to occur? Are they desirable or undesirable?

27. Top executives of large corporations often earn millions of dollars a year in salaries, bonuses, and benefits while the vast majority of people who work for them earn modest wages, sometimes no more than the minimum hourly amount required by law. Some people believe that an economic system that permits such disparity to exist is wrong and should be changed. Others argue that no change is possible without stifling human initiative. How might the economic system be changed? Should it be changed?

28. Because journalists serve the important function of collecting information for public dissemination, they have traditionally claimed the right to keep their sources of information confidential, even from the courts. That claim has been challenged many times in the courts, and reporters have on occasion been held in contempt of court and sent to jail for refusing to divulge their sources. In taking such action, judges have not denied the basic principle of confidentiality; they have merely asserted that it has definite limits. Do you agree with them?

29. Some people claim that video games are harmful to young minds. C. Everett Koop, former surgeon general of the United States, believes they are. Because of the emphasis in most games on "eliminate, kill, destroy," he says, the games produce "aberrations in childhood behavior." Needless to say, not everyone shares Koop's view. Some psychologists and educators believe that, far from being harmful to children, video games are in some ways helpful.[7] What benefits and/or drawbacks do you see in video games?

30. One of the causes of the antisocial behavior that is so prevalent today, according to some analysts, is the fact that the old-fashioned hero has been largely replaced by the anti-hero. If the media offered more wholesome, virtuous individuals for young people to model their lives after, these analysts reason, crimes of violence would decrease. Do you agree?

31. On at least two occasions, the city council of Evanston, Illinois, considered a proposal to tax the students of Northwestern University to offset the cost of unpaid services provided by the city. The Association of American Universities opposed the proposal, which they believed would serve as a lamentable model for other college communities.[8] But some people disagree, asserting that such a tax represents the fairest way to have everyone share the costs of the services they use and suggesting that municipalities across the country adopt the idea. What is your view?

32. In two separate cases, the U.S. Supreme Court ruled that the use of trained dogs to detect drugs is legitimate under certain circumstances. In the first case, it ruled that citizens' rights are not violated when dogs are used to sniff

airport luggage if police have reason to suspect that drugs are present. In the second case, it approved the use of dogs to sniff students' lockers, cars parked on school property, and students themselves when they are suspected of drug possession. (However, it outlawed the use of dogs for mass searches of students.)[9] Do you believe the Court judged wisely?

33.   Some believe that adults should be held financially responsible for their elderly parents when the parents are too poor or ill to care for themselves. Is this a reasonable view?

34.   In the past couple of decades, student evaluations of teachers have become one common measure of teacher effectiveness. Typically, students are given an opportunity, toward the end of the term, to fill out a questionnaire and rate their teachers. The overall ratings are then compiled and become one criterion for salary raises, promotion, and tenure. Not all teachers approve of students' evaluating them, however. Some argue that students are not trained evaluators and can too easily confuse popularity with effective teaching and punish the very teachers who are serving them best. What is your view?

35.   Suppose that a single woman becomes pregnant, has the baby, and then decides to give it up for adoption. Suppose, too, that the biological father learns of her adoption decision. Under what circumstances, if any, should he be able to block the adoption and claim the baby as his own?

36.   Some people argue that wealthy people have an obligation to share their riches with poor people. Do you agree? Does your answer depend on whether their wealth was honestly or dishonestly obtained (by themselves or their ancestors)? If they do have such an obligation, how should it be enforced if they choose not to honor it? Do rich countries have a similar obligation to poor countries?

37.   Most computer software carries a warning against copying, yet many people feel the warning is unreasonable. They believe that if they buy a program, it is theirs to do with as they wish, and that includes giving or selling a copy to someone else. Are they right?

38.   When television dish antennas first became available, owners were able to receive HBO and other pay-channel signals directly from the satellites, without paying for them. Then the pay-channel companies began to scramble their signals to prevent the owners of dish antennas from receiving pay channels without paying. Do you think the companies were within their rights to do so?

39.   Lawyers often defend clients who are guilty of the charges. Is this right? Does your answer depend on the seriousness of the offense? For example, would your answer be the same for driving while intoxicated as it would be for murder?

40.   Since the onset of the AIDS epidemic, many people have experienced the pain of seeing their loved ones die a slow death. When the victims have begged to be assisted in committing suicide, some people have been moved by pity to grant their request. Such actions are against the law in most states. Should the law be changed? If not, should people who aid others in committing suicide be charged with a crime?

41.   Fear of contracting AIDS has caused people to behave in untypical ways. For example, many refuse to have any social contact with a friend who has contracted the disease. Dentists and doctors have refused to work on patients with the disease. Undertakers have refused to embalm victims. Is such behavior justifiable?

42. To some people the Asian practice of acupuncture is pure superstition; to others it produces a real anesthetic or curative effect. Which view is correct?

43. For many years it was believed that children who receive early formal education have an advantage over those who start school at age five or six. Today, some educators challenge that view. They speculate that intellectual and emotional *harm* can result from putting very young children into structured learning situations. Which view is the more reasonable one for parents to accept?

44. The increase in violence in this country (and a number of other Western countries) in recent years has given new currency to an old issue. Are human beings naturally, instinctively aggressive, or is aggression *learned* behavior?

Notes

CHAPTER 1: WHO ARE YOU?

1. Cited in James Fallows, *Breaking the News: How the Media Undermine American Democracy* (New York: Pantheon Books, 1996), pp. 117–18.
2. Cole Campbell, editor of the *Norfolk Virginian-Pilot*, quoted in James Fallows, *Breaking the News: How the Media Undermine American Democracy* (New York: Pantheon Books, 1996), p. 246.
3. Ellen Hume, commentator, on *Reliable Sources*, CNN, June 22, 1999.
4. Larry Sabato, appearing on *60 Minutes*, CBS, July 4, 1999.
5. Maxwell Maltz, *Psycho-Cybernetics* (New York: Pocket Books, 1969), pp. 49–53.
6. Viktor Frankl, *The Unheard Cry for Meaning* (New York: Simon & Schuster, 1978), pp. 35, 67, 83.
7. Viktor Frankl, *Man's Search for Meaning* (New York: Washington Square Press, 1963), pp. 122–23.
8. Frankl, *Unheard Cry*, pp. 39, 90, 95.

CHAPTER 2: WHAT IS CRITICAL THINKING?

1. Chester I. Barnard, *The Function of the Executive* (Cambridge, Mass.: Harvard University Press, 1938), p. 303.
2. James Harvey Robinson, in Charles P. Curtis, Jr., and Ferris Greenslet, eds., *The Practical Cogitator, or the Thinker's Anthology* (Boston: Houghton Mifflin, 1945), p. 6.
3. Leonard Woolf, quoted in Rowland W. Jepson, *Clear Thinking*, 5th ed. (New York: Longman, Green, 1967 [1936]), p. 10.
4. Percey W. Bridgman, *The Intelligent Individual and Society* (New York: Macmillan, 1938), p. 182.
5. For a remarkably clear discussion of this complex subject, see Mortimer J. Adler, *Intellect: Mind over Matter* (New York: Macmillan, 1990).
6. William Barrett, *Death of the Soul from Descartes to the Computer* (Garden City, N.Y.: Doubleday, 1986), pp. 10, 53, 75.
7. John Dewey, *How We Think* (New York: Heath, 1933), p. 4.
8. Dewey, *How We Think*, pp. 88–90.
9. R. W. Gerard, "The Biological Basis of Imagination," *The Scientific Monthly*, June 1946, p. 477.
10. Gerard, "Biological Basis," p. 478.

CHAPTER 3: WHAT IS TRUTH?

1. Walter Lippmann, *Public Opinion* (New York: Harcourt Brace, 1922), p. 90.

2. Gordon W. Allport and Leo Postman, *The Psychology of Rumor* (New York: Russell & Russell, 1965 [1947]), p. 100.

3. Quoted in Francis L. Wellman, *The Art of Cross-Examination* (New York: Collier Books, 1962), p. 175.

4. "People Remember Things That Didn't Happen," *Tampa Tribune*, Nation/World section, February 16, 1997, p. 22.

5. *Time*, August 14, 1972, p. 52.

6. "Chaplin Film Is Discovered," *Binghamton* (New York) *Press*, September 8, 1982, p. 7A.

7. "Town's Terror Frozen in Time," *New York Times*, November 21, 1982, Sec. 4, p. 7.

8. "A Tenth Planet?" *Time*, May 8, 1972, p. 46.

9. Herrman L. Blumgart, "The Medical Framework for Viewing the Problem of Human Experimentation," *Daedalus*, Spring 1969, p. 254.

10. "Back to School," *New York Times*, March 11, 1973, Sec. 4, p. 4.

11. "The Murky Time," *Time*, January 1, 1973, pp. 57ff.

CHAPTER 4: WHAT DOES IT MEAN TO KNOW?

1. Barbara Risman, "Intimate Relationships from a Microstructural Perspective: Men Who Mother," *Gender and Society* 1(1), 1987, pp. 6–32.

2. S. Minerbrook, "The Forgotten Pioneers," *U.S. News & World Report*, August 8, 1994, p. 53.

3. Carol Tavris, *Anger: The Misunderstood Emotion* (New York: Simon & Schuster, 1982), p. 144.

4. Paul F. Boller, Jr., *Not So: Popular Myths About America from Columbus to Clinton* (New York: Oxford University Press, 1995), Chap. 5.

5. Boller, *Not So*, Chap. 2.

6. Judith A. Reisman and Edward W. Eichel, *Kinsey, Sex, and Fraud* (Lafayette, La.: Huntinton House, 1990).

7. Thomas Sowell, *Race and Culture: A World View* (New York: Basic Books, 1994), pp. 92–93.

8. Sowell, *Race and Culture*, Chap. 7.

9. A. E. Mander, *Logic for the Millions* (New York: Philosophical Library, 1947), pp. 40–41.

10. Rowland W. Jepson, *Clear Thinking*, 5th ed. (New York: Longman, Green, 1967), p. 123.

11. Karl-Erick Fichtelius and Sverre Sjolander, *Smarter Than Man? Intelligence in Whales, Dolphins and Humans*, trans. Thomas Teal (New York: Random House, 1972), p. 147.

12. Karl Menninger, *Whatever Became of Sin?* (New York: Hawthorne Books, 1973).

13. Thomas Fleming, "Who Really Discovered America?" *Reader's Digest*, March 1973, pp. 145ff.

14. "Scientists Say Chinese 'Discovered' America," *The* (Oneonta, New York) *Star*, October 31, 1981, p. 2.

15. "Shibboleth Bites Dust," *Intellectual Digest*, July 1973, p. 68.

16. "Empty Nests," *Intellectual Digest*, July 1973, p. 68.

17. "Psychic Senility," *Intellectual Digest*, May 1973, p. 68.

18. *Time*, August 20, 1973, p. 67.

19. *Nova*, PBS-TV, September 21, 1993.

20. Mortimer J. Adler, "A Philosopher's Religious Faith," in *Philosophers Who Believe: The Spiritual Journeys of Eleven Leading Thinkers*, ed. Kelly James Clark (Downers Grove, Ill.: InterVarsity Press, 1993), p. 215.

21. Mark A. Noll, *The Scandal of the Evangelical Mind* (Grand Rapids, Mich.: Eerdmans, 1994), p. 238.

22. Herbert Kupferberg, "Why Scientists Prowl the Sea Floor," *Parade,* July 29, 1973, pp. 12ff.

23. "Beer Test," *Parade,* May 13, 1973, p. 4.

24. Conversation with Rush Limbaugh in *The Limbaugh Letter,* February 1997, pp. 6–9.

25. David Egner, "Sioux Fight to Keep Black Hills Holy Land," *Binghamton* (New York) *Press,* December 7, 1982, p. 5A.

CHAPTER 5: HOW GOOD ARE YOUR OPINIONS?

1. Cited in Martin Gardner, *Fads and Fallacies in the Name of Science* (New York: Dover, 1952, 1957), pp. 12–13.

2. "Couple Awaits Resurrection of Their Son," *Binghamton* (New York) *Press,* August 27, 1973, p. 11A. Also, "Two Arrested in Son's 'Faith Heal' Death," *Binghamton* (New York) *Press,* August 30, 1973, p. 8A.

3. *20/20,* ABC News, July 22, 1982.

4. "Aid for Aching Heads," *Time,* June 5, 1972, p. 51.

5. Francis D. Moore, "Therapeutic Innovation: Ethical Boundaries . . . ," *Daedalus,* Spring 1969, pp. 504–5.

6. *Adolescence: Its Psychology and Its Relations to Physiology, Anthropology, Sociology, Sex, Crime, Religion, and Education,* vols. 1 and 2 (New York: Appleton, 1904).

7. "Egyptian Artifacts Termed Fakes," *The* (Oneonta, New York) *Star,* June 16, 1982, p. 2.

8. "Venus Is Pockmarked," *Binghamton* (New York) *Press,* August 5, 1973, 2A.

9. Cited in Carol Tavris, *The Mismeasure of Woman* (New York: Simon & Schuster, 1992), p. 199.

10. Nation/World section, *Tampa Tribune,* May 2, 1999, p. 24.

11. *Consumer Reports on Health,* August, 1999, p. 1.

12. Stanton Samenow, *Inside the Criminal Mind* (New York: Times Books, 1984).

13. John Locke, *The Conduct of the Understanding,* Part 3.

14. "Hashaholics," *Time,* July 24, 1972, p. 53.

15. Walter Sullivan, "New Object Seen on Universe Edge," *New York Times,* June 10, 1973, p. 76.

16. Karl-Erick Fichtelius and Sverre Sjolander, *Smarter Than Man? Intelligence in Whales, Dolphins and Humans,* trans. Thomas Teal (New York: Random House, 1972), pp. 135–36.

17. Ray Marshall and Marc Tucker, *Thinking for a Living: Education and the Wealth of Nations* (New York: Basic Books, 1992), pp. 17–20.

18. Bill Katz and Linda Sternberg Katz, *Magazines for Libraries* (New York: Bowker, 1992).

19. *A Current Affair,* Fox TV, April 28, 1989.

20. "Bars' Ladies' Nights Called Reverse Sexism," *Binghamton* (New York) *Press,* January 12, 1983, p. 5B.

CHAPTER 6: WHAT IS EVIDENCE?

1. W. I. B. Beveridge, *The Art of Scientific Investigation* (New York: W. W. Norton Co, 1951), p. 54.

CHAPTER 8: THE BASIC PROBLEM—"MINE IS BETTER"

1. Edwin Arthur Burtt, *Right Thinking: A Study of Its Principles and Methods*, 3rd ed. (New York: Harper & Brothers, 1946), p. 63.

2. Ambrose Bierce, *Devil's Dictionary* (New York: Dover, 1958), p. 66.

3. Cited in Thomas Gilovich, *How We Know What Isn't So: The Fallibility of Human Reason in Everyday Life* (New York: Free Press, 1991), p. 77.

4. Edmond G. Addeo and Robert E. Burger, *EgoSpeak: Why No One Listens to You* (Radnor, Pa.: Chilton, 1973).

5. Gordon Allport, *The Nature of Prejudice* (Reading, Mass.: Addison-Wesley, 1954), pp. 355–56.

6. G. K. Chesterton, *Charles Dickens* (New York: The Press of the Readers Club, 1942), p. 15.

7. "Theologian: U.S. Too Tolerant," *The* (Oneonta, New York) *Star*, May 30, 1981, p. 15.

8. "Jailed Rabbi Seeks Kosher Diet," *Binghamton* (New York) *Press*, May 23, 1982, p. 5A.

9. Reported on *Good Morning, America*, ABC News, November 4, 1982.

10. "Pregnant Teacher Stirs Town," *Binghamton* (New York) *Press*, December 22, 1982, p. 1A.

CHAPTER 9: ERRORS OF PERSPECTIVE

1. J. H. Plumb, "The Great Change in Children," *Horizon*, Winter 1971, pp. 4–12.

2. Thomas Sowell, *Race and Culture: A World View* (New York: Basic Books, 1992), p. 220.

3. George Will, *Suddenly* (New York: Free Press, 1992), pp. 313, 318.

4. Cited in Hadley Arkes, "German Judges and Undue Burdens," *Crisis*, July–August 1994, p. 16.

5. Solomon Asch, cited in Carole Wade and Carol Tavris, *Psychology*, 2nd ed. (New York: HarperCollins, 1990), p. 669.

6. Nat Hentoff, *Speaking Freely: A Memoir* (New York: Alfred A. Knopf, 1998).

7. Reported in George Will, *Suddenly* (New York: Free Press, 1992), p. 405.

8. Thomas A. Harris, *I'm OK—You're OK: A Practical Guide to Transactional Analysis* (New York: Harper & Row, 1969), pp. 22–23.

9. "Anna Freud, Psychoanalyst, Dies at 86," *New York Times*, October 10, 1982, p. 46.

10. Rona and Laurence Cherry, "The Horney Heresy," *New York Times Magazine*, August 26, 1973, pp. 12ff.

11. "Liberation Lawn," *New York Times*, May 23, 1982, Sec. 4, p. 11.

12. This approach was used in the 1982 California primary and reported in "Game Show Prizes Entice CA Voters," *The* (Oneonta, New York) *Star*, June 4, 1982, p. 1.

13. This idea was tested by an education researcher, Eileen Bayer. It proved successful. (Fred M. Hechinger, "Grandpa Goes to Kindergarten," *New York Times*, October 29, 1972, Sec. 4, p. 11.)

14. The Reagan administration discussed this plan and indicated it was not opposed to it. "U.S. Considering National ID Cards," *The* (Oneonta, New York) *Star*, May 21, 1982, p. 1.

15. Harry Atkins, "Football, Hockey Are X-Rated," *Binghamton* (New York) *Press*, December 19, 1982, p. 60.

CHAPTER 10: ERRORS OF PROCEDURE

1. Thomas Sowell, *Race and Culture: A World View* (New York: Basic Books, 1992).

2. "FAA's Regulations Ruffle Feathers of Hang Gliders," *Binghamton* (New York) *Press,* September 3, 1982, p. 1A.

3. Cited in James Fallows, *Breaking the News: How the Media Undermine American Democracy* (New York: Pantheon Books, 1996), pp. 117–18.

4. Quoted in Fallows, *Breaking the News,* p. 246.

5. "Long Sentences Sought for Repeat Offenders," *New York Times,* April 25, 1982, p. 63.

6. "Possessed Teen Gets Long Prison Term," *The* (Oneonta, New York) *Star,* December 19, 1981, p. 2.

7. "Woman Convicted of Making Ethnic Slur," *The* (Oneonta, New York) *Star,* May 14, 1982, p. 2.

8. "High School Class Uses Human Cadavers in Lab," *Binghamton* (New York) *Press,* December 15, 1982, p. 2C.

CHAPTER 11: ERRORS OF EXPRESSION

1. Thomas Sowell, *The Quest for Cosmic Justice* (New York: Free Press, 1999), p. 18.

2. Karla Valance, "This Time, the Rebel's on the Right," *Christian Science Monitor,* January 27, 1983, p. 1B; George Basler, "Student Paper Urges Theft and Graffiti," *Binghamton* (New York) *Press,* January 25, 1983, p. 1F.

3. "Witch's Church Tax Free," *The* (Oneonta, New York) *Star,* April 8, 1982, p. 17.

CHAPTER 12: ERRORS OF REACTION

1. Rowland W. Jepson, *Clear Thinking,* 5th ed. (New York: Longman, Green, 1967 [1936]), p. 81.

2. Harold Kolansky, M.D., and William T. Moore, M.D., "Toxic Effects of Chronic Marijuana Use," *Journal of the American Medical Association,* October 2, 1972, pp. 35–41.

3. "Bar License Church Veto Struck Down," *Binghamton* (New York) *Press,* December 14, 1982, p. 4A.

4. "Tough—But Flawed—Alcohol Tests," *Christian Science Monitor,* March 3, 1983, p. 24.

CHAPTER 13: THE ERRORS IN COMBINATION

1. George Will, *Suddenly* (New York: Free Press, 1992), p. 89. Will cites Norman MacRae as his source.

2. "An Exercise in Educational Flimflam," *Parade,* May 12, 1974, p. 17.

3. "Court Order Blocks Big Inmate Release," *The* (Oneonta, New York) *Star,* December 22, 1981, p. 12.

4. "Ruling Strikes Down Exempt Status," *The* (Oneonta, New York) *Star,* March 27, 1982, p. 1.

5. "State Rules Let Gays and Crooks Adopt Children," *Binghamton* (New York) *Press,* August 8, 1982, p. 1A.

6. "Ex-Policeman Says Sex Shift Cost His Job," *The* (Schenectady, New York) *Gazette,* August 28, 1982, p. 14.

7. "Abortion Sought for Retarded Woman," *Binghamton* (New York) *Press,* September 23, 1982, p. 8B.

CHAPTER 14: KNOWING YOURSELF

1. Reported in *First Things,* December 1996, p. 58.

2. *Burden of Proof,* CNN, February 24, 1997.

3. "Bill Limits Link Between Tobacco and Sports," Nation/World section, *Tampa Tribune*, February 23, 1997, p. 14.

4. Reported on *The Today Show*, NBC TV, August 26, 1996.

5. "Questioning Campus Discipline," *Time*, May 31, 1982, p. 68.

6. "Holiday Songs Haunt Schoolmen," *Binghamton* (New York) *Press*, December 16, 1982, p. 3A.

7. "Elizabeth Taylor vs. Tailored Truth," *Time*, November 8, 1982, p. 71.

8. Interview with Shirley MacLaine, *USA Today*, June 16, 1983, p. 11A.

CHAPTER 15: BEING OBSERVANT

1. Lawrence K. Altman, "Discovery 60 Years Ago Changed Doctors' Minds on Heart Attack Survival," *New York Times*, December 10, 1972, pp. 56–57.

2. Earl Ubell, "Lysozyme: One of the Body's Miracle Workers," *New York Times*, November 12, 1972, Sec. 4, p. 6.

3. "Attacking Disease," dialogue between Jacques Monod and Jean Hamburger, *Intellectual Digest*, May 1974, pp. 12–14.

4. Richard P. Feynman, *"Surely You're Joking, Mr. Feynman"* (New York: Bantam Books, 1985), esp. pp. 157–58.

5. *Binghamton* (New York) *Press*, March 22, 1989, p. 1A.

CHAPTER 16: SELECTING AN ISSUE

1. "Tragedy May Haunt Mancini," *Binghamton* (New York) *Press*, November 16, 1982, p. 4D.

CHAPTER 17: CONDUCTING INQUIRY

1. Lee Edson, "Will Man Ever Live in Space?" *New York Times Magazine*, December 31, 1972, pp. 10ff.

2. Gordon Gaskill, "Which Mountain Did Moses Really Climb?" *Reader's Digest*, June 1973, pp. 209–16.

3. Ron Cowen, "Hubble Telescope Dates the Universe," *Science News*, Vol. 155, No. 22, May 29, 1999.

4. Lucy Burchard, "The Snug Way," *Intellectual Digest*, February 1974, p. 67.

5. Editorial, *Atlanta Constitution*, April 14, 1996.

6. Editorial, *Washington Times*, March 31, 1996.

7. Editorial, *The* (Salt Lake City, Utah) *Desert News*, July 17, 1996.

8. Editorial, *The* (Toledo, Ohio) *Blade*, July 20, 1996.

9. Editorial, *The* (Sioux Falls, South Dakota) *Argus-Leader*, July 21, 1996.

CHAPTER 18: FORMING A JUDGMENT

1. "The 2000-Year-Old Woman," *Time*, September 17, 1973, pp. 55–56.

2. Joyce Brothers, "Answers to Your Questions," *Good Housekeeping*, November 1993, p. 100.

3. John Leo, "In Search of the Middle Ground," *U.S. News & World Report*, March 6, 1989, p. 30.

4. Quoted in Leo, "In Search of…," p. 30.

5. Barbara Lerner, "Self-Esteem and Excellence: The Choice and the Paradox," *American Educator*, Winter 1985.

CHAPTER 19: PERSUADING OTHERS

1. "Scientist Clones Lamb from an Adult Sheep," Nation/World section, *Tampa Tribune*, February 23, 1997, p. 14.

2. Reported by CNN, February 7, 1997.

3. Dr. Art Ulene, reporting on *The Today Show*, NBC TV, May 17, 1996.

4. William F. Buckley, *Firing Line*, PBS affiliate WEDU, Tampa, Florida, July 7, 1996.

5. "Court Exempts Presidents from Damage Suits," *The* (Oneonta, New York) *Star*, June 25, 1982, p. 1.

6. See, for example, Carolyn A. Ristau, "Do Animals Think?" in *Animal Intelligence*, eds. R. Hoage and L. Goldman (Washington, D.C.: Smithsonian Institution Press, 1983).

7. "Pacman Ilk Nips Surgeon General," *Binghamton* (New York) *Press*, November 10, 1982, p. 1A.

8. "Evanston, Illinois, May Tax University Students," *Time*, November 7, 1982, p. 33.

9. "School's Out for Drug-Sniffing Dogs," *USA Today*, June 28, 1983, p. 7A.

Index

ABC (American Broadcasting
    Company), 39
abortion, 31, 87–88, 107, 135, 166–168
absolutism, 90, 95, 125
abstracting services, 162
active knowing, 35–36
acupuncture, 205
Addeo, Edmond, 79–80
Adler, Mortimer, 39–40
adolescence, assumptions about concept, 87
adoption, 134, 204
Adventures of Huckleberry Finn (Twain), 80
advertising
    appeal to conformity, 89, 94
    beer and wine, 96
    celebrity endorsements, 54
    on children's TV programs, 157
    influence of, 201
    infomercials, 60
    with meaningless statements,
        109–110
    observing, 149
    tobacco company sponsorships, 142
    See also under television
affirmative action, 133
African Americans
    assumptions about, 43, 87
    common knowledge about, 33
    Ebonics dialect, 103, 105
    false analogies about, 110
    hasty conclusions about, 99
    and hate crime statutes, 122
    pressure to conform, 90
    self-esteem of, 37
    stereotyping, 81, 100
    Twain novel and, 80
aggression, and violence, 205
AIDS, 11, 153, 200, 204

alcohol abuse
    adoption and, 134
    binge drinking, 55
    blood alcohol tests, 122–123
    car impoundment for DUI drivers, 74
    co-dependency theory, 49
    driving under influence, 84
    reformed alcoholics, 71
Allah, 39
Allport, Gordon, 81
almanacs, 160
America: History and Life, 162
American Broadcasting Company
    (ABC), 39
American Indian Movement, 42
    See also Native Americans
American Legion, 133
anabolic steroids, 11, 66
analogy, false, 110–111, 128
analysis
    and background information, 160n
    of issues, 17
    limiting scope of, 152, 156
    summarizing, 169–170
Ancient Order of Hibernians, 122
anecdotal evidence, 169
anger, expressing, 33, 34
animals
    dogs, 133, 203–204
    fish, 37, 40
    intelligence of, 201
    whales, 37, 51
    in zoos, 122
anti-heroes, 203
antimiscegenation laws, 171
anti-poverty programs, 193
antisocial behavior, 55, 66
appearances, 41

arguments
  about, 67–68
  applications of, 74–76
  circular, 109, 127–128
  conditions in, 169
  considering both sides, 71
  consolidating, 168–170
  definitions of, 67–68
  difficult, 71–74
  with double standard, 98
  errors in, 68–69
  evaluation of, 69–71, 175–177
  focus on best, 194–195
  loaded, 174
  logic in, 69
  overwhelming with, 193–194
  parts of, 68–69
  persuasiveness of, 72
  relevancy of, 195
  soundness of, 195
  summarizing, 71
  understating, 190–191
art forgeries, 28–29
  See also hoaxes
articles, 161, 174
artificial hearts, 36
assault weapons, 119–120
assertions, 68
  identifying key, 168–169
  qualifying words, 169
  See also premises
assisted suicide, 204
Associated Press, 167
Association of American Universities, 203
assumptions
  knowledge implied by, 40–41
  terminology, 131–132
  unwarranted, 86–88, 124–125, 130, 131
astronauts, 92, 158–159
astronomers, 51
atheists, stereotyping, 100
athletes. See sports
attention span, 6, 10, 26, 157
attitudes
  identity including, 4
  inappropriate, 69
  inventory of, 139–141
  "mine-is-better," 78–83
  observing others', 144–145
  See also beliefs; viewpoints
attorneys
  irrational appeal to emotion, 112
  issue shifting, 107
audience, understanding viewpoint of,
    187–188
Augustine, Saint, 178

authority
  irrational appeal to, 112–113
  mistaken, 110, 128
  See also expert opinion; information
automatic rejection, 118–119, 128–129

Bacon, Francis, 50n
balanced views, 18, 179–180
Barrett, William, 15
Beausay, Bill, 96
beauty pageants, 96
beer and wine commercials, 96
behavior control, 202
beliefs
  "mine is better," 78–83
  and truth creation, 25, 28–29
  See also attitudes; viewpoints
bias
  in evidence evaluation, 64, 97–98, 126
  for or against change, 91–93, 125
Bible, 134–135, 159
bicycles, resistance to, 92
Bierce, Ambrose, 8, 79
Billings, Josh, 42
binge drinking, 55
biological fathers, 204
birth control, 11, 66, 157
Black Hills National Forest, 42
blacks. See African Americans
blood alcohol tests, 122–123
books
  college textbooks, 161n
  information from, 161–162
  self-improvement, 180
Boston Strangler, clothing of, 147
boxing, 154, 165–166
Boylston, Zabdiel, 48
Brady, Joseph L., 28
brain
  and behavior control, 202
  frontal lobotomy of, 36
  vs. mind, 14–15
  senility and, 37–38
brainwashing, 94
Brigham, Carl, 99n
Brothers, Joyce, 175–177
Budweiser, 89
burden of proof, shifting, 119, 129
Burger, Robert, 79–80
Bush, George W., 71

Canada, 142
cancer, 48, 49, 110–111, 181
cannibalism, 34
Carville, James, 7
Catholics, stereotyping, 100

cause-and-effect relationships, 103
celebrity endorsements, 54
celebrity testimony, 60
censorship, 113–114
census, 62, 163
Center for Media and Public Affairs, 41
certainty
    failure to achieve, 38–39
    in judgments, 64
    sufficient evidence, 164–165
    See also evidence, facts
certainty continuum, 101
change, bias for or against, 91–93, 125
Chaplin, Charlie, 28
chemical stimulation of brain, 202
Chesterton, G. K., 82
childhood
    adoption, 134, 204
    assumptions about concept, 87
    beauty and talent competitions, 11, 66
    child abuse, 142
    child labor, 92
    choosing up sides, 75
    and death, 199
    divorcing parents, 203
    false memories of, 26
    self-esteem, 180
    self-images, 8
    spanking, 55, 142
    strictness of parents, 22
    truth creation and, 24–25
    values learned in, 135–136, 185
    video games, 203
Chinese, 100, 172–173
cholesterol, 49
Christians. *See* religion
chronic laziness, 150
churches, legislation affected by, 121
    See also religion
cigarettes. *See* smoking
circular arguments, 109, 127–128
Civil War, 112
Clinton, Bill
    double-standard judgments on, 98
    impeachment trial of, 7, 57
    and partial-birth abortion bill,
        166–168
    and Paula Jones, 41, 120
Clinton, Hillary Rodham, 57
cloning, human, 199
clothing, 147
co-dependency theory, 49
CODESH (Council for Democratic and
    Secular Humanities), 53–54
coffee, Taster's Choice labels, 46
Coleridge, Samuel Taylor, 19–20

college
    abolition of intercollegiate sports, 202
    city taxation of students, 203
    cut systems, 190–191
    dining hall food and service, 196–198
    dormitory damages, 121
    gender-linked sports budget, 202
    higher-standards proposal, 142–143
    mandatory freshman composition, 11, 66
    as meaningful job requirement, 157
    pay for athletes, 185
    plagiarism, 143
    student newspapers, 113–114
    student responsibility, 191
    student/teacher dating, 75
    tenure system, 97, 98n, 199–200, 204
    textbooks, 161n
    value of, 134
    See also education; school; students;
        teachers
Columbus, Christopher, 33, 37
commentary, web searches for, 163
commercials. *See* advertising
commercial web sites, 163
common belief, irrational appeal to, 113
common knowledge, 33–35, 37–38
compulsory education, 202
computer databases, 162
computer software, copying, 75, 204
Comte, Auguste, 30
concentration, 21
concession, 191–192
conclusions
    defined, 68–69
    dictating in advance, 21
    distinguishing from premises, 72
    hasty conclusion, 90, 98–100, 126, 131–132
    identifying author's, 169
    jumping to, 65
    qualifying words, 169
conditioning, 10, 35–36
confidence, performance and, 8
conflicts, resolving, 172
conformity
    advertising appeal to, 89, 94
    collaboration experiment, 89
    mindless, 89–90, 125
    with other problems, 130–131
    situations for study, 94–95
congressional term limits, 200
consequences, 47–48
Constitution. *See* U.S. Constitution
contracts, 47
contradiction, 108–109, 127
controversial issue, 151n
controversy, 151

Cornell University, 146
Council for Democratic and Secular Humanities (CODESH), 53–54
courts. *See* laws
Crabbe, Buster, 25
creationism, 11, 66, 157
creative thinking, 16
crime
  background information, 160
  and economic backgrounds, 43
  getting tough with, 185
  hate crime statutes, 122
  juvenile crime, 142, 154–155
  life stories of criminals, 122
  Lombroso's phrenology theory, 174
  social theories on, 49–50
critic, attacking, 120–121, 129
critical thinkers
  characteristics, 17–19, 65
  and evidence, 58
  issue selection, 151
  "mine is better" thinking, 82
  questioning, 16
critical thinking
  about, 13–14
  and argument, 67–68
  basic activities, 20–21
  conscientious mode of, 52–53
  defined, 15–17
  in difficult arguments, 73–74
  evaluation and, 16
  fundamental principle of, 46
  inventory, 139–141
  misconceptions about, 17
  relativism opposed to, 91
  tools, 3
  writing and, 21
  See also thinking
crowding, psychology on, 164
cultural patterns, 100–101
curiosity
  critical thinking and, 18
  "puzzle drive," 146
Current Biography: Who's News and Why, 160

Darwinism, 30
dating
  students and teachers, 75
  teens and adults, 54
daydreaming, 16*n*
Dean Witter ad, 109
"Dear Abby," 121
Declaration of Independence, 75
defense budget, 75
Defense of Marriage Act, 170–171
de Fort, Charles Sylvester, 44

Delgado, José, 202
Department of Defense, 163
DeSalvo, Albert, 147
detached observation, 62–63
Devil's Dictionary (Bierce), 79
devil worship, 142, 157
Dewey, John, 18, 19
Dictionary of Slang and Unconventional English (Partridge), 160
dietary fiber, 49
dinosaurs, opinions about, 49
discoveries
  of America, 37
  intuition and, 19–20
  from observation, 147
  of truth, 28–29
discrimination
  ethnic/racial groups, 80–81
  against gay organizations, 122
  "ladies' nights" in bars, 55–56
  in rape laws, 202
  after sex-change operations, 135
  by stereotyping, 75
  against unmarried couples, 142
Dissertation Abstracts International, 162
distinctions, 178–179
DNA technology, 199
dogs
  drug-sniffing, 203–204
  sport fighting, 133
Dole, Bob, 166
dormitory damages, 121
double standard, 98, 126
Down's syndrome, 167
Draper, Patricia, 164
Dress for Success (Molloy), 147
drug abuse, 71
  adoption and, 134
  co-dependency theory, 49
  legality of searches, 203–204
Duk Doo Kim, 154
DWEMs (dead, white, European males), 100

Ebonics, 103, 105
education
  compulsory, 202
  fast-start programs, 205
  home schooling, 74
  obstacles to learning, 175
  school vouchers, 74, 89, 202
  See also college; school; students; teachers
educational web sites, 163
egocentrism, 79–80, 83
"egospeak," 79–80
"egothink," 80
Egyptian treasures, opinions about, 48

Eichel, Edward W., 34
either/or outlook, 88–89, 125
electrical stimulation of brain, 202
Elizaldo, Manuel, 38
Ellis, Albert, 141
emotional handicap, and adoption, 134
emotions
  appeals to, 6
  irrational appeal to, 111–112
  mental health, 154
  See also feelings
employers, 33, 34
enabling, 49
encyclopedias, 160
end, means justified by, 55, 65
English language, information about, 160
entertainers, 60
environment, 142
envy, 78*n*
Epictetus, 35, 41, 53
equality, 75
Equal Rights Amendment, 42
errors
  in arguments, 68–69
  combinations of, 124–137
  by experts, 48–50
  of expression, 106–115, 127–128
  kinds of, 50
  lessening chances of, 51–52
  of perspective, 86–93, 124–125
  of procedure, 97–105, 126–127
  proneness to, 50
  of reaction, 116–123, 128–129
  recognizing, 124–129
  terminology of, 131–132
  of wise, 27–28
Esposito, John, 180
ethics, codes of, 47
ethnic groups
  ethnocentrism, 80–81, 83
  hasty conclusion in testing, 99
  stereotyping, 100
ethnocentrism, 80–81, 83
evaluation
  of arguments, 69–71, 175–177
  critical thinking and, 16
  of evidence, 63–65, 97–98, 126, 173–174
  fairness in, 64
  in science, 172–173
Evanston, Illinois, 203
evidence
  about, 57–58
  applications of, 65–66
  assertions supported by, 169
  bias in consideration of, 97–98, 126
  conclusions supported by, 99

evaluation of, 63–65, 97–98, 126, 173–174
  experimental, 61, 169
  impartiality of, 174
  kinds of, 58–63
  making distinctions, 178–179
  preponderance of, 65, 165
  relevance of, 63
  sufficient, 64–65, 164–165
  See also certainty; facts
evil spirits, 55, 65
exaggeration, avoiding, 183–184
executive salaries, 203
experimental evidence, 61, 169
expert opinion, 48–50, 61
  See also authority
expression
  of anger, 33, 34
  errors of, 106–115, 127–128
  of judgments, 45*n*, 179
extraterrestrial life, 159
extreme views
  critical thinking and, 18
  Ku Klux Klan rallies, 11, 66, 157
eyewitness testimony, 59–60, 172

face-saving, 116–117, 130, 131
facts
  information on, 160
  inquiry into, 158
  interpretation of, 172–173
  relevant, in persuasion, 192–193
  treating opinion as, 53
  See also certainty; evidence
fairness, 47
faith, and knowledge, 39–40
  See also religion
faith healers, 45
false analogy, 110–111, 128
false memory, 26
falsity, of premises, 69–71
familiarity
  vs. correctness, 179
  and resistance to change, 91
family, identity influenced by, 5
family values, 201
Federal Aviation Administration, 102
Federal Bureau of Investigation, 75
feelings
  controlling, 19
  as guide to behavior, 184
  and imperfect perception, 25–26
  "mine is better" thinking, 83
  and oversimplification, 102
  vs. thinking, 15–16
  See also emotions
Feynman, Richard, 146

fiber, dietary, 49
field experiments, 61
films, 28, 49
fish, 37, 40
Flat Earth Society, 45
Fleming, Arthur, 145–146
Foley, Mick "Mankind," 7
foreign-made goods, 134
forgiveness, 121
formal observation, 62–63
Fox News, 120
Frankl, Viktor, 8–9, 11
Franklin, Benjamin, 48
Free Inquiry: A Secular Humanist Magazine, 53–54
free speech, 75–76, 98, 153, 180
free thinking, 89
frequency continuum, 101
Freud, Anna, 141
Freud, Sigmund, 92–93, 141
Frost, Robert, 92
Fuller, Thomas, 149
fundamentalists, stereotyping, 100
furniture-stripping discovery, 147

Galileo, 27, 91–92
gambling, 134, 200
"gangsta rap" music, 84
gender
    and manic depression, 146
    and married name, 121
    sex-change operations, 135
    and sports budgets, 202
    See also men; sexuality; women
General Academic Index, 162
generalizations, 58, 100–101
    See also overgeneralization
Germany, 88, 100
Glover, Ian, 39
Goethe, Johann Wolfgang von, 19–20
Golden Rule, 184
Gomberg, Edith, 49
Goring, C., 174
government web sites, 163
Greeks, 37
group judgment, 27
groups, individuals distinct from, 178
guaranteed annual wage, 202
guessing, 40–41
Guide to Reference Books (Sheehy), 161
guilt, 37
gullibility, 132
guns
    assault weapons, 119–120
    handgun bans, 199
    legislation proposals, 190

restricting sale of, 119–120
and U.S. Constitution, 43

habits, inventory of, 139–141
Hall, G. Stanley, 48
Hamblin, Ken, 105
hang gliders, regulating, 102
Harris, Sidney J., 138
Harvard Medical School, 48
hashish, 51
hasty conclusion, 90, 98–100, 126, 131–132
hate crime statutes, 122
Hawaii, same-sex marriages, 170–171
headaches, opinions about, 48
Headland, Thomas, 39
health, web searches, 163
Health and Psychosocial Instruments, 162
heart disease, 145
heart transplants, 36
heavy metal music, 84
Heiss, Jerold, 37
Henry, Carl F., 84
Hentoff, Nat, 89–90
Herculaneum, 28
Hernandez, Roger, 105
heroes/anti-heroes, 203
heroin, as painkiller, 28
Herrick, James B., 145
hierarchy of human needs, 8
Hill, Anita, 29
Hillel, Rabbi, 149
hippies, 89
Hispanics
    cultural patterns, 101
    stereotyping, 75, 81, 100
Hitler, Adolf, 82
HIV/AIDS, 11, 66
    See also AIDS
HMOs, suing, 74
hoaxes, 38–39, 48, 132
home schooling, 74
homophobia, 65, 176–177
Homo sapiens, 4
homosexuality, 132–133, 134
    fear of, 65, 176–177
    gay rights, 122
    same-sex marriages, 170–171
honesty, 18, 41, 47
Horace, 149
Horney, Karen, 93
Houck, Eric, 147
Human Events magazine, 53
humanistic psychologies, 8–9
human rights violations, 114
Humphrey, Nyles, 38

ideals, 47
ideas, confusing with people, 178
identity, 4–12
immigrants, 99
inappropriate personal questions, 107
income tax reform, 157
inconclusive results, 158–159
indexes, 160, 161, 162
individuality, 9–10, 11, 178
inferiority complex overstatement, 191
infomercials, 60
information
  abstracting services, 162
  from articles, 161
  background on issues, 160
  from books, 161–162
  computer databases, 162
  deficient, 26–28
  about English language, 160
  facts, 160
  on Internet, 163–164
  looking for, 159
  managing lengthy material, 168–170
  about people, 160
  research, 62–63
  retrieval technology, 162
  and search engines, 163
  statistics, 160
  See also authority
Information Please Almanac, 160
informed opinion, 51–52, 158
InfoTrak, 162
inquiry, 158–171
  defined, 158
  enough, 164–168
  into facts, 158
  managing lengthy material, 168–170
  into opinions, 158
insanity defense, 42
Institute of Rational-Emotive Therapy, 141
integrity, 47
intellectual honesty, 41
intelligence
  of animals, 201
  testing, 99n
International Index, 161n
Internet information, 163–164
Internet service providers, 163
interpretation
  of evidence, 20
  of facts, 172–173
  of opinions, 36
Interpretation of Dreams (Freud), 92–93
intolerance, 80–81
intuition, 19–20, 184
investigation, of evidence, 20

IQ testing, 99n
irrational appeal, 111–113, 128
Islam, 39, 179–180
issue analysis, 17
issues
  background information, 160
  contemporary, 199–205
  defined, 151
  examining both sides of, 166–168, 170–171
  limiting, 152
  selecting, 151–157
issue shifting, 106–107, 127
Italians, stereotyping, 81, 100

jails, overcrowding, 133
  See also prisons
James, William, 26
Japanese, 100–101
Jepson, Rowland W., 116
Jesus Christ, 39
Jews
  faith, 39
  and hate crime statutes, 122
  stereotyping, 81, 100, 131
Jones, Paula, 41, 120
journalism
  confidentiality of sources, 203
  newsworthiness, 41
  sensationalism, 7, 102–103
  See also media
*Journal of the American Medical
    Association*, 118
journals, articles in, 161
judgments, 20, 172–185
  appropriately specific subjects, 181
  certainty in, 64
  considered, 45
  critical thinking and, 18
  exact predicates, 181–182
  expression of, 45n, 179
  group, 27
  including appropriate qualifications,
    182–183
  matters of preference, 179
  premature, 98–100
  supportive line of reasoning, 67
Jurassic Park (film), 49
justice, 47
juvenile crime, 142, 154–155

Katz, Bill, 53–54
Katz, Linda Sternberg, 53–54
Kekule, Friedrich August, 19–20
Khomeini, Ayatollah, 179–180
King Tut, 28
Kinsey, Alfred, 33, 34

knowledge, 32–43
  active/passive, 35–36
  common knowledge, 33–35, 37–38
  difficulty of, 36–38
  and faith, 39–40
  hoaxes and, 38–39
  obstacles to, 40–41
  requirements of, 32–33
  of self, 11, 138–143
  testing, 33–35
Koch, Robert, 48
Koop, C. Everett, 203
Koreans, stereotyping, 81
Ku Klux Klan, 11, 66, 157
!Kung tribe, 164

laboratory experiments, 61
labor force
  child labor, 92
  imported unskilled, 33, 34
language, errors of, 50
laws
  abortion, 31, 87–88, 166–168
  aircraft regulation, 102
  antimiscegenation, 171
  children divorcing parents, 203
  divorce, 157
  divorce custody guidelines, 55, 65
  drug searches, 203–204
  equality in restaurant service, 102
  on fetal status, 148–149
  frivolous lawsuits, 96, 133
  gun control, 190, 199
  hate crime statutes, 122
  insanity defense, 42
  issues of, 151
  juvenile crime, 142, 154–155
  minimum drinking age, 55, 65
  as moral judgments, 47
  motorcycle helmets, 94
  partial-birth abortion, 166–168
  preponderance of evidence, 65
  on rape, 132, 202
  religious tax exemptions, 114–115
  right to defense, 204
  same-sex marriages, 170–171
  school religious holidays, 143
  sex discrimination, 55–56
  on surrogate mothers, 150
  tax-exempt status and lobbying, 133
  on tobacco company sponsorships, 142
  youthful offenders treated as adults, 74
lawyers, 107, 112
laziness, chronic, 150
learning, obstacles to, 175
  See also college; education; school; teachers

legal information
  sources, 162
  web searches, 163
Leibnitz, G. W., 15
LensCrafters slogan, 109
Leo, John, 180
Lerner, Barbara, 180
less-is-more rule, 151–152
Lexis-Nexis, 162
librarians, assistance from, 162
libraries, 53–54, 161–162
Lichter, Robert, 41
listening, 18
lobbying
  by special interest groups, 157
  with tax-exempt status, 133
lobotomy, frontal, 36
Locke, John, 15, 50
Loftus, Elizabeth, 26
logic, in arguments, 69
Lombardi, Vince, 150
Lombroso, Cesare, 174
Lord's Prayer, in school, 22
Loving couple, 171
lysozyme, 146

McDonagh, Sean, 38
MacLaine, Shirley, 143
magazines, 35, 161, 174
Magazines for Libraries (Katz and Katz),
  53–54
mail surveys, 62
Maltz, Maxwell, 8
Mancini, Ray "Boom Boom," 154
manic depression, 146
Marcos, Ferdinand, 38
marijuana, 74, 118
marriage
  abolition of, 184
  in Asian cultures, 201
  names after, 121
  same-sex, 170–171
Marshall, Barry, 49
Marshall, Ray, 52
Marx, Karl, 30
Maslow, Abraham, 8–9, 11, 34
mass culture, identity influenced by, 5–7
meaningless statements, 109–110, 128
means, justifying end, 55, 65
media
  hoaxes and, 38–39
  inaccurate reporting, 42
  influence of, 201
  manipulation by, 5–6
  newsworthiness, 41
  passive knowing from, 35–36

published reports as evidence, 59
undercover reporting, 200–201
violence and, 43
See also films; journalism; newspapers;
    television
medicine
    acupuncture, 205
    AIDS patients' rights, 204
    astronauts' health, 158–159
    Chinese, 172–173
    cloning technology, 199
    ethical decisions, 36
    expert opinions, 48–49
    interpretation of evidence, 172–173
    observation in, 145–146
    sexually transmitted diseases, 153, 200
    web searches, 163
Medline: PubMed, 162
memory
    imperfect, 26
    and truth, 25–26
men
    common knowledge about, 33
    male vs. female athletes, 157
    music video portrayals of, 11
    See also gender; sexuality
"Mending Wall" (Frost), 92
Menninger, Karl, 37
mental health
    of boxers, 154
    hashish and, 51
    manic depression, 146
    neurosis, 93
    stimulation of brain, 202
Mercedes, unwarranted assumptions, 132
Metropolitan Museum of Art, 48
military spending, 115
mind
    vs. brain, 14–15
    discipline of, 17–19
    passive vs. active, 15
mindless conformity, 89–90, 125
"mine is better," 78–83, 92, 124, 130
mistaken authority, 110, 128
moderation, irrational appeal to, 112
Molloy, John T., 147
Molony, Carol, 38
Monod, Jacques, 146
morality
    of frontal lobotomy, 36
    issues of, 151
    obligations, 194
    opinions on, 46–48
    premarital sex, 115
    and relativism, 91
    same-sex marriages, 170–171

sexual, 132–133
moral judgments, 46–48
morphine, as painkiller, 28
Morris, Dick, 120
Moses, 39, 159
motives, judging, 178
motorcycle helmets, 94
Mount Vesuvius, 28
movies, 28, 49
Muhammad, 39
murky time phenomenon, 30–31
music, 84
music video channels, 11
Muslims, 39, 179–180

names, after marriage, 121
National Basketball Association, 200
National Broadcasting Company
    (NBC), 39
National Collegiate Athletic
    Association, 185
National Geographic, 38
National Organization for Women, 182–183
Nation magazine, 53
Native Americans
    American Indian Movement, 42
    common knowledge about, 33, 34
    medical opinions of, 48
natural selection, 30
NBC (National Broadcasting Company), 39
needs, hierarchy of, 8
neurosis, theories about, 93
news
    serious coverage, 200
    web searches, 163
newspapers
    articles in, 161
    censoring student newspapers, 113–114
    inaccurate reporting, 42
    See also media
New York City
    Metropolitan Museum of Art, 48
    overgeneralizations about, 100
    St. Patrick's Day Parade, 122
New York State Social Services, 134
New York Times Encyclopedia Almanac, 160
Noll, Mark, 40
Northwestern University, 203
Norwegians, 30–31
nuclear first strikes, 55, 65

objectivity, 63–64
obligations, 47
observation, 144–150
    accuracy of, 173
    detached, 62–63

observation, *(continued)*
  formal, 62–63
  increasing capacity for, 147–148
  of others, 173–174
  range of application, 146–147
  reflecting on, 148–149
  See also perception
opinions
  about, 44–46
  acting on, 45
  borrowed, 57
  contemporary issues, 53–56
  corruption by errors, 50
  and evidence, 57–58, 65–66
  exchange of, 67
  of experts, 48–50, 61, 110
  as expression of judgment, 45
  forming correct, 52–53
  informed vs. uninformed, 51–52, 158
  inquiry into, 158
  interpretation of, 36
  mistaken, 46
  on moral issues, 46–48
  questioning, 53
  reader responses to articles, 161
  reexamining, 50
  treating as fact, 53
  untestable, 159
overgeneralization, 100–101, 126
oversimplification, 81, 90, 101–103, 127, 131–132
overstatement, 191
Owens, Susan, 37
Oxford English Dictionary, 160

paganism, 114–115
Paidika: The Journal of Paedophilia, 54
paid spokespersons, 60
panhandlers, 75–76
parents
  assumptions about children, 87
  biological fathers, 204
  children leaving home, 37
  divorced by children, 203
  financial responsibility for children, 150, 204
  identity influenced by, 5
  legal responsibility for children, 150
  notification of birth control usage by minors, 11, 66, 157
  strictness of, 22
  values taught by, 135–136, 185
Parrish, Michael, 49
partial-birth abortion, 166–168
participant observation, 62–63
Partridge, Eric, 160

passive knowing, 35–36
Pavlov, Ivan Petrovich, 10
penicillin, 146
penis envy, challenge to, 93
people
  confusing with ideas, 178
  information about, 160
  observing, 144–145
perception
  discovering meaning in, 52
  imperfect, 25–26
  See also observation
performance, confidence and, 8
personal experience, as evidence, 58
personal interview surveys, 62
perspectives
  errors of, 86–93, 124–125
  "mine is better," 78–83, 92, 124, 130
  testing, 91
persuasion
  about, 186
  allowing time for acceptance of views, 195–196
  common beginning position, 188–189
  concession of opponent's points, 191–192
  defined, 186
  focus on best argument, 194–195
  overwhelming with arguments, 193–194
  persuasive presentation example, 198
  positive approaches, 189–190
  relevancy of arguments, 195
  relevant facts, 192–193
  respect for audience, 187
  soundness of arguments, 195
  understanding audience's viewpoint, 187–188
  understating arguments, 190–191
  unpersuasive presentation example, 196–197
philosophy
  basis of Western, 138
  and truth creation, 29
  and world conflict, 195
phrenology theory, 174
physical handicap, and adoption, 134
physics, observation in, 146–147
place, identity influenced by, 4–5
plagiarism, 143
planets, 28, 30, 49
Pluto, discovery of, 28
Poles, stereotyping, 81, 100
political correctness, 157
politics
  attention span for, 6
  double standard, 98
  focus groups, 7

irrational appeal to emotion, 111–112
issue shifting, 107
issues of, 151
"mine is better" thinking, 82, 130
partial-birth abortion, 166–168
polls, 7
pressure to conform, 90
public skepticism, 133
in world conflict, 195
polygamy, 11, 66, 157
Pompeii, 28
pornography
ban on sale of, 150
clarifying issues of, 152–153, 156
inquiry into, 114, 165
Portugese, 101
positive approaches, 189–190
possessions, "mine is better," 78–79
post hoc fallacy, 103, 127, 146
prayer, in school, 22
preferences
identity including, 4
in judgments, 179
pregnancy, 48
See also abortion
premises
defined, 68–69
distinguishing from conclusions, 72
hidden, 72–74, 88
See also assertions
presidential elections, 71, 107
Princeton University, 143
prisons
housing of juvenile offenders, 155
overcrowding, 133
punishment vs. rehabilitation, 11,
66, 157
religious freedom in, 142
probability
dealing with, 180–181
force of, 65
problems, critical thinking and, 18, 22
procedure, errors of, 97–105, 126–127
prostitution, 157
Psychological Abstracts, 162
psychology
hasty conclusion in testing, 99
identity influenced by, 7–9
murky time phenomenon, 30–31
and truth creation, 29
PsycINFO, 162
PsycLIT, 162
public service messages, 201
published reports, as evidence, 59
Puritans, 33, 34, 37
"puzzle drive," 146

quarrels, 67
quasars, 51
questioning, 16–17
questions, avoiding, 107

race. See African Americans; ethnic groups;
ethnocentrism; Native Americans;
stereotyping
"Railroad Killer," 75
random sampling, 62
rape laws, 132, 202
rational appeal, 111–113
Rational-Emotive Therapy, 141
reaction
errors of, 116–123, 128–129
individuality in, 10
readers, persuading, 187–196
Reader's Digest Almanac, 160
Reader's Guide to Periodical Literature,
161, 162
reading, popular tastes, 6–7
reasonableness, demonstrating, 65, 165
reasoning
vs. intuition and feeling, 184
judgments using, 67
thinking and, 14
reflection
on observations, 148–149
practicing, 149–150
reincarnation, 143
Reisman, Judith A., 34
rejection, automatic, 118–119, 128–129
relativism, 24, 82, 90–91, 95, 108, 125
religion
abortion views, 87–88
biblical admonitions, 134–135
cults, 94
free exercise of, 75, 142
and homosexuality, 122
and knowledge, 39–40
"mine is better" thinking, 82
of Native Americans, 42
Santeria, 75
Satan worship as, 142
in school, 114, 115
school religious holidays, 143
school vouchers, 74, 89, 202
stereotyping, 100
tax exemptions, 114–115
truth and, 23
See also churches
reports, 59
Repplier, Agnes, 149
research
formal observation, 62–63
review of, 63

research, *(continued)*
  surveys, 62
  See also information
resistance to change, 91–93, 125
responsibility
  of college students, 191
  inquiry into, 166
  of parents for children, 150, 204
rights
  abortion, 87–88
  AIDS patients, 204
  to bear arms, 43
  boxers', 154
  of environment, 142
  Equal Rights Amendment, 42
  gay, 122
  human, 114
  to legal defense, 204
  prisoners', 142
  religious, 75, 142
  smoking, 36
Ring Record Book, 154
Risman, Barbara, 33
Rodman, Dennis, 7
Roe v. Wade, 87–88
Roget's Thesaurus, 14
Romans, 37
Roosevelt, Franklin D., 108
Rose, Pete, 134
Ruhling, Robert, 38
Rumor game, 36
Rushdie, Salman, 179–180

Sabato, Larry, 7
St. Patrick's Day Parade, New York
    City, 122
Saint Augustine, 178
salaries
  of sport superstars, 201
  of top executives, 203
Salazar, Zeus, 38–39
Samenow, Stanton, 49–50
same-sex marriages, 170–171
sampling, in surveys, 62
Santeria, 75
Satanic Verses (Rushdie), 179–180
Saturn, rings of, 30
schizophrenia, hashish and, 51
scholarly electronic indexes, 162
Scholastic Aptitude Test, 99n
school
  class attendance, 55, 66
  creationism in, 11, 66, 157
  displaying Ten Commandments in, 72
  Lord's Prayer in, 22
  religion in, 114, 115

religious holidays, 143
sex education in, 54, 157, 192
thinking in, 13–14
writing in, 21
See also college; education; students;
    teachers
school vouchers, 74, 88–89, 202
science
  cloning technology, 199
  interpretation of facts, 172–173
  observation in, 145–146
  relativity of truth, 30
search engines, 163
self-actualization, 8–9, 11
self-centeredness, 7, 80
self-esteem, 8, 11, 37, 66, 180
self-fulfilling expectations, 39
self-hypnotism, 8
self-image, 116–117, 139
self-improvement, 141
self-improvement books, 180
self-knowledge, 11, 138–143
self-transcendence, 9, 11
Seneca, 121
senility, 37–38
sensationalism, 7, 102–103
sense impressions, 148
sentiments, identity including, 4
sex education, 54, 157, 192
sexual harassment, 29
sexuality
  Kinsey's research, 33, 34
  premarital sex, 115
  prostitution, 157
  in psychological theory, 92–93
  Puritan, 33, 34
  sex-change operations, 135
  on TV, 122
  See also gender; homosexuality;
      pornography
sexually transmitted diseases, 153, 200
Sheehy, Eugene O., 161
Shepherd, Cybill, 110
shifting the burden of proof, 119, 129
shifting the issue, 106–107
simplification, 101
  See also oversimplification
Simpson, Nicole Brown, 108
Simpson, O. J., 108
sin, 37
Sinai desert, 159
slavery
  assumptions about, 87
  common knowledge about, 33, 35, 37
  irrational appeal to moderation, 112
Smith, C. Lavett, 40

smoking
  advertising, 36
  beliefs and, 29
  as conformity, 130–131
  and evidence, 181
social theories
  on crime, 49–50
  identity influenced by, 7–8
society, evolution of, 30
Sociological Abstracts, 162
sociology, 30
Socrates, 138
software, copying, 75, 204
solar system
  Galileo and, 27, 91–92
  planets, 28, 30, 49
Sowell, Thomas, 101
Spanish, 101
spanking, 55, 65, 142
speech, freedom of, 75–76, 98, 153, 180
Spencer, Herbert, 30
sports
  abolition of intercollegiate sports, 202
  anabolic steroid testing, 11, 66
  boxing classified as, 154
  gambling by participants, 134, 200
  gender-linked college budgets, 202
  identity influenced by, 5
  instant replay in, 25
  male vs. female athletes, 157
  pay for college athletes, 185
  rating system proposal, 96
  superstar salaries, 201
  tobacco company sponsorships, 142
Sri Lankans, 101
Starr, Kenneth, 57
statistics
  as evidence, 61–62, 169
  finding, 160
Stella, Vikki, 167
stereotyping, 75, 81, 100–101, 126, 131
Stern, Howard, 7
Stone Age tribes, uncertainty about, 38–39
stratified sampling, 62
straw man, 119–120, 129
student newspapers, censoring, 113–114
students
  evaluation of teachers, 204
  responsibility of, 191
  taxation of, 203
  teachers dating, 75
  See also college; education; school
studies, reviews of, 63
style vs. substance, 178
subject continuum, 101
subjectivism, 24

substance vs. style, 178
suicide, 30, 31, 157, 204
Supreme Court. *See* U.S. Supreme Court
surgical gloves, errors about, 27
surrogate mothers, 150
surveys, as evidence, 62
survival of the fittest, 30
systematic sampling, 62

talk shows, 7, 8, 60, 74, 108, 201
Tarzan, 25
Tasaday tribe, 38–39
Taster's Choice coffee labels, 46
Tavris, Carol, 34
taxation, referendums for, 74
teachers
  dating students, 75
  effectiveness and class size, 63
  hoax experiment, 132
  opinions about, 52
  respect for, 55, 66
  setting attendance policies, 184–185
  student evaluations of, 204
  tenure system, 97, 98*n,* 199–200, 204
  See also college; education; school
technical indexes, 162
technology, 162, 169
telephone surveys, 62
television
  beer and wine commercials, 96
  children's program advertising, 157
  cigarette commercials, 36
  commercial aims, 201
  commercials, 5–6
  contradictions by industry moguls, 108
  dish antenna reception, 204
  evaluating evidence from, 174
  hours watched, 5–6
  influence of, 201
  infomercials, 60
  laugh and applause tracks, 202
  music video channels, 11
  observation of, 148
  passive knowing from, 35–36
  rating systems, 200
  sensationalism of war, 22
  serious news coverage, 200
  sexuality, 6, 122
  suicide as topic, 31
  talk shows, 7, 8, 60, 74, 108, 201
  undercover reporting, 200–201
  violence, 6, 122
  See also media
Ten Commandments, 72
tenure system, 97, 98*n,* 199–200, 204
term limits, 200

testimonial evidence, 25, 29, 169
testimony
  celebrity, 60
  eyewitness, 59–60
testing
  hasty conclusion in, 99
  of intelligence, 99*n*
  of perspectives, 91
thalidomide, 48
thinking, 13–17
  categories of, 1
  "egothink," 80
  either/or outlook, 88–89, 125
  in everyday life, 141
  vs. feeling, 15–16
  good and poor, 14
  improving, 141
  intuition and, 20
  "mine is better," 81–83, 124
  monitoring, 53
  in school, 13–14
  synonyms for, 14
  See also critical thinking
Thomas, Clarence, 29, 98
thorotrast, 48
time
  identity influenced by, 4–5
  murky time phenomenon, 30–31
tobacco. *See* smoking
tolerance, irrational appeal to, 113
tradition, 92*n*, 112
truth
  about, 23–25
  challenges to accepted, 27–28
  discovery vs. creation, 28–29
  and memory, 25–26
  of premises, 69–71
  relativity of, 30–31, 90–91, 108
tuberculosis, 48
Tucker, Marc, 52
Tut, King, 28
Twain, Mark, 80

UFOs, 29, 157
ulcers, 49
ultralight motorized aircraft, 102
uncritical thinking, 52–53
undercover reporting,
    200–201
uninformed opinion, 51–52
University of Turin, 174
unpublished reports, as evidence, 59
untestable opinions, 159
unwarranted assumptions, 86–88, 124–125,
    130, 131
U.S. Census Bureau, 62, 163

U.S. Constitution
  abortion rights, 87–88
  equal protection guarantees, 133
  free exercise of religion, 75
  gun control, 43, 190
U.S. Supreme Court
  antimiscegenation laws, 171
  assumptions about, 87–88
  blood alcohol tests, 122–123
  church decision-making powers, 121
  drug search ruling, 203–204
  presidential immunity, 200
  same-sex marriages, 170–171
  Thomas nomination, 98

values
  family, 201
  learned in childhood, 135–136, 185
Van Buren, Abigail, 121
Venus, 49
Vesuvius, Mt., 28
Veterans of Foreign Wars, 133
Victorians, 34
video games, 203
viewpoints
  of audience, 187–188
  balanced, 18, 179–180
  extreme, 11, 18, 66, 157
  "mine is better," 78–83
  observing others', 144–145
  See also attitudes; beliefs
violence
  and aggression, 205
  and anti-heroes, 203
  in boxing matches, 154
  and frontal lobotomy, 36
  in media, 43
  solutions to, 115
  on TV, 6, 122
voting, 11, 66, 133, 157

wage, guaranteed annual, 202
war, "mine is better" thinking, 79
wardrobe engineering, 147
wealth, sharing, 204
Webster's Biographical Dictionary, 160
Webster's New Dictionary of Synonyms, 160
weightlessness, inquiry into, 158–159
welfare system, 75
  adoption and, 134
  either/or outlook, 88
  guaranteed annual wage, 202
Westlaw, 162
whales, 37, 51
Whatever Became of Sin? (Menninger), 37
White, Byron, 87, 200

Will, George, 87–88
wine and beer commercials, 96
wisdom
    conventional, 33–35, 37–38
    errors in, 27–28
women
    common knowledge about, 11,
        33, 66
    "ladies' nights" in bars, 55–56
    male vs. female athletes, 157
    medical opinions about, 48
    in military service, 134
    music video portrayals of, 11
    as teachers, 52
    See also gender; sexuality

women's liberation,
    182–183
workaholism, 150
World Almanac, 160
world conflict, 194–195
World Wide Web, 162, 163–164
writing
    critical thinking and, 21
    with persuasion, 187–196
    in school, 21

Yale University, 202
Yen, Douglas, 38

zoos, 122